Quantitative Analysis

QUANTITATIVE ANALYSIS

PAUL E. MERRITT

Professor of Chemistry,
The State University College at Potsdam, New York

Under the editorship of Jacob Kleinberg,
Professor and Chairman of the Department of Chemistry,
University of Kansas

D. C. HEATH AND COMPANY BOSTON

Library of Congress Catalog Card Number: 64–17488

Printed March 1965

Preface

This book has developed during several years of teaching quantitative analysis. All the thirty three experiments have been successfully used in the author's classes from time to time. Clearly many more experiments are included than can be used in two semesters of work, allowing for variation in the program from year to year or between sections. The growing importance of instrumental methods is reflected in the inclusion of several instrumental determinations. All experiments, both classical and instrumental, have been developed or selected to illustrate the analytical principles discussed in the text. In general, students can be expected to make nine or ten determinations each semester.

The book consists of four parts. In Part I are given the general considerations of analytical chemistry: the use of the analytical balance, general laboratory operations, sampling and the preparation of the sample for analysis. This last topic is designed to give the student some appreciation of sampling problems and the effect these problems can have on final analytical results.

Part II is concerned with volumetric methods of analysis. Here are chapters in acid-base theory, oxidation-reduction methods including electromotive force measurements and potentiometric titrimetric methods, and volumetric methods involving complex formation. In the latter is included the use of chelons in analytical chemistry, illustrated by the discussion of ethylenediaminetetraacetic acid and its use in analytical titrations.

Separation methods and selected gravimetric determinations are found in Part III. The discussion of analytical separations is of a general nature, with references included to which the student may be directed for a more complete and thorough discussion of each type of separation method.

An introduction to instrumental methods of analysis is given in Part IV. Using visible absorption spectroscopy as an illustration, the basic principles of absorption spectroscopy and the types of instrumentation available are discussed. Selected electrogravimetric procedures as well as electrometric methods of analysis are presented.

Usually the author covers volumetric methods and a part of the material on gravimetric methods during the first semester. Gravimetric methods are continued and the section on instrumental methods is covered during the second semester. Although the author prefers to begin the experimental work with

Part II, volumetric methods, the book is designed so that Part II can just as conveniently follow Part III—gravimetric methods.

The author wishes to thank all those who have contributed ideas and helpful suggestions in the development of this text. He is especially grateful to those students in his course in quantitative analysis who have used the material and offered their criticisms. He would like to thank his colleagues Dr. Alexander Major and Mr. Thomas Wallace, as well as Dr. Charles H. Stauffer of the St. Lawrence University who read sections of the manuscript and Dr. Ernest Griswold, University of Kansas, for his editorial assistance. To two student secretaries, Ann Marie Yates and Jacquelyn Kauffman, go thanks for the typing of the first draft of the manuscript.

PAUL E. MERRITT

Contents

Laboratory Experiments

PART I

GENERAL CONSIDERATIONS

CHAPTER **1**

Introduction

Analytical chemistry is divided generally into **qualitative analysis** and **quantitative analysis.** Qualitative analysis attempts to answer the question—What? Quantitative analysis deals with the question—How much?

Qualitative analysis is the study of the composition of a material and the separation and identification of the components that make up the compound or the mixture. Schemes of separation and identification are well known for both organic and inorganic substances.

Quantitative analysis is the examination of a substance to determine the amount of each of the constituents in it. As in qualitative analysis, quantitative methods for organic and inorganic analyses are generally well known.

Modern analytical chemistry has been described as the characterization and control of materials. Characterization of materials implies a greater number of physical measurements and fewer chemical measurements. This in turn implies instrumentation and a larger number of individual determinations. In classical terms, this increase in the number of individual determinations requires separation procedures that are more specific. The trend in modern analytical chemistry is to make more and more analyses on the original sample in such a manner that the sample may be returned. The emphasis is being shifted from classical wet methods of analysis to instrumental methods. Instrumental methods of analysis are becoming more and more important in modern analytical chemistry. This in no way detracts from the importance of noninstrumental methods, because most of the instrumental methods are comparison methods and need standards on which to base the comparisons. The analytical chemist who more and more places greater reliance upon instruments needs the standards that are determined by the analysts who rely on classical methods. Without a doubt a greater responsibility is now being placed on determinations made by an analyst than ever before.

Much has been said about the fact that the analytical chemist will be replaced by automation. This may no doubt become the fate of the "button pusher" but not of the true analytical chemist. There will always be a place in the chemical group for the analytical chemist who must advise and help with the solution of such problems as methods of sampling, the type of preparation and separation necessary, and the general method of analytical attack.

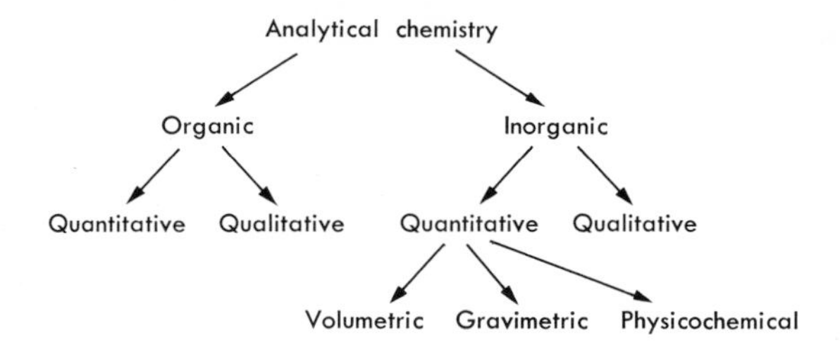

Fig. 1.1. Areas of analytical chemistry.

The analytical chemist uses both the theoretical and the descriptive material of chemistry to describe chemical reactions on the basis of experimentally determined composition. A broad and thorough training in all phases of chemistry is necessary for the prospective analytical chemist.

Classification of Analytical Chemistry

The entire field of chemistry described as analytical chemistry can be divided and subdivided into smaller arbitrary units (see Figure 1.1). The two large divisions, based on the kinds of materials dealt with, are organic and inorganic. Both of these divisions can be subdivided according to "what?" or "how much?"—qualitative and quantitative. Qualitative organic analysis and qualitative inorganic analysis are usually studied in different courses. Qualitative organic analysis is generally postponed until the student has had one or more courses in organic chemistry. Qualitative inorganic analysis is more likely to be a part of the first course in chemistry given in the undergraduate curriculum.

Quantitative inorganic analysis can be further subdivided in terms of the types of methods employed. There are, in general, three classes of methods: volumetric (titrimetric), gravimetric, and physico-chemical (instrumental).

Volumetric methods, sometimes called titrimetric methods since these methods involve a titration, are those in which the final determination of the quantity of the substance desired is made by a direct or indirect measurement of a volume of standard reagent reacting with the substance in a chemical reaction.

Gravimetric methods require the separation in a weighable form of the constituent being determined, from a measured amount of the substance containing the desired constituent. The final measurement in this case is one of weight.

Physico-chemical methods (instrumental methods) are those that involve a final measurement of some physical property that is a function of the composition of the system as a whole. In many cases preliminary treatment of the sample or a separation may be necessary before such a measurement can be performed. In general, specialized instrumentation is required to make this measurement; hence the term "instrumental methods." For example, a colorimeter or spectrophotometer is used to measure absorption or transmission of monochromatic light by the system being studied; or a potentiometric circuit is used to follow the change in potential of a system during an oxidation-reduction titration; or a conductivity bridge is used to measure conductance.

Analytical procedures can be conducted on any one of several scales of operation in common use today. These scales are classified as macro, semimicro, micro, and ultramicro, depending upon the weight of materials used. When the sample weights range from several grams to a few tenths of a gram, these operations are spoken of as macro operations. Semimicro operations are those performed on samples of ten to one hundred milligram quantities. There is no sharp line of demarcation between macro and semimicro analytical techniques. Micro analytical procedures deal with samples in the range of one to ten milligrams. In this area a balance of special design is required to weigh with the sensitivity necessary for this type of analytical operation. The use of radioactive material has extended the analytical operation into the ultramicro area, where a few millionths of a gram of material may be analyzed.

Analysis may be either **ultimate** or **proximate.** An ultimate analysis is determining the percentages of the various elements in a substance. A proximate analysis (or condensed analysis) is finding the percentage of a group of substances that may be determined using a common procedure. Determining the loss on ignition in a limestone analysis when the loss may consist of various substances is an example of proximate analysis. Either a **partial** or a **complete** analysis may also be accomplished. A partial analysis is defined as an analysis of one or more constituents in the sample, but not all. In a complete analysis all the substances that can be detected by a careful qualitative analysis are determined.

Constituents can be classified as **major** if they are present in amounts greater than one percent, and **minor** if less than one percent. Those that are present in amounts less than one tenth of one percent are considered **trace** amounts.

Operations Required for Analysis

There are several laboratory operations that are common to both volumetric and gravimetric methods and in many cases to physico-chemical methods. The operations can be listed as

(1) Sampling
(2) Drying the sample
(3) Weighing the sample
(4) Dissolving the sample

(5) Preliminary treatment to obtain the constituent in a form suitable for measurement
(6) Measurement
(7) Calculation of the amount of the desired constituent.

After the preliminary treatment of the solution to get the constituent in a form for measurement, the measurement operation will be different for each of the three methods of analysis. As previously stated, for volumetric methods the measurement will be one of volume resulting from a titration. Gravimetric methods require that the preliminary treatment include a separation of the constituent in a weighable form or in a form that can be converted into another substance of weighable form related numerically to the desired constituent. The final measurement will then involve obtaining a weight. Physico-chemical methods may follow all the steps in the list or may deviate from the list given in that it may not be necessary to dissolve the substance. The measurement may be made directly on the sample. In the spectrographic analysis of metal alloys, the sample is used without any kind of preliminary chemical treatment.

In general, volumetric methods are less time consuming than gravimetric methods. By judicial use of reagents precipitations can be made more specific than volumetric methods. Physico-chemical methods are rapid, in many cases, and offer a great saving in time when applied to routine analytical procedures.

Experience in all three methods is a part of the elementary quantitative analysis course. More complete descriptions of the principles of separation and of special physico-chemical methods are given in advanced analytical chemistry courses.

CHAPTER **2**

The Analytical Balance; General Laboratory Procedures

Since the results of most chemical analyses are expressed in terms of weight percentages, it is evident that the operation of weighing is of fundamental importance in quantitative analysis. For this reason the beginning analytical chemist must become very familiar with the operation of the analytical balance, and he must learn to use it correctly and efficiently.

TYPES OF ANALYTICAL BALANCES

Analytical balances are of two main types: **double beam balance** (double pan balance) and **constant load balance** (single pan balance).

Double Beam Balances

Double beam balances can be further classified as: rider balances, chain balances, notched beam balances, and keyboard balances.

The rider type balance is common among analytical balances designed for students. This type of balance makes use of a small piece of platinum or aluminum wire called a **rider** to establish weights less than 10 milligrams. Some balances of this type are less expensive and often as accurate as some of the more elaborate balances.

Chain type balances use a fine gold chain, one end of which is suspended from the beam, with the other end attached to a sliding vernier or a drum. The chain is moved up or down by means of a shaft which projects outside the balance on the side. By moving the end of the chain on the sliding device downward, weight is in effect added to the right-hand pan. Moving the sliding device upward removes weight from the right-hand pan.

Notched beam balances are chain balances that have ten equally spaced notches in the beam in which a dumbbell-shaped rider weight can be placed by means of a movable rod. Thus, all pan weights of less than one gram are eliminated in this type of balance. The balance is so designed that the rider

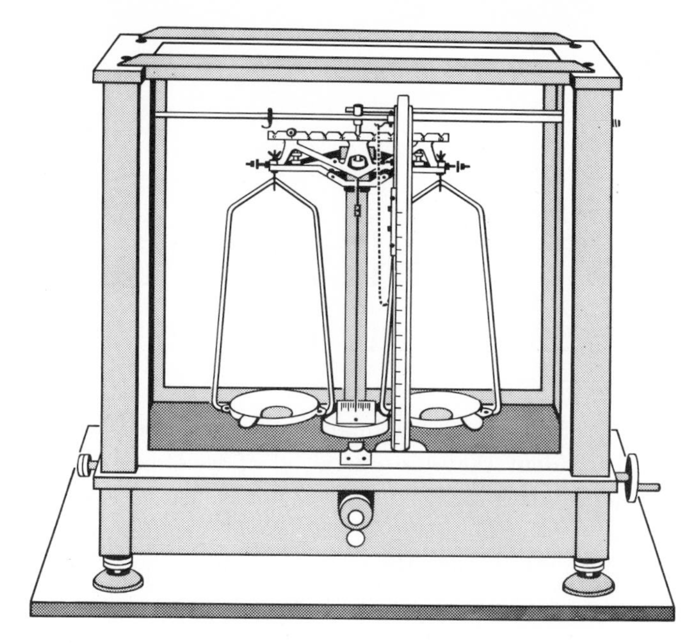

Fig. 2.1. Notched beam, chain type double beam balance.

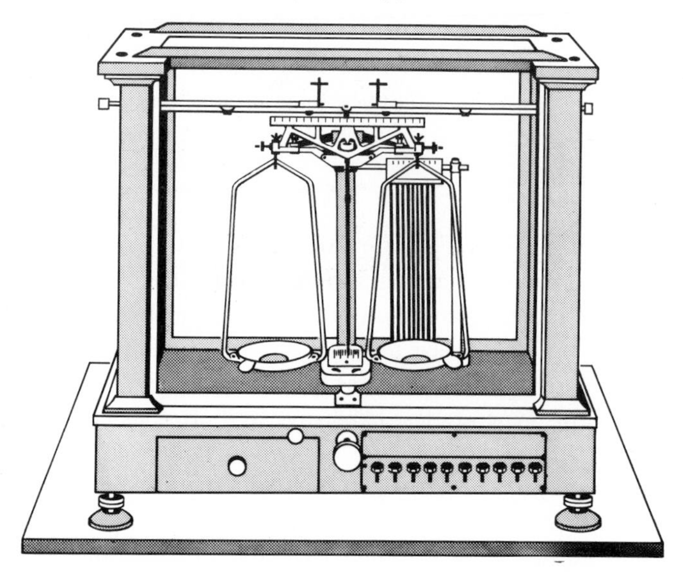

Fig. 2.2. Keyboard type double beam balance.

must always be on the beam when a weighing is being made. Figure 2.1 illustrates this type of balance.

Keyboard balances use a mechanical arrangement of levers and keys to manipulate special rider weights of less than one gram. The numbers and weights of the riders vary for different balances. When a key is pressed down,

Fig. 2.3. Constant load balance, Mettler Model H15, showing the digital read out and optical scale. *Courtesy Mettler Instrument Corporation*

the weight indicated by that key will be placed on a rack on the right-hand balance pan and will become an effective weight on the balance arm. Figure 2.2 illustrates an example of a keyboard balance.

Constant Load Balances

A constant load balance consists of a single pan with a set of concealed weights suspended from a single beam. A fixed weight counterpoises this combination. The weight of the object placed on the pan is obtained by removing weights from the beam equal to the total weight of the object. Since the beam is always under constant load, the sensitivity of the balance is therefore constant. The weights are removed by means of control knobs. Depending on the type

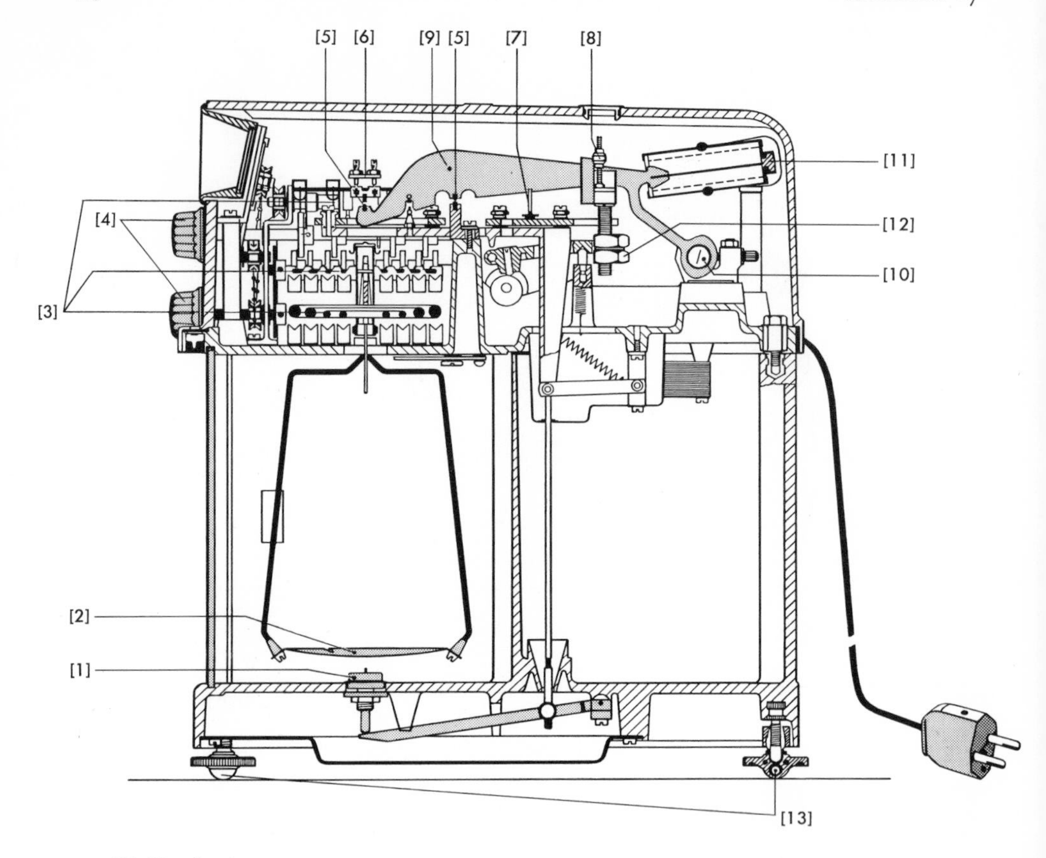

(1) Pan brake
(2) Pan
(3) Set of weights
(4) Weight control knobs. Arrest knob (not shown in this drawing) is on upper left side of the balance when facing the front.
(5) Sapphire knife edge
(6) Stirrup for hangers and weights
(7) Lifting device
(8) Movable weight for adjustment of sensitivity
(9) Beam
(10) Engraved optical scale (not shown)
(11) Air damper
(12) Counterweight
(13) Foot screws

Fig. 2.4. Schematic diagram of the Mettler constant load balance showing various parts. *Redrawn from diagram courtesy Mettler Instrument Corporation*

of balance, the lower limit of the weights that can be removed varies. Weights less than the lowest limit of the removable weights can be registered optically and automatically on an illuminated scale or by a digital readout system for all significant figures.

Figure 2.3 shows a constant load balance using an optical scale. Figure 2.4 shows the principal parts of this type balance. Balances of this type allow weighings to be made in much less time than with double pan balances and are very simple to operate.

OPERATION OF THE DOUBLE BEAM BALANCE

Before using a balance the following steps should be taken.

(1) Brush the balance pans with a camel's-hair brush to assure that they are clean.
(2) Check that the balance is level.
(3) Make sure that the operation of raising and lowering the beam rest mechanism is smooth.
(4) Check the operation of the pan arrests to assure that they touch the pans when the beam is lowered.
(5) Make sure that the needle swings freely and about equally on either side of the midpoint of the graduated card attached to the beam post.

There are several methods of direct weighing, and in each of these methods it is necessary to determine the equilibrium position of the beam. The difference between methods is in the means of determining the equilibrium position of the beam.

Determining the No Load Rest Point

The first step in any method of direct weighing is to determine the no load rest point, called the zero point. This is the equilibrium position of the pointer attached to the beam when both pans are empty. To find this position the beam arrest is carefully lowered and the pan rests are released to allow the beam to swing freely. If the amplitude of the oscillations is not great enough, the balance door may be opened and the air gently fanned against the left pan with the hand. Or if the balance has a rider on the beam, the rider may be lifted momentarily; this will cause the beam to start swinging. After closing the balance door, allow two or three swings before taking any readings. There are several techniques to be used to find the no load rest point.

1. Method of Long Swings

When the pointer is swinging freely about five divisions on either side of the center mark on the scale, the farthest point reached on the right and left sides is recorded to the nearest tenth of a division. An odd number of consecutive readings are taken on one side and an even number on the other. It is customary to take three readings on the left and two on the right. The set of readings to a given side is added separately and the average for each side is obtained. The averages are added and divided by two. If the scale readings to the left are designated minus values (−), and those on the right, positive values (+), then the algebraic sum of the averages divided by two is the no load rest point (N.L.R.P.). For example:

	Readings to the left		*Readings to the right*
(1)	−4.3	(1)	+4.5
(2)	−4.0	(2)	+4.1
(3)	−3.7		

$$\frac{-12.0}{3} = -4.0 \qquad \frac{+8.6}{2} = +4.3$$

$$\frac{4.3 + (-4.0)}{2} = \frac{0.3}{2} = +0.15 \text{ N.L.R.P.}$$

If the balance is in correct adjustment, the no load rest point will lie within one division of the center of the scale. If the no load rest point lies more than two divisions from the center of the scale, consult with the instructor before continuing.

2. Method of Short Swings

For the usual analytical weighing in which it is not necessary to have an accuracy greater then 0.1 mg., the method of short swings can be used to find the no load rest point. In this method, after the beam and the pan arrests have been released and the beam is swinging freely, two readings are taken, one on either side of the center, on successive swings. The readings are added and divided by two; this gives the mean value, which indicates the center of the swing and thus gives the no load rest point. Using the first two readings in the previous example, the computation is as follows:

$$\frac{-4.3 + 4.5}{2} = +0.1$$

The deviation of this result from the true no load rest point previously computed is so small as to be entirely negligible for the usual analytical balance.

3. The Single Deflection Method

One arm of the balance to be used for this method is made permanently heavier than the other. When the beam is lowered very carefully and the pans released, the pointer moves a number of divisions to one side. The end of the swing is taken as the zero point on the scale.

Determining the Load Rest Point

The **load rest point,** or simply rest point, is found by first placing the object to be weighed on the left pan and the weights which will cause the equilibrium position to be reached on the right pan. The method of determining the load rest point can then be any of the three listed for the no load rest point determination.

Determining the Sensitivity

In weighing an object, the weights can be adjusted so that the load rest point and the no load rest point coincide, or the change in weight required to reach coincidence can be calculated from the sensitivity of the balance.

The sensitivity of a balance varies with the weight on the pan. Therefore it must be determined for several different loads. The term **sensitivity** as used here is the displacement of the load rest point in scale divisions from the no load rest point, produced by the addition of one milligram of weight.

The procedure for determining the sensitivity is as follows: Exactly one milligram is added to the right pan. The beam is set swinging and the load rest point determined. The difference, expressed in scale divisions, between the no load rest point and the load rest point is the sensitivity. For example, if there are two divisions between the no load rest point and the load rest point, then the sensitivity is 2 divisions per milligram. The reciprocal value, in this case 1 mg./2.0 divisions, is sometimes stated as the sensitivity of a balance.

To use sensitivity in the weighing procedure, the sample is weighed to the nearest milligram, the load rest point being obtained in the usual manner. The number of scale divisions and direction that the load rest point is displaced from the no load rest point is recorded. Using the sensitivity, the weight that must be added or subtracted is calculated. The direction of the displacement will determine whether the calculated amount will be added or subtracted to the weight that is on the pan.

GENERAL LABORATORY OPERATIONS

The analytical chemist is concerned with the qualitative and quantitative composition of specific samples of matter. It is most imperative during the determination of composition not to add impurities caused by using reagents that are not of the purest quality, nor to use equipment that is not clean, nor to practice poor housekeeping in the laboratory.

Habits of maintaining the analytical laboratory desk in a neat and orderly manner do not assure accurate analytical determinations, but such habits can eliminate many sources of error. It is much easier to choose areas in a determination where a high order of accuracy is not required than to go from sloppy laboratory technique to the point of accuracy and precision demanded by many determinations. Therefore it is advisable for the analytical chemist (and the student of quantitative analysis) to keep the desk space assigned to him in a neat and orderly condition.

Cleaning Glassware

The glassware that is in the desk should be kept clean and ready for use at all times. In general, glassware other than burets, pipets, and similar items can be cleaned by washing with a good detergent. After being cleaned with a detergent, the glassware is rinsed thoroughly with several applications of water and finally rinsed with distilled water. Care should be taken during the washing and rinsing to be sure that no film of detergent is left on the clean surface.

Burets, pipets, and similar pieces of glass transfer equipment can be cleaned by using cleaning solution. A satisfactory cleaning solution can be prepared by adding 15 grams of powdered sodium or potassium dichromate to 500 ml. of concentrated sulfuric acid. The resulting solution is allowed to cool, after which the solution is decanted through a funnel containing glass wool into a pyrex bottle with glass stopper. After repeated use the appearance of a green color indicates that the solution is exhausted.

When a buret is to be cleaned it is filled with cleaning solution and the solution allowed to remain in the buret for about 15 minutes. The cleaning solution is then returned to the bottle. The buret is rinsed thoroughly with water, and a check is made of whether or not water clings to the side walls of the buret in droplets. If water clings in droplets, the buret is not clean. In this case the cleaning solution is used again in a repetition of the foregoing procedure. After it has been established that the inside surface of the buret is clean, the buret is rinsed with distilled water.

If the buret is to be used immediately, it is rinsed with several small portions of the liquid to be measured and then filled with this liquid. If it is not to be used immediately, it should be filled with distilled water and stored.

Pipets can be cleaned using cleaning solution. There is one precaution: **Never draw cleaning solution into a transfer pipet using your mouth.** A suction bulb is used to fill the pipet to a point above the fill line (see Figure 2.5). The cleaning solution is allowed to drain out. The pipet is rinsed with water thoroughly and finally rinsed with distilled water. Before using it, the pipet is rinsed with a small portion of the solution to be transferred.

Use of Volumetric Equipment

In order to eliminate errors resulting from misuse of various pieces of apparatus used in volumetric determinations, a discussion of the technique for using specific pieces of volumetric apparatus is in order.

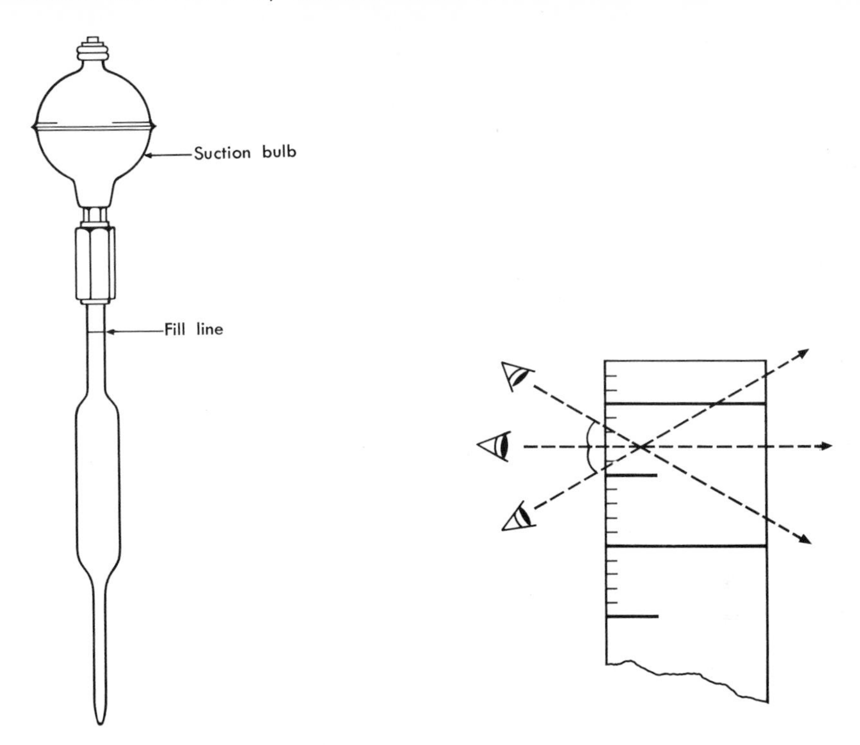

Fig. 2.5. Transfer pipet with suction bulb.

Fig. 2.6. Parallax errors in reading a buret.

BURET

The procedure for assuring that the buret is clean has been covered in the section concerned with the cleaning of glassware. The stopcock of the buret should be greased with a small amount of lubricating grease (Vaseline or silicone stopcock grease) such that it will turn without sticking or leaking. The layer of grease should not be so thick that in the rotation of the stopcock, particles of grease are pushed into the aperture of the stopcock and on down into the delivery tube causing the tip to become clogged. The buret is rinsed with the solution to be used and then filled to a level above the zero mark in the buret. The solution is run down to the zero mark. This insures that the delivery tube below the stopcock is filled.

When reading a buret, the analyst must be careful to read the meniscus in such a manner that there is no error due to parallax (see Figure 2.6).

During the titration, drops that hang from the tip of the buret delivery tube should be removed with a stirring rod and added to the solution, since they have already been measured. When running in large volumes, it is necessary to allow a short time for drainage down the sides of the buret before recording a reading.

Transfer Pipets

Transfer pipets are used to remove accurately measured portions from the main volume of a solution. These portions are called **aliquots.** The pipet is calibrated to deliver a specified volume at a given temperature, usually 20°C. To fill a pipet, some type of suction bulb is used (see Figure 2.5). The liquid to be measured is pulled up into the pipet to a level above the fill line and then the level is adjusted such that the meniscus is exactly at the fill line. The pipet is withdrawn from the solution, the meniscus being held to the fill line, and the solution in the pipet is allowed to empty into the desired container. Holding the tip of the pipet close to a wall of the container minimizes loss by spattering. The pipet is allowed to drain and the tip of the pipet is touched to the surface and then withdrawn. Generally there is a drop of solution left in the delivery tip of the pipet. This drop is not blown out or shaken out since the calibration is such that the stated volume does not include this drop. Once this transfer has been made quantitatively, there is in the container an accurately measured volume of solution.

Volumetric Flasks

Volumetric flasks are calibrated to contain a stated volume (*e.g.* 250 ml.) of a solution at a specified temperature, usually 20°C, when filled to a line etched on the neck of the flask (see Figure 2.7).

When preparing a solution in a volumetric flask, a small amount of solvent is added to the flask and then the required amount of solute is added. The solute is dissolved in the small portion of solvent. After the solution of the solute, solvent is added until the meniscus of the solution coincides with the line on the neck of the flask. While doing this dilution, be careful that neither solute nor solvent is allowed to remain on the neck of the flask above the line. After the solution has been made up to the line, it is thoroughly mixed by inverting the stoppered flask several times. When mixing is complete, a known volume of solution of a known concentration has been prepared.

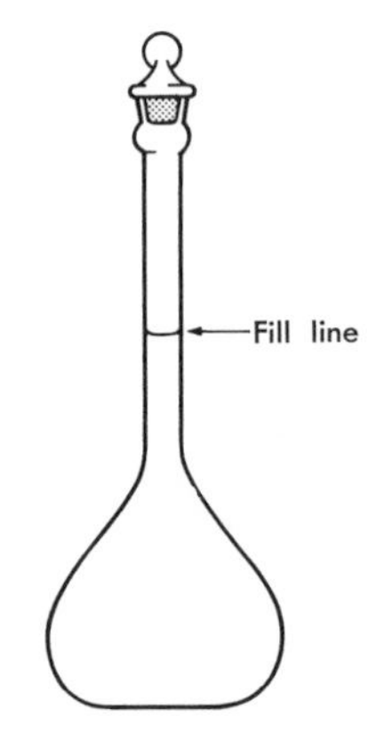

Fig. 2.7. Volumetric flask.

GRAVIMETRIC OPERATIONS

The major unit operations that are uniquely characteristic of the gravimetric method of analysis are as follows:

(1) Precipitation
(2) Digestion
(3) Filtration
(4) Washing
(5) Ignition
(6) Weighing

It can readily be seen that all of the above operations are focussed on the process of precipitation. In some gravimetric methods, some of the steps that are listed can be combined or in a few cases eliminated altogether. Even so, these are the general operations that are associated with gravimetric analytical methods. For this reason a short discussion of each operation is presented so that an understanding of the technique of the operation, the role the operation plays, and the place of the operation in the overall gravimetric determination will be obtained.

Precipitation

Gravimetric precipitations are made in beakers. In most analytical procedures, the amount of reagent necessary to bring about a precipitation is specified. If this information is not given, the amount may be determined by calculation, using the concentration of the reagent and an approximation of the weight of the constituent present. A moderate excess of the precipitating agent is usually added. Many times a large excess is undesirable because the precipitate may dissolve by the formation of a complex ion and because such an excess constitutes a waste of the precipitating agent. A good practice is to add a 10% excess of the precipitant. In all cases, the supernatant liquid (mother liquor) should be tested for completeness of precipitation. This can be done by adding a small volume of the precipitant and observing whether additional precipitate is formed.

Digestion

After precipitation, generally the precipitate is allowed to stand in contact with the supernatant liquid for a specified period of time before filtration. During this time the solution is kept above room temperature. This allows the particles to increase in size, since the smaller particles are more soluble than the larger ones. The increase in size of the particles decreases the total surface area and thus decreases the surface coprecipitation phenomenon, resulting in a purer precipitate. This process, taking place at an elevated temperature to aid in dissolving the smaller particles and to cause the larger particles to grow, is called **digestion.**

Filtration

After the precipitate has been digested, it must be collected by filtration. This can be accomplished by using filter paper or filtering crucibles. The nature of the precipitate and the temperature to which it finally will be ignited generally dictate the type of filter to be used.

Types of Filter Paper

Before beginning the filtration, the size and texture of **quantitative** paper which is best suited for the particular filtration is determined. If the precipitate is to be subjected to high temperature, an acid-washed paper relatively free of inorganic content and producing low ash should be used. Examples of such a paper are Whatman or Schleicher and Schuell analytical ashless filter paper. The ash content of one circle of Whatman No. 40, 9 cm. paper is 0.000090 gram. Whatman papers are rated as follows:

Medium—medium speed and retentiveness (Whatman 40)
Soft—more rapid, less retentive (Whatman 41)
Dense—more retentive, less rapid (Whatman 42)
Thin—very retentive, low ash weight (Whatman 44)
Hard—rapid, strong, very low ash weight (Whatman 41H)

The choice of a paper is dependent on the nature of the precipitate. The size of the filter chosen is dependent on the amount of precipitate and not on the amount of liquid to be filtered. The precipitate should not fill more than one half of the filter; preferably only one third should be filled. Coarse precipitates and gelatinous precipitates can be filtered through paper of high quality.

Whatever size or porosity of paper is chosen, it must be remembered that when doing quantitative determinations, quantitative, ashless paper must be used. Qualitative papers, quite differently constituted, should be used for nonquantitative filtering.

Types of Filtering Crucibles

Precipitates that are not gelatinous and are of such a nature that, after ignition at a low temperature, they give a product of definite known composition, can be filtered using filtering crucibles. One such crucible is the **Gooch crucible.** The Gooch crucible is a porcelain crucible with a perforated base. The filtering medium used in this crucible is acid-washed asbestos fiber. This type of filtering crucible is useful for filtration of precipitates that might be reduced during ignition in the presence of filter paper, and is preferable for filtering solutions which attack paper—*e.g.* potassium permanganate.

The asbestos mat is freshly prepared for each filtration. To prepare, place the Gooch crucible in a suction filtering apparatus, and into the crucible, without suction, pour a small portion of a well-shaken aqueous suspension of asbestos fibers. The amount of the suspension to be added should fill about one-third of the crucible. Suction is applied gently to draw the water through the base of the crucible leaving an even layer of asbestos. This layer should be thin enough so that when the crucible is held up to the light the outlines of the holes in the bottom of the crucible are visible. A mat formed in this manner is a very satisfactory filtering medium.

Filtering crucibles are also constructed with a porous base. There are three types of porous base filtering crucibles: (1) sintered porcelain, (2) sintered glass, and (3) Munroe.

(1) *Sintered porcelain crucibles* are porcelain crucibles with a porous porcelain mat as a filtering medium. These crucibles (Selas crucibles) are excellent for many filtrations. They can be heated to a high temperature in an electric muffle furnace or inside a plain crucible using a gas burner. The greatest disadvantage of porous base filtering crucibles when compared with filter paper or Gooch crucibles is the difficult task of cleaning out a precipitate after using the crucible. The one advantage over filter paper is that porous base crucibles, like the Gooch crucibles, can be used in a suction filtration apparatus.

(2) A *sintered glass crucible* is a glass-walled crucible with a porous glass mat as the filtering medium. Crucibles of this type are commercially available in several grades of porosity. This crucible is very convenient to use, because no preparation is necessary as with the Gooch crucible, and it is unnecessary to remove the filtering medium as must be done with filter paper. Since glass cannot stand high temperatures, sintered glass crucibles are used for precipitates that can be dried effectively at temperatures around 100°C.

(3) The *Munroe crucible* is a platinum crucible with a spongy platinum pad as the filtering medium. Such a crucible can be heated to a high temperature. This crucible is expensive.

Technique of Filtration

When filter paper and a funnel are used as a means of filtration, the circle of paper is folded directly in half and then once again through the center so the edges of the two halves do not quite meet (see Figure 2.8). The top corner of the smaller folded segment is torn off to give a tighter fit at the top of the funnel. The apical angle of the cone will be slightly greater than 60°. When this filter cone is placed in a 60° funnel, it will not quite fit the walls of the funnel at the apex but will at the top. The single larger fold is opened and the paper placed in the funnel. The top of the filter paper should fall about

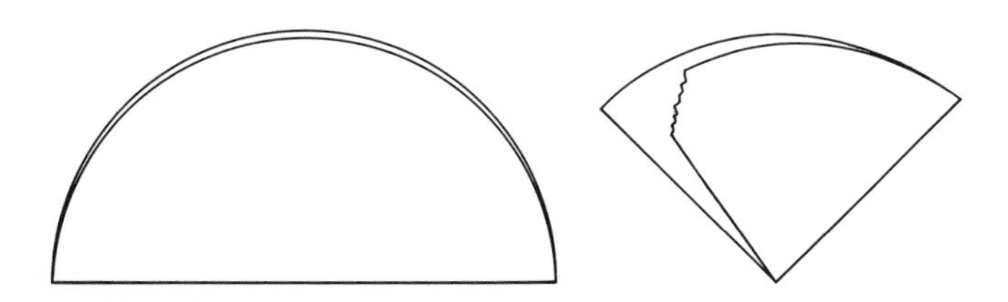

Fig. 2.8. Method of folding quantitative filter paper. Notice that one folded segment is smaller than the other.

Fig. 2.9. Quantitative filtration. This method of filtering the supernatant liquid does not disturb the precipitate.

one-half to one centimeter below the rim of the funnel. The paper is moistened with distilled water, and the upper third of the paper is gently pressed against the glass funnel with the finger. For proper operation of the filter, the stem of the funnel should fill up when water is placed in the filter. If bubbles appear in the water column in the stem, this indicates that air is seeping in around the paper. The paper should then be carefully refitted to the glass all the way around to assure no seepage of air into the stem. When the paper is fitted correctly, there will be an unbroken column of liquid in the stem. This unbroken column of liquid creates a gentle suction as the liquid passes down the stem.

After the paper is fitted correctly, the funnel is placed in the funnel rack and a clean beaker placed under the stem. The stem should touch the side of the beaker to prevent splashing. The stem should be well inside the beaker but should never extend into the liquid in the receiving beaker (see Figure 2.9).

Solutions should ordinarily be filtered hot through filter paper since the passage of a liquid through the pores of the paper is retarded by friction. The retardation for water at 100°C is less than one-sixth that at 0°C. Where the solubility effects are appreciable, however, it is advisable to filter a cold solution.

The supernatant liquid should be filtered first without disturbing the precipitate. This is accomplished by carefully pouring the liquid down a stirring rod into the funnel (see Figure 2.9). It is necessary to be careful that the

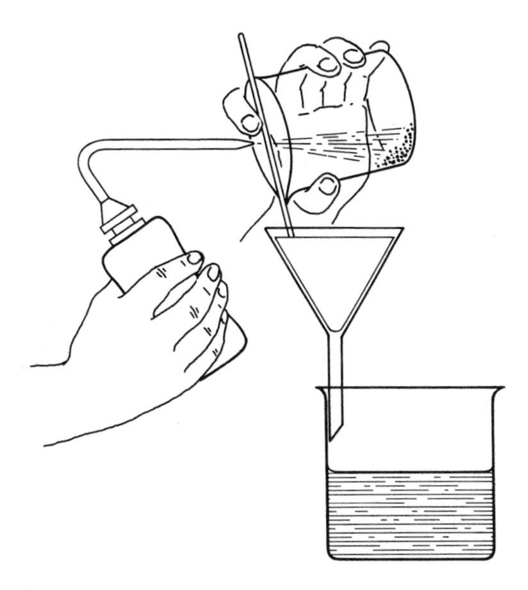

Fig. 2.10. Transferring a precipitate.

liquid level in the filter is kept about one-half centimeter below the top of the paper and that the stirring rod does not puncture the paper. Keep the precipitate in the beaker as long as possible. In many cases the first washing of the precipitate can be conducted in the beaker. The suspension of the precipitate and the wash water should be poured down the stirring rod into the filter. Again the suspension of the precipitate should be kept below one-half centimeter from the top of the paper.

Wash back into the beaker any of the precipitate that may have adhered to the stirring rod. Place the rod across the top of the beaker such that about one inch of the rod projects beyond the lip of the beaker. Take the beaker in the left hand with the thumb and fingers encircling the beaker, and place the index finger of the left hand over the rod and across the top of the beaker, thus holding the rod in place. Hold the beaker over the filter in the position indicated in Figure 2.10; direct a jet of water from a wash bottle into the beaker and wash out the precipitate into the filter. Be careful not to overflow the top of the filter paper and not to splatter the solution or the suspension.

After the beaker has been washed in this manner, usually there will still be small amounts of precipitate adhering to the walls. These are removed by moistening the walls and rubbing gently with a policeman (see Figure 2.11).

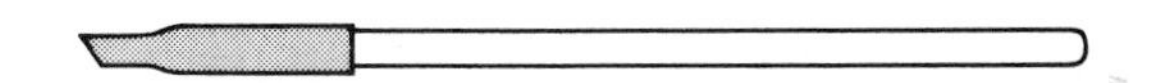

Fig. 2.11. Stirring rod with rubber policeman.

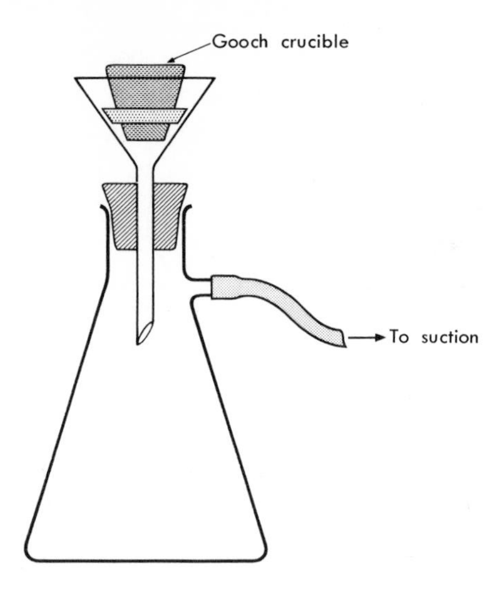

Fig. 2.12. Gouch crucible and suction filtering apparatus.

The whole interior of the beaker is gone over very carefully so as to dislodge all the particles. When this has been completed, the policeman is rinsed and removed from the beaker. The small amount of precipitate thus dislodged is washed into the filter as before. The beaker should be examined very carefully for specks of precipitate or surface that was not rubbed. If necessary, the treatment with the policeman should be repeated.

Except for minor modifications, the directions given for filtering precipitates on paper also apply to filtrations using filtering crucibles.

When a crucible is used for filtering, it must first be washed with water or dilute acid to remove any soluble substances. It is dried to constant weight at the same temperature at which the precipitate is later to be heated. The crucible is set up in a suction apparatus as shown in Figure 2.12. A gentle suction is applied. The supernatant liquid from the precipitation beaker is carefully poured into the crucible with the aid of a stirring rod used in the same manner as when filtering with paper. The precipitate is transferred to the crucible in the same manner as described in the previous section.

Washing

When the precipitate has been transferred quantitatively to the filter paper, washing should begin immediately. A precipitate should not be allowed to stand in a filter for any length of time before being washed. If the precipitate dries, it cakes up and cracks. It is virtually impossible to wash a dried precipitate free of soluble impurities.

The selection of a wash liquid depends on the precipitate. The solubility of the precipitate and its ability to peptize (return of the coagulated precipitate to its original colloidal form) are two factors that dictate the choice of wash liquid. If an electrolyte is used as the wash liquid to minimize the effects of peptization, one should be used that is easily volatilized and will leave no appreciable residue. Ammonia, ammonium salts, or dilute acids are often used. To minimize solubility losses, use a reasonably small volume of a wash liquid containing an ion in common with the precipitate. Washing is done more efficiently by using many small portions of a wash liquid rather than a few large portions. In most cases, eight or ten washings will be sufficient.

Rapid filtration and efficient washing can be accomplished by performing as much of the washing as possible in the beaker. The supernatant liquid is poured through the filter, wash liquid is added, the beaker swirled gently, and the precipitate allowed to settle. The supernatant liquid is again poured through the filter. This procedure is repeated several times and then the bulk of the precipitate is transferred to the filter. The precipitate is then washed with several portions of the wash liquid.

When filter paper is used, the precipitate is washed down into the apex of the cone with a gentle jet of wash liquid. When a Gooch crucible is used, the jet of wash liquid should not be strong enough to pierce the filter mat. The jet should not strike the precipitate in the bottom of the crucible.

Drying, Ignition, and Weighing

The precipitate must be dried to remove the moisture left by the wash liquid. It is usually not adequate to dry at room temperature. In many cases, drying at 110°C for two hours is not sufficient to remove all the water retained by the precipitate. In most cases, the precipitate must be transformed into a substance of more definite composition and this plus the removal of the filter paper requires heating well above 110°C. Therefore, a well-drained filter usually can be placed directly in a weighed crucible and dried therein over a low flame before ignition.

When filter paper is used for the filtration, it and its contents are removed from the filter. The paper is folded carefully around the contents and placed in a weighed crucible previously brought to constant weight under the same conditions as those of the ignition of the precipitate. The crucible is placed in a nichrome wire triangle mounted over a burner (see Figure 2.13). The ignition takes place in two steps: the smoking off, or ashing, of the filter paper, and ignition of the precipitate at the desired temperature.

The ashing procedure must be conducted carefully. The paper should not burn with a flame because the precipitate might be excessively reduced. A small flame in a burner is generally sufficient to keep the paper ashing off slowly, and a crucible cover can be used to extinguish any flame that may appear due to local overheating. The ashing procedure should be accomplished slowly and carefully to eliminate splattering and loss of precipitate. When the

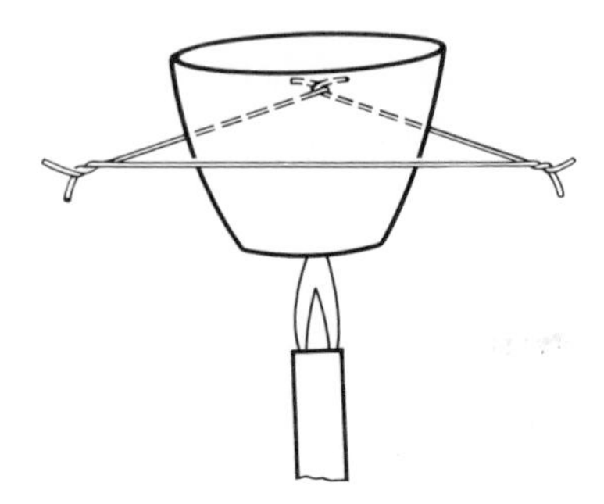

Fig. 2.13. Ignition in a porcelain crucible supported by a nichrome wire triangle.

paper has been completely reduced to ash, the temperature of the crucible is brought up to the desired value and the ignition is usually continued for about 30 minutes. The crucible should not be enveloped by flame and must be placed so that the bottom of the crucible is in contact with the blue oxidizing flame. If the crucible is in contact with the center cone or the yellow part of the flame, a tightly adhering black soot is formed on the crucible.

When the ignition period is ended, the crucible is allowed to cool for a few moments in the air before being placed in a desiccator. It must remain in the desiccator to come to room temperature. The time required is usually about 30 minutes. The crucible is weighed and the weight recorded.

The crucible is then reheated to the ignition temperature for 15 minutes. It is cooled in air, placed in the desiccator until cool, and weighed. The ignition, cooling, and weighing should be repeated until the crucible and its contents achieve constant weight.

A Gooch, Munroe, or sintered porcelain crucible should be inserted in a regular crucible during ignition so that the burner gases will not come in contact with the precipitate.

In all cases, the empty crucible must have previously undergone the same ignition procedure that is necessary when the precipitate is present. The alternate ignition and weighing should be carried out until two successive weighings give reasonably constant results, such as ± 0.5 mg. This is considered to be constant weight.

Having the weight of the crucible empty and the weight of the crucible and its contents, the weight of the contents can be obtained by difference.

Laboratory Experiment 1

Weighing Techniques

DETERMINATION OF THE NO LOAD REST POINT

Place the balance in operation as described previously (see page 11) and record the number of scale divisions of the swings to the right and to the left, using the method of **long swings.** Calculate a no load rest point. Repeat the procedure. Record the values obtained.

Using the method of **short swings,** find the no load rest point. Record this value.

DETERMINATION OF SENSITIVITY

Determine the sensitivities for loads of 0, 5, 10, 20, and 50 grams.

For sensitivity at loads other than 0 gram, the same load should be placed on each pan. Since there might be slight differences in weights, the rest point should be determined without the additional 1 mg. weight and then with the additional 1 mg. weight. Record the differences in rest point values and the calculated sensitivity at each weight load in tabular form. Using the values from this table, plot a sensitivity curve using linear graph paper. Plot divisions per milligram *vs.* load in grams.

EXPERIMENTAL WEIGHING OF A SAMPLE

Most of the weighing of samples is done by finding the difference in weight between the sample and container and the empty container. The weighing bottle and contents are weighed first, the sample removed and the bottle weighed again. The difference in weight is the weight of the sample. To practice this weighing technique, carry out the following steps:

(1) Weigh a clean dry weighing bottle A and record the value observed.

(2) To a second clean weighing bottle B, add about three grams of the crystalline material supplied.

(3) Weigh the weighing bottle B and the contents. Record the weight.

(4) Transfer about one-third of the contents of weighing bottle B to the previously weighed weighing bottle A.

(5) Reweigh both of the weighing bottles and record the weights.

(6) Calculate the weight of the sample removed from weighing bottle B. Calculate the weight of the material added to weighing bottle A. These two weights should agree within 0.5 mg. or 0.0005 gram.

(7) Repeat the weighing until the results are satisfactory.

SINGLE PAN BALANCE

Place the single pan balance in operation according to the procedure described by the instructor.

With no load on the pan, the zero point of the balance is adjusted with the zero adjustment control knob. After adjusting the zero point, perform the following:

(1) Weigh two weighing bottles A and B and their contents used in the previous weighing exercise. Record the weights of both weighing bottles to the nearest 0.1 mg.

(2) Transfer the contents quantitatively from weighing bottle A to weighing bottle B. Reweigh both bottles and record the weight to the nearest 0.1 mg.

(3) The difference in weight of the empty weighing bottle A and the weight of the same bottle and contents found in (1) is recorded. This weight added to the weight of weighing bottle B prior to the transfer of material should be the same as the weight of weighing bottle B found in (2).

(4) Repeat the operation until the weights calculated in part (3) agree within 0.5 mg.

Compare the advantages and disadvantages of weighing using a chainomatic double pan balance and a single pan balance.

CHAPTER 3

Sampling and Sample Preparation

Often the most important operation in the analysis of a given sample is the procedure used to obtain the sample. The beginning student in analytical chemistry many times is not concerned with the sampling process. The sample that he is given for analysis will be, in most cases, hand picked and is completely homogeneous, so that the problem of sampling is not one that seems to be of great importance. Since the analysis requires time and can be costly, the history of the sample should be known. Therefore the student of quantitative analysis should have some understanding of the importance and the significance of the sampling procedure.

Since the analytical chemist is concerned with the control of quality, as well as with composition, the sampling process could be of major importance. The application of statistical methods to the sampling process has brought the sampling technique to a point where it may be considered an accurately controlled process. Regardless of this fact, the taking of representative samples requires training and experience.

The terminology of the sampling process may be very familiar, but, with the increasing precision of the process and the attempts by the International Union of Pure and Applied Chemistry to establish the terms used in testing materials, it is desirable to present the proposed definitions of the terms that are applicable in this book.

Sample is a portion of the material that is representative of the total bulk. The size of the sample can range from a single drop of a completely homogeneous liquid to several grams of powder, or, as in quality control, it may be series of observations of a given specific property.

Gross sample is the sample prepared by mixing all the increments.

Analysis sample is the sample taken for the determination or test. This sample is expected to be homogeneous and to represent the entire bulk of the material.

Grab sample is a sample that is taken at random by the person doing the sampling. The analysis may be made on the grab samples individually or they may all be combined into a gross sample and then an analytical sample may be taken.

Fig. 3.1. Riffle Splitter. *Courtesy Soiltest, Inc.*

Sampling process is the series of steps that are specified for the taking of a sample so that the final sample will have all the essential characteristics of the bulk.

METHODS OF SAMPLING

The methods and techniques of sampling differ with the physical state of the material to be sampled.

Solids

There is no single general method that can be given for the sampling of all solid materials. The method depends on the type of material and the conditions of sampling. A simple grab sample (sometimes referred to as a hand sample) is not very accurate. To maintain a representative sample using this method of sampling requires constant supervision and strict control over the sampler. If this is not done, then the sampler may either consciously or unconsciously prejudice his taking of the sample.

To pick a representative sample, the method of coneing and quartering may be used. The material to be sampled is placed in a conical shaped pile. A thorough mixing is accomplished by removing material at the base of the cone and placing it on the top of a new pile. During this process samples are taken from various points around the circumference of the base of the old cone. The new cone is afterwards flattened until a circular layer of uniform thickness is obtained. The flattened cone is then quartered and the opposite quarters selected by chance are retained, remixed, and the process of coneing and quartering is repeated The analytical sample is taken from the material that has been finally retained.

Larger lots of material can be divided into sections and increment samples taken from each section and combined to form the gross sample. To this gross sample can be applied the method of coneing and quartering to obtain a representative sample.

Mechanical sampling is faster and more accurate than hand sampling. To use mechanical sample machines requires that the sample be in motion. The gross sample that is obtained is used to provide the laboratory sample, and the analysis sample can be taken from it. To reduce the size of the gross sample to a smaller increment, **riffles** can be used. A riffle is a series of troughs divided into an even number of segments, each set of two adjacent segments delivering the material into opposite sides of the trough. Thus each portion of sample falling on a pair of adjacent segments is divided in half. Such a riffle is shown in Figure 3.1.

In addition to the method and technique of taking a sample, another variable is introduced when one is dealing with solid samples. This is the particle size in the sample. In many cases this is the most important characteristic of the sample. The decomposition and/or solution of the sample often depends on the particle size.

Liquids

The sampling of homogeneous liquids is much simpler than the sampling of either solids or gases. The sample for analysis requires only an extraction of a portion of the liquid material. If the liquid is not homogeneous, sampling requires the use of many techniques and is dependent upon the type of mixture to be sampled.

Samples can be taken from various levels within the container and analyzed separately or they can be combined to form a gross sample. If liquids are immiscible, they present a definite sampling problem if the size of the container and the amount of each of the substances is not known. Special sampling tubes can be constructed to enable the sampler to obtain a sample from each layer. If this is not possible, then rapid mixing is undertaken and a sample is taken from the mixture. This sample is placed in a graduated cylinder and the layers can be used to provide samples for analysis. Several samples can be taken under conditions of mixing and placed in graduates of similar cross section. From the heights of the various levels within the graduates, the reproducibility of the sampling technique can be estimated.

Liquids can be sampled from the stream (line of flow) at various points and at various times. It must be recognized that the points and times of sampling must not coincide with any periodic variation; otherwise the sampling procedure will be biased. To eliminate the chance of bias, the sample must be taken only after a thorough study of known or suspected periodic variations.

Gases

The problems involved in sampling gaseous mixtures are quite different, and many times more difficult, than in the sampling of either liquids or solids. Gases are usually collected by the displacement of a liquid in which they are immiscible. The most satisfactory liquid is mercury. Sampling mixtures of gases under pressure in the liquefied state and atmospheric sampling require a rather complicated procedure, a complete discussion of which is beyond the scope of this volume.

DRYING THE SAMPLE

After a solid analytical sample has been obtained, it is necessary to dry it to remove the adsorbed water. If care is not taken to dry the sample and to store it in a desiccator containing a good desiccant, the chance for the exchange of water between the atmosphere and the sample is excellent. The composition of the sample may be changed significantly by this process. The water content of the sample must be known or the analytical results will be just an estimate of the composition. If the water content is known and the analysis was performed on a wet sample, the result can be converted to a dry basis, or, if performed on a dry basis, the results can be expressed on an "as is" basis. This term generally means that the results represent the analysis of the original wet material.

The most common method of drying a sample is to put the material to be analyzed in a weighing bottle and to place the bottle in an oven set at 100–105°C for one hour or more. This will remove the adsorbed water, allowing for a reproducible state of dryness for successive samples. Not all of the nonessential water is removed by drying at this temperature. Nonessential water is water that is adsorbed on the surface or mechanically entrapped within the crystal and has no stoichiometric proportions to the other atoms in the compound. If it is necessary to remove the nonessential water completely, higher temperatures must be used. Change in composition or secondary reactions must be considered among the possibilities if higher temperatures are used. Such processes as loss of water of crystallization or oxidation could take place.

After the sample is heated in the oven, the loosely stoppered weighing bottle is stored in a desiccator until cool. After the substance in the weighing bottle has reached room temperature, the bottle is weighed with its top on securely.

WEIGHING THE SAMPLE

It is customary to prepare replicate samples for analysis. Triplicate samples are usually carried through the analysis but in some cases quadruplicate samples may be desirable. A fourth sample is advisable when the procedure is attempted for the first time. Three samples would remain in case of an error in procedure that would cause the rejection of one sample.

To keep the number of weighings to a minimum, samples are weighed by difference. The weighing bottle and its contents are weighed. A portion of the substance is removed by pouring it into a container in which the sample will be dissolved. The bottle and its contents are weighed again. The difference in weight of the bottle before and after the removal of the portion is the weight of the sample taken from the bottle.

The weighing bottle should be handled with a clean cloth, small tongs, a piece of chamois, or a strip of paper pinched around it in such a manner that the bottle can be handled without the fingers touching it.

Powders and solid materials can be transferred by pouring through a powder funnel. This procedure is particularly useful when transferring the solid material to a volumetric flask or similar container. A camel's hair brush can be used to transfer the final traces of the powder. In general, the funnel should be washed with the solvent being used to dissolve the sample, in order to be sure that all of the sample has been removed from the powder funnel.

Liquids can be weighed in small flasks or containers having ground glass stoppers. The containers are required to be stoppered to prevent the evaporation of the sample.

A common practice in routine analytical procedure when weighing an exactly predetermined weight of sample is to use a tare. A **tare** is a piece of metal that is the exact weight of the sample required plus the weight of the watch glass on which the solid sample is placed. The solid sample is added to the watch glass with a spatula until the state of balance is attained. The sample weight can be reproduced very easily from sample to sample.

Under no circumstances are solids or liquids weighed directly on the balance pan. Liquids are weighed in a container, and solids are weighed either in a container or on a watch glass.

DECOMPOSITION AND DISSOLUTION OF SAMPLES

Once a representative sample is obtained and weighed, the next step in a wet analysis is to dissolve the sample. The decomposition and dissolution of the sample must not involve the loss of material and should not introduce any substance that will complicate the analysis. The latter requirement is one that is often compromised, since the best method of solution may require the addition of some interferences that must be recovered at a later time in the procedure.

Acids are used extensively because the excess usually can be removed by volatilization. Fusion with acid and alkaline fluxes is a common method used to bring material into solution. The disadvantage in this method is that material is introduced which is difficult to remove and in many cases is undesirable. Organic solvents can be used to dissolve organic materials. A variety of solvents and solvent mixtures, described in the literature, are available to aid in the problem of dissolution of organic materials. The inorganic sample is dissolved in water whenever possible. With the aid of suitable acids, fluxes, or complexing agents, nearly any inorganic material can be brought into solution.

Acids

Acids can be classified as oxidizing and nonoxidizing. The principal oxidizing acids are nitric, hot concentrated sulfuric, and hot concentrated perchloric. The common nonoxidizing acids are hydrochloric, phosphoric, dilute sulfuric, and dilute perchloric.

1. Nitric Acid

This is a strong oxidizing agent. It can be used to attack active metals, inert metals, nonferrous alloys, and the acid-insoluble sulfides. The excess of acid can be removed by displacement with sulfuric acid or by destroying it with excess hydrochloric acid.

2. Hot Concentrated Sulfuric Acid

This is an excellent solvent for sulfides. It dissolves all of the common metals. It can be used to displace the anion of a more volatile acid from solution by evaporation to fumes of sulfur trioxide.

3. Concentrated Perchloric Acid

This acid is the most versatile of all acids. It dissolves most all of the common metals. It is a strong oxidizing agent when hot and destroys organic matter rapidly and efficiently. Extreme **caution** must be maintained because many easily oxidizable substances react with explosive violence. Evaporations using perchloric acid should be conducted in a hood that has a **short, direct** discharge to the atmosphere to minimize the build up of perchlorates in the fume system. Such a build up can result in a disastrous explosion.

4. Hydrochloric Acid

Hydrochloric acid dissolves those metals that are above hydrogen in the electromotive series. The reaction is slow with lead, nickel, cobalt, cadmium, and a few other metals above hydrogen. Ferro-alloys are soluble in this reagent. The acid-soluble sulfides are soluble in hydrochloric acid as are most oxides and the salts of weak acids. Some silicates can be decomposed in dilute acid leaving behind a residue of silica that can be removed if its presence interferes in subsequent steps.

5. Dilute Sulfuric Acid

The active metals are soluble in dilute sulfuric acid. As with hydrochloric acid, the action may be too slow to be used when the potential is near that of hydrogen (*e.g.* lead).

6. Dilute Perchloric Acid

This behaves quite differently from concentrated perchloric acid. It can be used routinely as a strong acid solution for the dissolution of substances such as carbonates, oxides, and phosphates of most common metals.

Combinations of two acids or an acid and a complexing agent can be used as a means of dissolving the sample. Any combination that is effective in bringing a sample into solution without the loss of any of its components can be used.

Fluxes

Fused salt media used to decompose samples to make possible their dissolution are called **fluxes.** The flux is mixed with the sample in a ratio of 10 or 20 to 1, flux to sample, and heated in a suitable crucible to a temperature at which the flux will become molten. When the melt becomes clear and homogeneous, the reaction is usually complete. After the mass has cooled, it is extracted with water or dilute acid to bring the solid cake into solution. The flux can be either alkaline or acidic.

1. Sodium Carbonate

This is the most commonly used alkaline flux for the fusion attack on silicates. The fusion is effected in a platinum crucible. Sodium or potassium hydroxide cannot be used in platinum. In this case a gold or nickel crucible is used.

2. Borax

This is a strong decomposing agent and can be used with advantage on refractory minerals such as chromite. Boron introduced in the fusion may provide interference in later analytical procedures.

3. Potassium Pyrosulfate

Potassium pyrosulfate is an extremely powerful acid flux, forming a melt at about 300°C. It is used for dissolving oxides that are difficult to bring into solution, but is of little value for the decomposition of silicates. It can be used with platinum or silica crucibles. If heating occurs too rapidly, sulfur trioxide fumes will be liberated. Thus the temperature should be no higher than necessary to keep the salt well fused until the particles of powder have been dissolved.

4. Sodium Peroxide

Sodium peroxide is one of the most effective of the alkaline oxidizing fluxes. It attacks most substances, making it difficult to find a crucible in which to conduct the fusion. Nickel or iron crucibles can be used, and the metal that is introduced by the attack of the alkaline melt is usually not a serious interference. Crucibles of the metal zirconium are especially resistant to the action of fused sodium peroxide.

The dissolution of the sample requires that the method be effective and not require too long a time. If the proper method for dissolving the sample is chosen, both of these requirements can be attained. If, in addition to the solution of the sample, some separation can be achieved, more time will be saved in the accomplishment of the analysis.

PART II

VOLUMETRIC METHODS OF ANALYSIS

CHAPTER **4**

Introduction to Volumetric Analysis

In *volumetric* analysis, the chemist determines the volume of a solution, the exact concentration of which is known, required for reaction with a known amount of sample to be analyzed. The solution of known concentration is called the **standard solution.** The process used to carry out the addition of the standard solution to complete the chemical reaction is known as a **titration.** The volume of the solution added is measured with a buret. Volumetric methods are often called titrimetric methods since they require a titration.

The standard solution is added in an amount that is chemically equivalent to the amount of the substance being determined in the sample. The point at which this equivalency is satisfied is called the **equivalence point.** To provide a means of determining when the equivalence point has been reached requires the addition of an auxiliary reagent called an **indicator.** The indicator will undergo a visual change when the reaction between the standard solution and the substance being titrated is virtually complete. The point at which this visual change takes place in the titration is called the **endpoint** of the reaction. The experimentally determined endpoint is not exactly the same as the theoretically calculated equivalence point. The degree of agreement between these two values is dependent on the choice of indicator. The indicator which gives the closest agreement between the endpoint and the equivalence point is the most desirable. The difference in volume between the experimentally determined endpoint and the calculated equivalence point is called the **titration error.** The choice of indicator is such that the titration error will be as small as possible; in any case it should be within the experimental error of the method in use. One means of determining the extent of this error is to determine the **indicator blank.** This can be accomplished by titrating with the standard solution a solution containing all of the reagents except the substance to be determined. The volume of the standard solution required to cause the desired change in the indicator is the indicator blank and is used to determine the titration error.

Volumetric methods differ from gravimetric methods in that the amount of reagent is accurately measured, and only an amount equivalent to the substance being titrated is added. Most reactions that take place quantitatively can be measured on the basis of a titration. Gravimetric methods depend on the separation of the substance in a weighable form from the remainder of the solution, whereas in volumetric methods any type of reaction can occur.

Types of Volumetric Methods of Analysis

Volumetric methods are generally classified according to the kind of reaction that takes place during the titration.

Acid-Base Reactions

Acids can be titrated with a standard solution of a base; bases can be titrated with a standard solution of an acid. The two processes are called acidimetry-alkalimetry. The reaction of hydrogren ion with hydroxyl ion in aqueous solution is called **neutralization.** The following equation generally represents the reaction that takes place, regardless of the specific acid or base.

$$H^+ + OH^- \rightleftharpoons H_2O$$

Oxidation-Reduction Reactions

Volumetric methods of this type are based on reactions which involve a transfer of electrons. An oxidizing agent may be titrated with a standard solution of a reducing agent, and the reverse can also be done. Reactions using oxidizing agents such as potassium dichromate, potassium permanganate, cerium(IV) sulfate, iodine, and reducing agents such as iron(II) sulfate, arsenic(III) oxide, tin(II) chloride, sodium thiosulfate, and copper(II) ion are encountered frequently and are well known.

Precipitation Reactions

These volumetric methods make use of the formation of a precipitate when a standard solution is added. An example of this kind of reaction is the determination of halides using silver nitrate.

$$Ag^+ + Cl^- \rightarrow AgCl$$

Complex Formation Reactions (Chelometric Methods)

Methods of this type depend on the formation of a complex ion with the standard solution of the complex forming reagent (chelon). An important example of this kind of volumetric method is the use of ethylenediaminetetraacetic acid (EDTA) solution in the determination of various metallic ions and in the determination of the hardness of water.

Requirements for a Volumetric Reaction

For a given reaction to be used as a basis for a titration, the following requirements must be fulfilled:

(1) The reaction must proceed quantitatively as represented by the equation for the reaction. Side reactions make the principal process of little value for analytical purposes. Therefore, there should be no side reactions.

(2) The reaction should be rapid. Since the rate of chemical reaction depends on several factors, such as concentration of reactants, temperature, and presence of catalysts and inhibitors, slow reactions can be made to proceed at a more favorable rate by making appropriate changes in the conditions.

(3) The reaction should proceed essentially to completion. The reaction equilibrium should favor the formation of the products since an excess of reagent is usually not added to force the reaction to completion.

(4) A means of determining the equivalence point is necessary. Indicators that undergo a color change are the most convenient. Other methods, such as sudden changes in potential, conductivity, or similar properties, can be used.

The reactions that fulfill the above requirements the best are reversible reactions. An example of this type of reaction is the quantitative neutralization of an acid or a base. The reactions proceed rapidly, directly, and with the possibility of an exact determination of the equivalence point. Irreversible reactions are difficult to treat from a theoretical basis since significant equilibrium constants are not available. These reactions have a higher probability of side reactions. There are many reactions that satisfy all the necessary requirements for a volumetric method except that a suitable indicator is not available. This is often the case in precipitation and complex formation methods of volumetric analysis.

Steps in a Volumetric Analytical Determination

Many of the operations involved in a volumetric analytical determination are common to all analytical methods. The selection, preparation, and dissolution of the sample are steps that need to be completed for all determinations. These operations have been discussed in Chapter 3. Volumetric methods differ in those steps required for the preparation and standardization of the reagent solution and in the method of making the final measurement—the titration of the sample.

Primary Standard Requirements

The reaction of the primary standard with the solution to be standardized must satisfy the general requirements for volumetric reactions. In addition the primary standard must meet the following specifications:

(1) It must be readily available in a form of known purity. It is preferable that the substance be a solid.

(2) The reagent must be of a definite constant composition.

(3) It must be stable at temperatures used for drying. Reagents that easily absorb moisture present difficulties in weighing, and therefore do not make desirable primary standards. Hydrates are not usually employed because of the difficulty in drying them without the removal of water of hydration causing a partial decomposition. This makes the purity and composition of the reagent indefinite.

(4) The substances should have a relatively high equivalent weight. This will allow the size of the sample to be large enough to satisfy the precision required in weighing to attain the necessary accuracy without the need of exceptionally large volumes of titrant. Low equivalent weight substances may be used, however, since large samples can be weighed and dissolved and aliquot portions taken for standardization.

(5) The substance must be soluble under the conditions of the reaction. Since most of the common reactions in analytical determinations take place in aqueous medium, the primary standard must be soluble in water.

Listed below are some of the reagents that are frequently used for primary standards and the type of standardization reaction employed.

Acidimetry-alkalimetry. Reagents: sodium carbonate (Na_2CO_3), sulfamic acid (HSO_3NH_2), potassium acid phthalate ($KHC_8H_4O_4$), constant boiling hydrochloric acid (HCl), 2,4,6-trinitrobenzoic acid ($HC_7H_2O_2(NO_2)_3$), benzoic acid ($HC_7H_5O_2$).

Oxidation-reduction. Oxidizing agents: potassium dichromate ($K_2Cr_2O_7$), potassium bromate ($KBrO_3$), potassium iodate (KIO_3), Iodine (I_2).

Reducing agents: sodium oxalate ($Na_2C_2O_4$), tin(II) chloride ($SnCl_2$), arsenic(III) oxide (As_2O_3), electrolytic iron (Fe), iron(II) sulfate ($FeSO_4$), sodium thiosulfate ($Na_2S_2O_3$).

Precipitation or complex formation. Reagents: silver (Ag), silver nitrate ($AgNO_3$), various metal salts depending on the particular reaction being used.

Preparation of a Standard Solution

A standard solution may be prepared in either of two ways. If the reagent to be used in the preparation of the titrating solution can be obtained in a condition of known purity, it may be weighed directly and a solution of known concentration be prepared. The accurately weighed sample is placed in a volumetric flask, dissolved, and diluted to the exact volume in the manner described in Chapter 2 on the use of volumetric equipment. The concentration of the resulting solution will be known with the same accuracy as are the weight of the standard and the volume of the flask.

There are not many reagents that can be used for the direct preparation of a standard solution. One of the reagents most commonly used in this way is potassium dichromate; its purity can be known accurately, and it does not change during the sample weighing procedure.

The second way, the usual one, for the preparation of a standard solution is to make up a solution to the approximate concentration required, and then to standardize the solution by comparison with a reagent of known concentration.

Standardization of a Solution

The process of comparing a solution with a reagent of known concentration or analysis is called **standardization.** A primary standard or a secondary standard may be used for this purpose. The use of secondary standards, reagents that have been standardized against a primary standard, increases the possibility of error because of the additional operations required.

To perform the standardization, an accurately weighed portion of the pure, dry, primary standard is dissolved and titrated with the solution to be standardized. The size of the weighed sample of the standard should be such that about 30–40 milliliters of solution will be required to reach the equivalence point. This minimizes the errors of reading the buret and of the determination of the endpoint. Knowing the weight of the primary standard and the volume of solution needed to reach the endpoint, the concentration of the reagent can be calculated.

The calculations involved in finding the amount of the constituent being determined (whether by use of volumes and concentrations of solutions, or by weights of precipitates, or other kinds of information) are ultimately based on chemical formulas and equations and are called **stoichiometric calculations** or **stoichiometry.**

Preservation of Standard Solutions

Special precautions are required for storage and preservation of standard solutions. The solution should be kept in tightly stoppered containers to prevent evaporation, which will cause an increase in concentration. It is very important that the container be shaken well to mix the contents thoroughly before any of the solution is withdrawn. This will ensure uniform composition of the portion removed as well as of the solution remaining in the stock container. Unused parts of the withdrawn portion should not be returned to the original container, because of the danger of contaminating the main portion of the solution.

It is necessary to store some standard solutions in stoppered dark bottles, or to keep the clear bottles in the dark to prevent the occurrence of light catalyzed decomposition. This precaution is important when solutions of potassium permanganate, silver nitrate, and similar light sensitive solutions are to be stored. Standard solutions of sodium thiosulfate must be protected from decomposition by bacteria. Some standard solutions, such as sodium hydroxide solution, require protection from atmospheric gases. In the case of sodium hydroxide, carbon dioxide from the atmosphere reacts with the solution to cause a change in concentration.

Common Errors in Volumetric Determinations

Some of the most frequently occurring errors in volumetric determinations are associated with the determination of the concentration of the standard solution. The standardization value may be incorrect as a result of the uncertainty in the purity of the primary standard, decomposition of the solution on standing, poor choice of indicator, improper calibration of volumetric equipment, and changes in temperature.

Most other common errors are the result of careless laboratory technique. Errors in weighing, mechanical losses of solution during titration or during transfer of solutions, improper mixing of solutions, dirty burets, pipets, and similar volumetric apparatus, and errors in judgment of the endpoint are some of the most frequently occurring errors that can be eliminated by careful laboratory work.

The larger the number of operations that are performed in a determination, the greater the possibility of error. Therefore it is best to keep the number of operations used in each analysis at a minimum.

Stoichiometry of Volumetric Methods

In an earlier section (see page 41) stoichiometry was defined as the calculations involved in obtaining the percentage of the constituent being determined. To determine this stoichiometric relationship it is first necessary to review the various ways of expressing concentrations.

1. Weight Per Unit Volume

The concentration of the solution is expressed in terms of the number of grams of solute per liter of solution. It can also be given in the number of milligrams of solute per milliliter of solution. This is a simple and direct method of expressing the concentration but inconvenient from the stoichiometric point of view, since substances do not react gram for gram but on a molecule basis.

2. Percentage Composition

The concentration given in this manner is expressed as grams of solute per 100 grams of solution. Thus a 1% solution is prepared by dissolving one gram of solute in 99 grams of solvent.

3. Volume Ratio

Frequently a solution of a reagent is given in the numerical ratio of the concentrated reagent to water. For example, ammonium hydroxide (1:2) is prepared by mixing one volume of concentrated ammonium hydroxide with two volumes of water. Generally this means of expressing concentration is used for reagents not being used as standard solutions.

4. Molar Methods and Formal Methods

Since one gram molecular weight (mole) of any solute contains the same number of molecules, using this means of expressing concentration eliminates the disadvantages that result from the use of solutions prepared by weight-per-unit-volume methods. A one **molar** solution is a solution that contains one gram molecular weight of solute per liter of solution. Therefore 40.0 grams of sodium hydroxide (1 mole) dissolved in one liter of solution results in the formation of a one molar solution of sodium hydroxide (1 M NaOH). A solution of similar strength can be prepared by dissolving 40.0 milligrams of sodium hydroxide in one milliliter of solution. The mathematical expression used to calculate the molarity of a given solution can be expressed as

$$M = \frac{W_g}{M.W. \times V_l}$$

where M is the molarity, W_g is the number of grams of solute, $M.W.$ is the gram molecular weight of the solute, and V_l is the volume of the solution measured in liters. This expression can also be written using units of milligrams for weight of the sample, the molecular weight, and milliliters for volume of the solution.

The number of moles of solute can be obtained from the expression

$$n = M \times V_l$$

where n represents the number of moles of solute. Using the volume of the solution measured in milliliters, the number of millimoles will be obtained. Thus equal volumes of two solutions having the same molarity contain the same number of moles and they will contain the same number of molecules.

A one **formal** solution is prepared by dissolving one gram formula weight of a solute in one liter of solution. To prepare a one formal solution of sodium hydroxide (1 F NaOH), 40.0 grams of sodium hydroxide is dissolved in sufficient distilled water to give one liter of solution. It is apparent that molarity and formality are identical in value.

It is advantageous to express concentrations in terms of molarity or formality because the stoichiometric relationships between the reactants are in simple ratios.

5. Normal Solutions

A one **normal** solution is prepared by dissolving one gram equivalent weight of a solute in one liter of solution. A solution prepared by dissolving one milligram equivalent weight in a milliliter of solution is also one normal (1 *N*). This definition of normality can be expressed according to the relationship

$$N = \frac{Eq.}{V_l} \qquad \text{or} \qquad N = \frac{Meq.}{V_{ml}}$$

where N is the normality, $Eq.$ is the number of gram equivalents of solute, $Meq.$ is the number of milligram equivalents of solute, V_l is the volume of solution measured in liters and V_{ml} is the volume measured in milliliters.

The number of gram equivalents of a solute can be determined by dividing the weight of solute to be added, by the gram equivalent weight of the solute. In the same manner, the number of milligram equivalents (milliequivalents) can be obtained by dividing the weight of the solute measured in milligrams, by the milligram equivalent weight. Mathematically these two definitions can be expressed as

$$Eq. = \frac{W_g}{gr.\ eq.\ wt.} \qquad Meq. = \frac{W_{mg}}{mg.\ eq.\ wt.}$$

where $Eq.$ is the number of equivalents, $Meq.$ is the number of milliequivalents, W_g is the weight of solute in grams, W_{mg} is the weight of the solute in milligrams, *gr. eq. wt.* is the gram equivalent weight of the solute, and *mg. eq. wt.* is the milligram equivalent weight of the solute.

The type of reaction that the reagent undergoes determines the value of the gram equivalent weight or the milligram equivalent weight. A given substance can have a gram equivalent weight of one value in acid-base reactions and an entirely different value in an oxidation-reduction reaction. For specific definition of the gram equivalent weight see the discussion of the various types of volumetric methods in the following chapters.

Since the normal solutions used in a given type of volumetric reactions (*e.g.* acid-base, redox) are all referred to a common standard, they have the advantage of being equivalent. On the basis of the definition of normality, the number of milligram equivalents present in a given volume of a solution can be obtained from the relationship

$$V_s \times N_s = Meq._s$$

where V_s is the number of milliliters of standard solution and N_s is the normality of the standard solution. Since the number of milliequivalents of the reagent in the standard solution must equal the number of milliequivalents of the solute in the solution being determined, the fundamental stoichiometric principle in volumetric methods of analysis can be stated as follows:

$$Meq._s = Meq._x$$

Since the $Meq._s = Meq._x$ and $Meq._x = V_x \times N_x$, then

$$V_s \times N_s = V_x \times N_x$$

In titrations, this is the basic relationship between the volume and the concentration of two solutions, one being the standard solution whose concentration is known and the other being a solution whose concentration is to be calculated.

When the actual concentration of the solution to be titrated is unknown but the weight of the sample or solute dissolved is accurately known, the following mathematical statement gives the relationship between the weight and the volume of the solution used in the titration.

$$V_{ml} \times N = \frac{W_{mg}}{mg.\ eq.\ wt.}$$

where V_{ml} is the volume of the solution added in the titration, measured in milliliters, N is the normality of the solution added, W_{mg} is the weight of the substance being determined and *mg. eq. wt.* is the milligram equivalent weight of the substance being determined.

It is apparent that this relationship can be used in calculating the normality of a standard solution on titration with a primary standard.

The relationship that will give the percentage of the analyzed constituent in the sample is

$$\frac{V_{ml} \times N_s \times mg.\ eq.\ wt.\ A \times 100}{W_{mg}} = \%A$$

where V_{ml} is the volume measured in milliliters of the standard solution of normality N_s (*mg. eq. wt.*), A is the milligram equivalent weight of constituent A, W_{mg} is the weight of the sample containing constituent A, measured in milligrams, and 100 is the factor to give percentage of constituent A.

CHAPTER 5

Theory of Neutralization

Methods that are employed to determine the acidity or basicity of a sample by titration, using a standard solution of a base or an acid, have been classified under the general title of acidimetry-alkalimetry. The process of reaction of an equivalent amount of an acid and a base is called **neutralization.** The essential reaction in neutralization is that of hydrogen ion and hydroxyl ion combining to form water; or it may involve combination of one of these ions with another ion to form some other weak electrolyte. Reactions representative of acidimetric-alkalimetric methods of analysis are described in Chapter 4.

Theories of Acid-Base Reactions

According to the classical theory an acid is a substance that provides hydrogen ions in aqueous solution, and a base is a substance that gives hydroxyl ions in aqueous solution. This definition is illustrated by the general equations

$$HA \rightleftharpoons H^+ + A^- \quad \textbf{(5.1)}$$

$$BOH \rightleftharpoons B^+ + OH^- \quad \textbf{(5.2)}$$

The reaction of neutralization can be represented in the following manner:

$$HA + BOH \rightleftharpoons H_2O + B^+A^- \quad \textbf{(5.3)}$$

Because of the slight ionization of water, the equilibrium of the reaction favors the formation of the products; thus the reaction is said to be essentially complete.

Classical acid theory by definition requires that the solution must contain free hydrogen ions (H^+), or protons. It is highly unlikely that centers of such large charge-to-size ratio could exist as such in water solution since the water molecule is a rather strong dipole. The hydrogen ion more accurately exists in water solution in a solvated form (hydronium ion) represented by the equation

$$H^+ + H_2O \rightleftharpoons H_3O^+ \quad \textbf{(5.4)}$$

Thus the reaction written in equation 5.1, representing the dissociation of an acid, is more properly written as

$$HA + H_2O \rightleftharpoons H_3O^+ + A^- \quad (5.5)$$

The difference between equations 5.1 and 5.5. is immaterial, if it is realized that the concentration of the water in any reaction in aqueous solution is essentially constant and that each time H^+ is written the writer understands that the hydronium ion is a closer representation of the actual species in solution. For convenience the hydrogen ion in aqueous solution will be represented by H^+ rather than H_3O^+ in later sections of this text.

Brönsted and Lowry have shown that classical theory is not entirely satisfactory to explain the neutralization reaction. They extended the classical definition of acids and bases to include as acids all substances that have a tendency to split off protons—proton donors—and as bases all substances that have a tendency to combine with protons—proton acceptors. In the light of this extension there should always be some ionic dissociation of common acids or bases in aqueous solution. For example,

$$H^+ + \underset{\text{(base)}}{H_2O} \rightleftharpoons \underset{\text{(acid)}}{H_3O^+} \quad (5.6)$$

The dissociation of an acid in water is due to the basic properties of water. The dissociation of an acid in a polar solvent is shown by the general equation

$$\underset{\text{(acid)}}{HA} + \underset{\text{(base)}}{S} \rightleftharpoons \underset{\text{(acid)}}{SH^+} + \underset{\text{(base)}}{A^-} \quad (5.7)$$

If the solvent has no basic properties (aprotonic solvent), the dissolved acid will remain completely in the undissociated form. In such aprotonic solvents as benzene and other hydrocarbons this is the case. Yet upon the addition of a base in the form of a trace amount of water, dissociation of the acid will occur.

The general equations to represent the formation of conjugate acid-base pairs can be illustrated as follows:

$$\text{acid}_1 + \text{base}_2 \rightleftharpoons \text{acid}_2 + \text{base}_1 \quad (5.8)$$

$$HCl + H_2O \rightleftharpoons H_3O^+ + Cl^- \quad (5.8a)$$

$$H_2O + NH_3 \rightleftharpoons NH_4^+ + OH^- \quad (5.8b)$$

$$H_3O^+ + OH^- \rightleftharpoons H_2O + H_2O \quad (5.8c)$$

$$H_3O^+ + Ac^- \rightleftharpoons HAc + H_2O \quad (5.8d)$$

It should be noted that water can act either as an acid or a base. The dissociation of water is given by the equation

$$H_2O + H_2O \rightleftharpoons H_3O^+ + OH^- \quad (5.9)$$

There are many other polar solvents that have similar amphoteric properties. Alcohols are examples.

The Brönsted-Lowry theory offers many interesting analogies between neutralization (proton transfer) and redox reactions (electron transfer).

Lewis defined acids and bases in terms of electron pair donors and acceptors. Acids are electron pair acceptors and bases are electron pair donors. Using this definition, the process of neutralization is not restricted to the transfer of a proton. An example of neutralization using the Lewis definition is

$$\underset{\text{(acid)}}{BF_3} + \underset{\text{(base)}}{:NH_3} \rightleftharpoons F_3B:NH_3 \tag{5.10}$$

The lone electron pair of the nitrogen is donated to the available vacant orbital of the boron atom to be shared between the two atoms. Thus the boron trifluoride is the acid and ammonia is the base.

Notwithstanding the utility of these modern concepts, the classical concepts are in common use and therefore will be used extensively in the following discussion of neutralization.

Neutralization Equilibria

The fundamental reaction in the chemistry of water as it affects the neutralization process can be expressed as

$$H_2O \rightleftharpoons H^+ + OH^- \tag{5.11}$$

The equilibrium point of this reaction lies well toward the left; therefore, water is essentially a nonionized compound.

The Law of Mass Action can be applied to this equilibrium reaction to give a dissociation constant for water.

$$K_i = \frac{[H^+][OH^-]}{[H_2O]} \tag{5.12}$$

The brackets in the equation indicate that the concentration of the substance within the brackets is expressed in moles per liter. The molar concentration of water is a very large number and remains essentially constant for all aqueous neutralization reactions. A new constant called the ion product of water, K_w, can be defined as follows:

$$K_w = K_i[H_2O] = [H^+][OH^-] \tag{5.13}$$

The value of K_w, since it is derived from the Law of Mass Action, is temperature dependent. At room temperature, 25°C, the numerical value of K_w is 1×10^{-14}.

From equation 5.11, the concentration of hydrogen ion and hydroxyl ion in pure water must be equal, since the ions are formed in equivalent amounts upon the dissociation of water. Since $[H^+] = [OH^-]$, then equation 5.13 can be reduced to

$$[H^+]^2 = 1 \times 10^{-14} \qquad (5.14)$$
$$[H^+] = 1 \times 10^{-7}$$

The concentration of the hydrogen ions in pure water is 0.0000001 M. If the hydrogen ion concentration is greater than this, as is true with acids, the concentration of the hydroxyl ions must be correspondingly less. This is true because the product of the hydrogen ion concentration and the hydroxyl ion concentration is equal to K_w.

If the molar concentration of hydrogen ion, $[H^+]$, or hydroxyl ion, $[OH^-]$, is known, it is very simple to determine the molar concentration of the other in aqueous solution. For example, in an aqueous solution that is 0.01 M in hydrogen ion, the hydroxyl ion concentration is

$$[OH^-] = \frac{K_w}{[H^+]} = \frac{1 \times 10^{-14}}{1 \times 10^{-2}} = 1 \times 10^{-12}\ M.$$

In the same manner, the concentration of the hydrogen ion in an aqueous solution that is 0.05 M in hydroxyl ions can be calculated as follows:

$$[H^+] = \frac{K_w}{[OH^-]} = \frac{1 \times 10^{-14}}{5 \times 10^{-2}} = 2 \times 10^{-13}\ M.$$

*p*H and *p*OH

To eliminate some of the inconvenience of handling the numbers involved in the small concentration of hydrogen ions and hydroxyl ions in neutralization reactions, Sörenson in 1909 proposed that an exponential system be adopted. He called the new term, used as a measure of the hydrogen ion concentration, *p*H. Mathematically, *p*H can be defined as

$$p\text{H} = \log \frac{1}{[H^+]} = -\log [H^+] \qquad (5.15)$$

$$[H^+] = 10^{-p\text{H}} \qquad (5.16)$$

These two expressions are identical mathematically. Using the same type of definition, the hydroxyl ion concentration can be expressed in the logarithmic system as follows:

$$p\text{OH} = \log \frac{1}{[OH^-]} = -\log [OH^-] \qquad (5.17)$$

$$[OH^-] = 10^{-p\text{OH}} \qquad (5.18)$$

If the concentration of the hydrogen ion, $[H^+] = 10^{-7}$, then

$$pH = -\log [H^+] = -\log 10^{-7} = -(-7) = 7$$

Many times, the pH of a solution is known and the value of the corresponding hydrogen ion concentration is desired. The mathematical manipulations are illustrated by the following example.

What is the hydrogen ion concentration of a solution whose pH is 4.5?

$$\begin{aligned} pH &= -\log [H^+] \\ 4.5 &= -\log [H^+] \\ \log [H^+] &= -4.5 = (-5.0 + 0.5) \\ [H^+] &= 3.16 \times 10^{-5}\,M. \end{aligned}$$

To determine the pH of a solution whose hydrogen ion concentration is known requires that the operations be the reverse of those illustrated for converting pH to hydrogen ion concentration.

Applying the notation of Sörenson—where the term p denotes the negative logarithm (−log)—to the value of the ion product of water, K_w, then

$$pK_w = -\log K_w = -\log 1 \times 10^{-14} = 14$$

Using equation 5.13, and taking the negative logarithm of both sides of the equation, the relationship is

$$-\log [H^+] + (-\log [OH^-]) = -\log (1 \times 10^{-14}) \qquad \textbf{(5.19)}$$

From the definition of pH and pOH by equations 5.15 and 5.17, respectively, equation 5.19 can be written as follows:

$$pH + pOH = 14 \qquad \textbf{(5.20)}$$

Neutralization occurs when $[H^+] = [OH^-]$. The value at which the pH equals the pOH is 7 (equation 5.20). A solution whose pH is 7 is said to be neutral. Those solutions whose pH is greater than 7 are said to be basic, and those whose pH is less than 7 are acidic.

A scale of acid strength based on the pH of aqueous solutions has been constructed and is shown diagrammatically in Table 5.1.

A more thorough discussion of the measurement of pH and its use in volumetric titrations will be found in a later section (see page 59).

Acid-Base Indicators

A substance that signals the equivalence point in a volumetric titration is called an **indicator.** In neutralization reactions the indicator must be a sub-

TABLE 5.1

pH–pOH Scale of Acid Strength

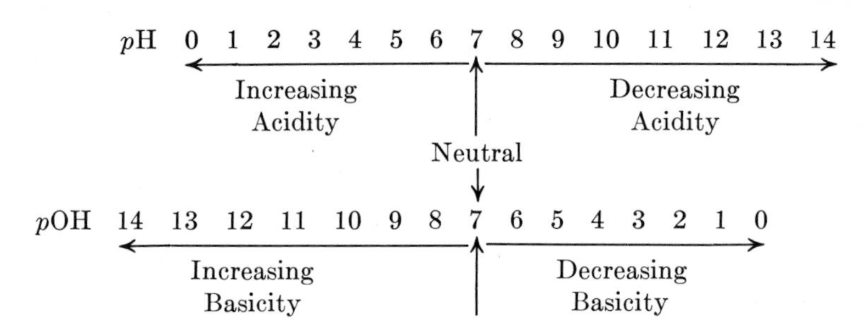

stance whose colorimetric properties depend on the hydrogen ion concentration in the reaction mixture. The color of these substances, usually weak organic acids or bases themselves, must vary over a very small range of hydrogen ion concentration. There can be either two-color indicators, those that change from one color to another, or one-color indicators, those that change from a color to colorless or vice versa. An example of a two-color indicator is methyl orange. It is yellow in basic solution and pink in acid solution. Phenolphthalein illustrates a one-color indicator. It is red in basic solution and colorless in acid solution.

The equilibrium that represents the dissociation of an indicator is identical with that of any weak acid or base. If the formula of an indicator, a weak acid type, is expressed as HIn, then the equation representing its dissociation is

$$\underset{\text{(color A)}}{\mathrm{HIn}} \rightleftharpoons \mathrm{H^+} + \underset{\text{(color B)}}{\mathrm{In^-}} \tag{5.21}$$

The color of the unionized form is different from the color of the ionized form of the indicator.

The ionization constant of the indicator, K_{in}, sometimes referred to as the indicator constant can be shown to be

$$K_{in} = \frac{[\mathrm{H^+}][\mathrm{In^-}]}{[\mathrm{HIn}]} \tag{5.22}$$

Upon rearrangement,

$$[\mathrm{H^+}] = K_{in}\frac{[\mathrm{HIn}]}{[\mathrm{In^-}]} \tag{5.23}$$

The color of the indicator will depend on the relative concentration of HIn, the unionized form, and In^-, the ionized form, of the indicator. Since K_{in} is constant, the ratio $[HIn]/[In^-]$ is dependent on the concentration of the hydrogen ion. In some cases color change of the indicator is due to a molecular rearrangement. As a result of this fact, the simplified explanation used here is not strictly correct. The ionization process of the indicator, however, appears to be the limiting case; therefore the simplified form of the explanation can be used in this discussion. Using the pH notation, equation 5.23 can be expressed as

$$-\log [H^+] = -\log K_{in} + \left(-\log \frac{[HIn]}{[In^-]}\right)$$

$$pH = pK_{in} + \log \frac{[In^-]}{[HIn]} \tag{5.24}$$

The detection of a change in color of the indicator when visual methods are used depends on the color perception of the observer. The average observer can detect 10 parts of the color of one form in the presence of 100 parts of the color in the other form. From equation 5.24, the pH range through which it is normally possible to observe a color change is shown to be

$$pH = pK_{in} + \log \tfrac{1}{10} = pK_{in} - 1$$

$$pH = pK_{in} + \log \tfrac{10}{1} = pK_{in} + 1$$

$$pH = pK_{in} \pm 1 \tag{5.25}$$

The range of color change corresponds to a hundredfold change in hydrogen ion concentration. Using a spectrophotometer, the range can be increased by a factor of 10 on either the acidic or the basic side of the indicator.

The color and structure of some representative indicators in both the acid form and the basic form are given in Table 5.2.

A variety of indicators is suitable for neutralization reactions. These indicators have been described in the literature. The most suitable indicators are those that give a sharp color change over a narrow pH range. Table 5.3 gives a series of indicators with pH range, pK_{in}, and color change. This information is useful in acid-base titrations.

A single indicator solution, called a universal indicator, that will give different colors over a wide range of pH can be prepared by mixing several indicators. The indicators are properly selected so that they cover the range desired. Paper can be impregnated with these mixed indicator solutions and used to determine the pH of a solution.

One example of a universal indicator is a mixture of phenolphthalein, methyl red, dimethylaminoazobenzene, bromthymol blue, and thymol blue in ethyl alcohol solution. After solution, sodium hydroxide is added until the solution becomes yellow. The color changes that occur are: red at pH 2, orange at pH 4, yellow at pH 6, green at pH 8, and blue at pH 10. Although the accuracy never exceeds one pH unit, nevertheless, universal indicators are useful for approximate pH determinations.

TABLE 5.2

Examples of Acidic and Basic Form of Some Common Acid-Base Indicators

Acidic Form	Name	Basic Form
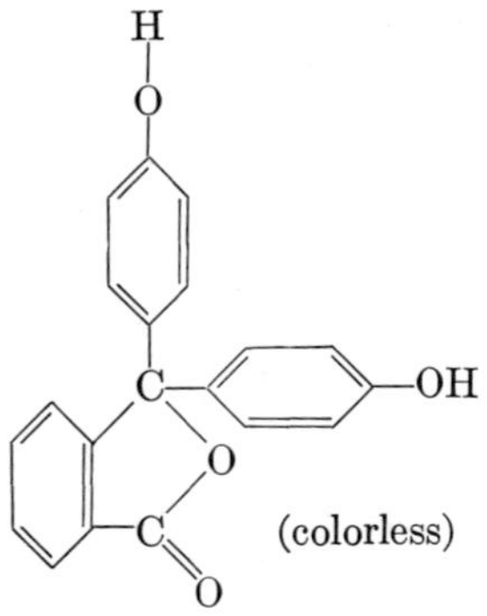 (colorless)	Phenolphthalein	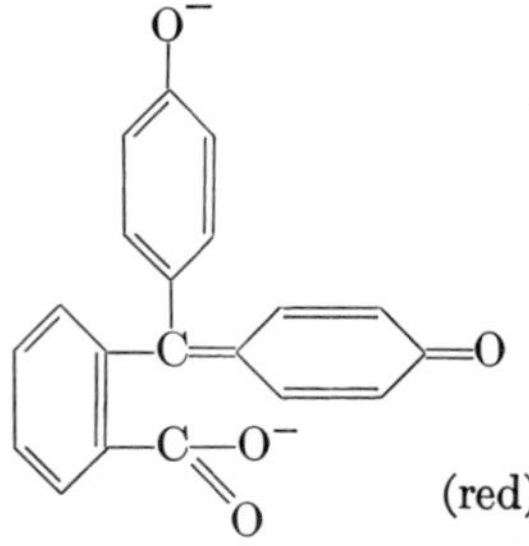 (red)
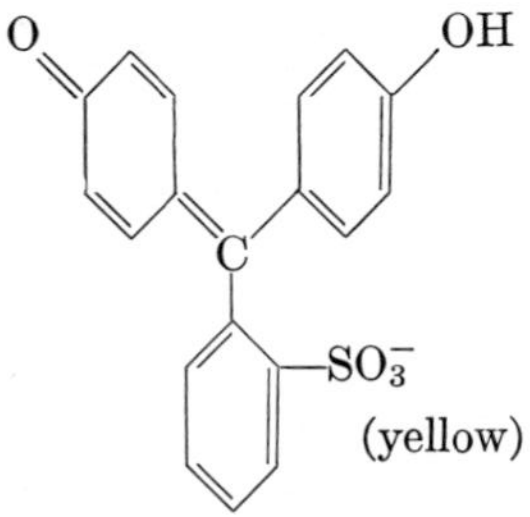 (yellow)	Phenol Red	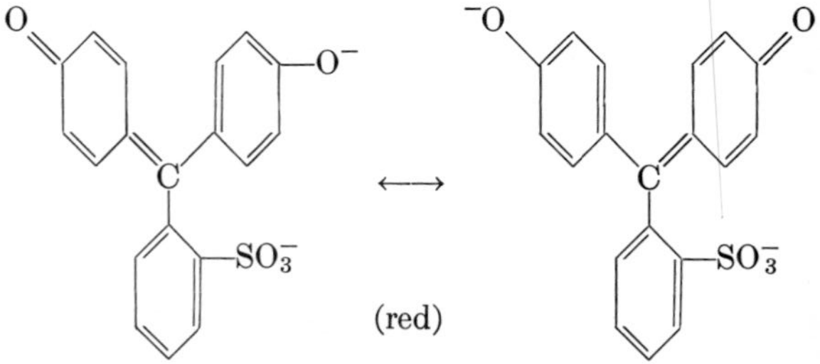 (red)
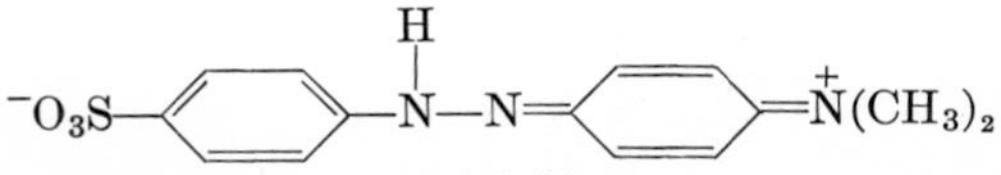 (pink)	Methyl Orange	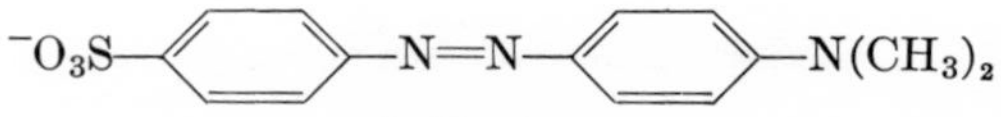 (yellow)

TABLE 5.3

Acid-Base Indicators and pH Range of Color Change

INDICATOR	pK_{in}	pH RANGE	ACID COLOR	BASIC COLOR
Crystal Violet	1.0	0.0–2.0	Green	Blue
m-Cresol Purple	1.5	0.5–2.5	Red	Yellow
Thymol Blue	1.65	1.2–2.8	Red	Yellow
Methyl Yellow	3.3	2.9–4.0	Red	Yellow
Bromphenol Blue	3.85	3.0–4.6	Yellow	Blue
Methyl Orange	3.46	3.1–4.4	Pink	Yellow
Bromcresol Green	4.66	4.0–5.6	Yellow	Blue
Methyl Red	5.0	4.2–6.3	Red	Yellow
Chlorphenol Red	6.0	5.0–7.0	Yellow	Red
Bromcresol Purple	6.12	5.2–6.8	Yellow	Purple
Bromthymol Blue	7.10	6.0–7.6	Yellow	Blue
Phenol Red	7.81	6.8–8.4	Yellow	Red
m-Cresol Purple	8.3	7.6–9.2	Yellow	Purple
Thymol Blue	8.9	8.0–9.6	Yellow	Blue
Phenolphthalein	9.7	8.3–10.5	Colorless	Red
Thymolphthalein	9.9	9.0–10.5	Colorless	Blue
Alizarine Yellow	11.1	10.0–12.0	Yellow	Lilac

The procedure for using impregnated papers is as follows: place a drop of the test solution on the paper and compare the color with a color chart to determine the value of the pH.

Mixtures of two indicators, or of an indicator and a dye, can be used to narrow the pH range and sharpen the color change of ordinary indicators. Bromcresol green mixed with methyl red in the ratio of 3:2 is an example of such an indicator mixture. The color change occurs at pH 5.1. The acid color is red and the alkaline color is green.

Buffer Solutions

Solutions that resist changes of their hydrogen ion or hydroxyl ion concentration are called **buffer solutions.** These buffer solutions are mixtures of a weak acid and its salt or a weak base and its salt. One of the common buffer systems is a solution containing acetic acid and sodium acetate. The buffering action in this case depends on the rather large initial concentration of both the acetic acid and the acetate ion in solution. The following equation may be used as an explanation of the buffer action.

$$HAc \rightleftharpoons H^+ + Ac^- \quad (5.26)$$

The addition of a strong acid to a solution buffered by the acetic acid-acetate mixture results in a shift of the equilibrium shown in equation 5.26 to the left.

If a strong base is added, the hydroxyl ion will combine with the hydrogen ion causing a shift in the equilibrium of equation 5.26 to the right. The effectiveness of the buffering action is determined by the ratio of the acetate ions to acetic acid, $[Ac^-]/[HAc]$, which is not greatly affected by the displacement of the equilibrium in either direction. The net result is that the pH of the solution remains essentially constant.

The point of maximum effectiveness of a given buffer system is attained when the concentration of the unionized acid, [HA], and the concentration of the salt, $[A^-]$, are equal. The value of the pH at this point is equal to the value of the pK_a of the weak acid.

Application of the equilibrium principle to the dissociation of the weak acid, HA, leads to the relationship

$$pH = pK_a + \log \frac{[A^-]}{[HA]} \quad \textbf{(5.27)}$$

If $[A^-] = [HA]$, then

$$pH = pK_a$$

Equation 5.27 can be used as a means of calculating the pH of buffer solutions where [HA] and $[A^-]$ are known.

A similar method of calculation can be applied to buffer solutions prepared by using a solution of a weak base and its salt.

To illustrate the action of a buffer solution, the following example can be used.

A buffer solution is prepared by mixing 50 ml. each of 1 M acetic acid and 1 M sodium acetate. To one 50 ml. portion of this buffer solution is added 1 ml. of 0.1 M hydrochloric acid and to the other 50 ml. portion is added 1 ml. of 0.1 M sodium hydroxide.

The pH of the buffer solution is calculated as follows:

$$pH = pK_a + \log \frac{[Ac^-]}{[HAc]}$$

$$pH = 4.74 + \log \frac{[\frac{50}{100}]}{[\frac{50}{100}]}$$

$$pH = 4.74$$

Upon the addition of 1 ml. of 0.1 M hydrochloric acid, the value of the pH is obtained as follows:

$$[HAc] = \frac{(0.5 + 0.1)}{51} = \left[\frac{0.6}{51}\right]$$

$$[Ac^-] = \frac{(0.5 - 0.1)}{51} = \left[\frac{0.4}{51}\right]$$

$$pH = 4.74 + \log \frac{\left[\frac{0.4}{51}\right]}{\left[\frac{0.6}{51}\right]} = 4.56$$

When 1 ml. of 0.1 M sodium hydroxide is added the resultant pH is found in the same manner.

$$[\text{HAc}] = \frac{(0.5 - 0.1)}{51} = \left[\frac{0.4}{51}\right]$$

$$[\text{Ac}^-] = \frac{(0.5 + 0.1)}{51} = \left[\frac{0.6}{51}\right]$$

$$p\text{H} = 4.74 + \log \frac{\left[\frac{0.6}{51}\right]}{\left[\frac{0.4}{51}\right]} = 4.92$$

The change in pH of the buffer solution is very small compared to the rather large addition of hydrogen ion and hydroxyl ion.

There are descriptions in the literature of many sets of buffer solutions. The mixtures are usually simple to prepare from original materials that are readily obtainable in the pure form. Some of the most common preparations of buffer solutions are those of Clark and Lubs, found in reference 1 listed at the end of this chapter. Other lists can be found in references 2 and 3.

Buffer action plays an important part in physiological processes and biological phenomena, as well as in analytical and industrial chemical processes. Many separation processes in analytical chemistry depend on the careful control of hydrogen ion concentration as well as other ion concentrations.

Gram Equivalent Weight in Neutralization Reactions

The value of one gram equivalent weight of a substance taking part in a neutralization reaction can be defined as the weight of the substance that will furnish, react with, or be chemically equivalent to one gram atom of hydrogen (1.008 grams) in the reaction in which it occurs. For example, in the reaction of hydrochloric acid and sodium hydroxide, the gram equivalent weight of hydrochloric acid is its gram molecular weight, since there is one gram atom of replaceable hydrogen in one mole of acid. If sulfuric acid is used in a neutralization reaction, the gram equivalent weight of sulfuric acid is one half its molecular weight in grams because there are two gram atoms of replaceable hydrogen per mole. A general expression for the determination of the equivalent weight of a substance used in a neutralization could be given as

$$\text{Eq. Wt.} = \frac{\text{Mol. wt. of substance}}{\text{No. of replaceable hydrogen atoms}} \tag{5.28}$$

Therefore, as stated earlier, the equivalent weight of hydrochloric acid is

$$\text{Eq. Wt.} = \frac{\text{M.W. HCl}}{1} = \frac{36.5}{1} = 36.5$$

The equivalent weight of sodium hydroxide is the molecular weight, since sodium hydroxide requires one gram atom of hydrogen for complete neutralization. Thus, sodium hydroxide will replace one gram atom of hydrogen and according to equation 5.18,

$$\text{Eq. Wt.} = \frac{\text{M.W. NaOH}}{1} = \frac{40}{1} = 40$$

The equivalent weights as well as the number of equivalents per mole of several common substances used in neutralization reactions are given in Table 5.4.

Equal volumes of hydrochloric acid and acetic acid of the same normality have the same neutralizing power. These two acids have very different degrees of ionization. Equivalent weights are based on the ability to neutralize and not on the degree of ionization.

The following examples illustrate the stoichiometry involved in neutralization methods.

EXAMPLE I. What weight of sodium carbonate is required to prepare one liter of a 0.1 *N* solution? What is its molarity?

Solution:

A 0.1 *N* solution is prepared by dissolving 0.1 equivalent of sodium carbonate in water and making the solution up to one liter in a volumetric flask.

0.1 equivalent Na_2CO_3 = 0.1 × gr. eq. wt. Na_2CO_3. Since the equivalent weight of Na_2CO_3 is the mol. wt. Na_2CO_3 divided by 2 due to its reaction with two gram atoms of hydrogen ion, it is $\frac{106}{2}$, or 53.

TABLE 5.4

Equivalent Weights of Common Reagents Used in Neutralization Reactions

COMPOUND	EQUIVALENT WEIGHT	EQUIVALENTS PER MOLE
Na_2CO_3	$\frac{Na_2CO_3}{2}$	2
$HC_2H_3O_2$	$\frac{HC_2H_3O_2}{1}$	1
$NaHCO_3$	$\frac{NaHCO_3}{1}$	1
Na_3PO_4	$\frac{Na_3PO_4}{3}$	3
$KHC_8H_4O_4$	$\frac{KHC_8H_4O_4}{1}$	1
$H_2C_2O_4 \cdot 2H_2O$	$\frac{H_2C_2O_4 \cdot 2H_2O}{2}$	2
CaO	$\frac{CaO}{2}$	2

The weight required to prepare one liter of a 0.1 N solution is

$$0.1 \times 53 = 5.3 \text{ grams}$$

Since there are two equivalents per mole of Na_2CO_3, the molarity is calculated as follows:

$$\frac{0.1 \text{ eq./liter}}{2 \text{ eq./mole}} = 0.05 \text{ mole/liter} = 0.05\ M.$$

EXAMPLE II. A solution of H_2SO_4 has a specific gravity of 1.110 and contains 15.7% by weight. What is the normality of this solution?

Solution:

$$\text{Specific gravity} = \frac{\text{wt. in grams 1 ml. } H_2SO_4}{\text{wt. in grams 1 ml. } H_2O}$$

$$1.110 = \frac{W_g\ H_2SO_4}{1}$$

1 ml. H_2SO_4 solution weighs 1.110 grams.

The solution contains 15.7% H_2SO_4 by weight, thus in 1 ml. of solution, the weight of H_2SO_4 is

$$1.110 \times .157 = 0.175 \text{ gram } H_2SO_4\text{/ml.}$$

The milligram equivalent weight of H_2SO_4 is the milligram molecular weight divided by 2 since there are two replaceable hydrogen ions. The milliequivalent weight is

$$\frac{H_2SO_4}{2} = \frac{98}{2} = 49$$

The number of milliequivalents in 175 milligrams of H_2SO_4 is

$$\frac{175}{49} = 3.58 \text{ milliequivalents/ml.}$$

By definition,

$$\text{Normality} = \text{milliequivalents/milliliter}$$

Therefore the H_2SO_4 solution is 3.58 N.

Mechanics of Titration

The process of titration has been described as the addition of a standard solution to complete the chemical reaction. In neutralization reactions, an acid or a base is titrated using a standard solution of a base or an acid. The acidity determined is not the same as the acidity of a solution as given by pH. The acidity measured by pH is the instantaneous hydrogen ion concentration as it exists in solution determined under equilibrium conditions. The acidity by titration is the total acidity of the solution measured by the complete neutralization of the reserve hydrogen ion content under nonequilibrium conditions. It is possible to follow the change in acidity or basicity of the solution by observing the change of *p*H after successive additions of the standard solution. Using this technique, it is possible to determine the endpoint of the reaction from the curve that is obtained by plotting the value of *p*H *vs.* the number of milliliters of standard solution added. Such a curve is called a **titration curve.** The value of the *p*H at the endpoint can be obtained graphically and it can be compared with the calculated value of the *p*H for the equivalence point of the neutralization reaction.

Molar concentrations rather than effective concentrations or activities will be used in the stoichiometric equilibrium calculations. In dilute solutions the differences are very small and correction factors can be used if more rigorous calculations are required.

Strong Acid-Strong Base

A strong acid or strong base is defined as one that is fully ionized in solution. The salts that are formed on neutralization are, with very few exceptions, completely ionized in solution. In a dilute solution a strong acid is completely ionized, making the value of the hydrogen ion concentration equal to the molarity of the acid, if the acid is monoprotic. The value of the hydrogen ion concentration of a 0.01 M solution of hydrochloric acid is also 0.01 M. The calculation of the *p*H of a strong acid or strong base solution is the direct application of the definition of *p*H, since the hydrogen ion concentration or the hydroxyl ion concentration and the molarity of the strong acid or base are identical. For example, the *p*H of a hydrochloric acid solution that is 0.01 M is calculated in the following manner.

$$\begin{array}{ccccc} \mathrm{HCl} & = & \mathrm{H^+} & + & \mathrm{Cl^-} \\ 0.01 & & 0.01 & & 0.01 \end{array}$$

$$p\mathrm{H} = -\log{[\mathrm{H^+}]} = -\log{(0.01)} = 2$$

The calculation of the *p*H of a strong base is done in a similar manner, since the hydroxyl ion concentration is equal to the molarity if the base contains one equivalent per mole.

The salts of strong acids and strong bases do not affect the acidity or basicity of a solution (using the assumption made earlier that molarities rather than activities are used). When a solution of a strong acid is completely neutralized by a solution of a strong base with no other solute present, the overall reaction can be shown as

$$\mathrm{H^+} + \mathrm{OH^-} \rightleftharpoons \mathrm{H_2O} \tag{5.29}$$

The *p*H at the equivalence point will be the same as the *p*H of the solvent. This value is $p\mathrm{H} = 7$ at room temperature when water is the solvent.

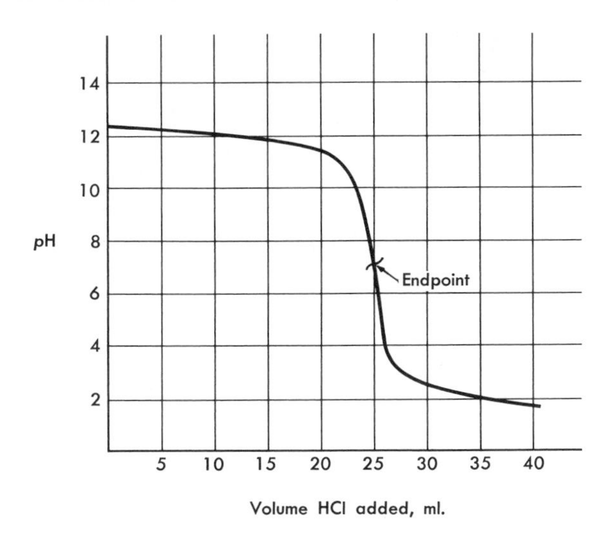

Fig. 5.1. Titration curve of 25 ml. 0.1 *M* NaOH titrated with 0.1 *M* HCl.

If the change in *p*H is followed during neutralization of 25 ml. of 0.1 *M* sodium hydroxide by 0.1 *M* hydrochloric acid, a titration curve, shown in Figure 5.1, is obtained. The *p*H of the equivalence point is 7 and the volume of 0.1 *M* hydrochloric acid required is shown to be 25 ml.

Strong Acid-Weak Base

A weak base is one that is not completely ionized in solution. The concentration of the hydroxyl ion in solution will be less than the molarity of the weak base. The calculation of the *p*H of the solution of a weak base and the *p*H at the equivalence point when it reacts with a strong acid in a neutralization reaction, can be developed from the equilibrium constant relationships between the ionized and the unionized forms of the weak base.

The titration curve that results when 25 ml. of a 0.1 *M* weak base, such as ammonium hydroxide, is titrated with a 0.1 *M* solution of a strong acid, such as hydrochloric acid, can be constructed by plotting the *p*H versus volume of strong acid added. The resultant curve is shown in Figure 5.2. The equivalence point from the titration curve is about *p*H 5.3.

The titration curve may also be constructed from the calculated *p*H values rather than from the values obtained experimentally. The *p*H at the equivalence point can be calculated and compared with the *p*H obtained from the experimentally obtained titration curve. These calculations are divided into several steps.

STEP I. *p*H *of the solution prior to the addition of the standard acid.* The value of the *p*H is calculated from the ionization constant, K_b, relationship of

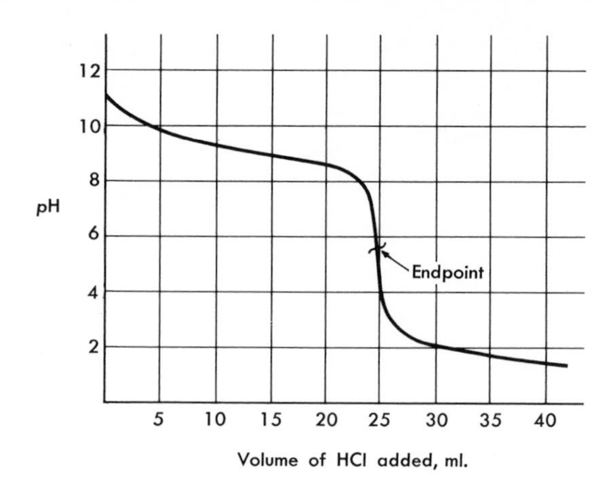

Fig. 5.2. Titration curve of 25 ml. of 0.1 *M* ammonium hydroxide titrated with 0.1 *M* hydrochloric acid.

the weak base. For ammonium hydroxide, the ionization equilibrium can be written as

$$NH_4OH \rightleftharpoons NH_4^+ + OH^- \quad \textbf{(5.30)}$$

The ionization constant, K_b, is expressed as

$$K_b = \frac{[NH_4^+][OH^-]}{[NH_4OH]}$$

$$[OH^-] = K_b \frac{[NH_4OH]}{[NH_4^+]} \quad \textbf{(5.31)}$$

The pOH can be calculated using the hydroxyl ion concentration. The pH of the solution can be obtained from the relationship $pH = 14 - pOH$. In the titration example given, the pH of a 0.1 *M* NH_4OH solution prior to the addition of standard acid is calculated as follows:

The ionization constant, $K_b = 1.75 \times 10^{-5}$. From equation 5.30, $[NH_4^+] = [OH^-]$. Therefore,

$$[OH^-] = \frac{1.75 \times 10^{-5}(0.1 - [OH^-])}{[OH^-]}$$

For an approximation, the term $(0.1 - [OH^-])$ can be reduced to 0.1, since the $[OH^-]$ can be neglected because it is so small in comparison with 0.1. This simplifies the calculation to

$$[OH^-]^2 = (1.75 \times 10^{-5})(0.1)$$

$$[OH^-] = \sqrt{1.75 \times 10^{-6}} = 1.32 \times 10^{-3}$$

$$pOH = -\log(1.32 \times 10^{-3}) = 2.88$$

$$pH = (14 - 2.88) = 11.12$$

STEP II. *The calculation of pH prior to reaching the equivalence point after the addition of standard acid.* The ionization constant equilibrium relationship is used as a basis for calculation. The concentration of the ammonium ion in the solution is obtained from the amount of standard acid added. To illustrate this step in the procedure, the calculation of the pH after the addition of 10 ml. of 0.1 M hydrochloric acid is shown.

After 10 ml. of 0.1 M HCl has been added, there remains 1.5 mmoles of ammonium hydroxide in 35 ml. of solution. This is shown by the following:

$$\begin{aligned} 25 \times 0.1 &= 2.5 \text{ mmoles } NH_4OH \text{ at the beginning} \\ 10 \times 0.1 &= \underline{1.0} \text{ mmoles HCl added} \\ &\quad\ 1.5 \text{ mmoles } NH_4OH \text{ remains} \end{aligned}$$

The total volume of the solution after the addition of 10 ml. of HCl is the original 25 ml. plus the 10 ml. added, giving a total of 35 ml.

The concentrations of the species in solution can be expressed as

$$[NH_4^+] = \frac{1.0}{35} \qquad [NH_4OH] = \frac{1.5}{35}$$

The number of millimoles of NH_4^+ that are formed is the same as the number of millimoles of hydrochloric acid that have been added. This can be seen from the equation

$$NH_4OH + HCl \rightleftharpoons NH_4^+, Cl^- + H_2O$$

For each millimole of hydrochloric acid added, one millimole of NH_4^+, Cl^- is formed.

Substituting the concentrations above in equation 5.31, the following is obtained.

$$[OH^-] = \frac{(1.75 \times 10^{-5})\left(\frac{1.5}{35}\right)}{\left(\frac{1.0}{35}\right)}$$

$$[OH^-] = \frac{(1.75 \times 10^{-5})(1.5)}{1.0} = 2.63 \times 10^{-5}$$

$$pOH = -\log(2.63 \times 10^{-5}) = 4.58$$

$$pH = (14 - 4.58) = 9.42$$

STEP III. *The calculation of the pH at the equivalence point.* To determine the pH at the equivalence point, the effect of the hydrolysis of the salt of the weak base and strong acid formed during the titration must be taken into consideration. There are two equilibria that must be satisfied.

$$NH_4OH \rightleftharpoons NH_4^+ + OH^- \qquad (5.32)$$

$$NH_4^+ + H_2O \rightleftharpoons NH_4OH + H^+ \qquad (5.33)$$

The equilibrium constant for equation 5.33 can be written as

$$K_{eq} = \frac{[NH_4OH][H^+]}{[NH_4^+][H_2O]} \tag{5.34}$$

Since this is an aqueous solution, $[H_2O]$ is a constant; therefore,

$$K_{eq}[H_2O] = K_h = \frac{[NH_4OH][H^+]}{[NH_4^+]} \tag{5.35}$$

where K_h is the hydrolysis constant.

The equilibrium constant, in this case the ionization constant, K_b, for equation 5.32 can be written according to the following equation:

$$K_b = \frac{[NH_4^+][OH^-]}{[NH_4OH]} \tag{5.36}$$

Substituting in equation 5.36 from the equation for the ion product of water,

$$[OH^-] = \frac{K_w}{[H+]}$$

the ionization constant relationship becomes

$$K_b = \frac{[NH_4^+]\,K_w}{[NH_4OH][H+]} \tag{5.37}$$

Rearranging,

$$\frac{K_w}{K_b} = \frac{[NH_4OH][H^+]}{[NH_4^+]}$$

The hydrolysis constant

$$K_h = \frac{[NH_4OH][H^+]}{[NH_4^+]} = \frac{K_w}{K_b} \tag{5.38}$$

From the hydrolysis of the ammonium ion shown in equation 5.33, it can be seen that $[NH_4OH] = [H^+]$. Thus equation 5.38 becomes

$$\frac{[H^+]^2}{[NH_4^+]} = \frac{K_w}{K_b}$$

$$[H^+] = \sqrt{\frac{K_w}{K_b}[NH_4^+]} \tag{5.39}$$

For the general case,

$$[H^+] = \sqrt{\frac{K_w}{K_b}C} \tag{5.40}$$

where C is the concentration of the salt formed at the equivalence point.

Taking the negative logarithm of each side of equation 5.40, the following relationship is obtained.

$$-\log [H^+] = -(\tfrac{1}{2}\log K_w - \tfrac{1}{2}\log K_b + \tfrac{1}{2}\log C)$$

$$pH = \tfrac{1}{2}pK_w - \tfrac{1}{2}pK_b - \tfrac{1}{2}\log C \qquad \textbf{(5.41)}$$

Equation 5.41 is the general expression for the value of the pH at the equivalence point for the titration of a weak base and a strong acid. This expression can be used for the calculation of the pH *only* at the equivalence point.

What is the pH at the equivalence point in the example being considered? Using equation 5.40 and substituting the values for K_w and K_b, then

$$[H^+] = \sqrt{\frac{1 \times 10^{-14}}{1.75 \times 10^{-5}} C}$$

To determine the value of C, it is necessary to calculate the $[NH_4^+]$ at the equivalence point. This can be accomplished as follows:

$$25 \times 0.1 = 2.5 \text{ mmoles HCl added}$$

The volume of the solution is 50 ml., since 25 ml. of acid has been added to the original 25 ml. of base. There are 2.5 mmoles of NH_4^+ in solution, since a millimole of NH_4^+ is produced for each millimole of HCl added.

The concentration of the ammonium ion is

$$[NH_4^+] = \frac{2.5}{50} = 0.05 = C$$

Then,

$$[H^+] = \sqrt{\frac{(1 \times 10^{-14})(5 \times 10^{-2})}{1.75 \times 10^{-5}}}$$

$$[H^+] = 5.35 \times 10^{-6}$$

$$pH = -\log (5.35 \times 10^{-6}) = 5.27$$

STEP IV. *The calculation of* pH *after passing the equivalence point.* After the equivalence point has been passed, the pH of the solution can be calculated from the concentration of the hydrogen ion added.

In the example used, what is the pH of the solution after the addition of 10 ml. of 0.1 M hydrochloric acid beyond the equivalence point?

$$10 \times 0.1 = 1.0 \text{ mmole HCl added}$$

$$50 + 10 = 60 \text{ ml. total volume of solution}$$

The pH can be calculated directly from the hydrogen ion concentration as follows:

$$[H^+] = \tfrac{1}{60} = 0.0167 = 1.67 \times 10^{-2}\ M$$

$$pH = -\log (1.67 \times 10^{-2}) = 1.78$$

Strong Base-Weak Acid

A weak acid is one that is not completely ionized. The treatment of this type of titration is similar to the strong acid-weak base titration. The calculation of the *p*H of the solution of a weak acid or the *p*H at the equivalence point in a neutralization reaction can be accomplished by using the same method as in the strong acid-weak base example. The hydrolysis of the salt formed during the reaction offers an explanation for the value of the *p*H at the equivalence point.

If 25 ml. of 0.1 *M* acetic acid (HAc) is titrated with 0.1 *M* sodium hydroxide, what is the *p*H of the solution (I) before the addition of base, (II) when 5 ml. of standard base has been added, (III) at the equivalence point, and (IV) when 10 ml. of base has been added beyond the equivalence point?

STEP I. To calculate the *p*H before the addition of any base, the ionization constant relationship of the acetic acid is used.

$$HAc \rightleftharpoons H^+ + Ac^-$$

$$K_a = \frac{[H^+][Ac^-]}{[HAc]}$$

$$1.80 \times 10^{-5} = \frac{[H^+][Ac^-]}{0.1 - [Ac^-]}$$

Since $[H^+] = [Ac^-]$ and $[Ac^-]$ is very small compared to 0.1, then

$$1.80 \times 10^{-5} = \frac{[H^+]^2}{0.1}$$

$$[H^+] = \sqrt{1.80 \times 10^{-6}} = 1.34 \times 10^{-3}$$

$$pH = -\log(1.34 \times 10^{-3}) = 2.87$$

STEP II. The ionization constant is used to determine the *p*H of the solution after the addition of 5 ml. of 0.1 *M* NaOH. The concentration of the acetate ion in solution is determined by the amount of sodium hydroxide added.

$$25 \times 0.1 = 2.5 \text{ mmoles HAc in solution}$$

$$5 \times 0.1 = \underline{.5} \text{ mmole NaOH added} = \text{mmole } Ac^- \text{ formed}$$

$$2.0 \text{ mmoles HAc unreacted}$$

The total volume of the solution is

$$25 + 5 = 30 \text{ ml.}$$

The concentrations can be expressed as

$$[Ac^-] = \frac{0.5}{30} \qquad [HAc] = \frac{2.0}{30}$$

Thus,

$$1.80 \times 10^{-5} = \frac{[H^+]\left(\frac{0.5}{30}\right)}{\left(\frac{2.0}{30}\right)}$$

$$[H^+] = 7.20 \times 10^{-5}$$

$$pH = -\log(7.20 \times 10^{-5}) = 4.14$$

STEP III. At the equivalence point, the calculation of pH depends on the hydrolysis reaction of the acetate ion, which in turn is dependent upon the ionization constant of the acetic acid.

$$Ac^- + H_2O \rightleftharpoons HAc + OH^-$$

$$K_h = \frac{[HAc][OH^-]}{[Ac^-]} \quad (5.42)$$

By a treatment similar to that used in the strong acid-weak base titration, the following relationship is obtained.

$$[H^+] = \sqrt{\frac{K_wK_a}{[Ac^-]}} \quad (5.43)$$

The general relationship is

$$[H^+] = \sqrt{\frac{K_wK_a}{C}} \quad (5.44)$$

where C is the concentration of the salt formed at the equivalence point. Expressing equation 5.44 in terms of the pH notation, it becomes

$$pH = \tfrac{1}{2}pK_w + \tfrac{1}{2}pK_a + \tfrac{1}{2}\log C \quad (5.45)$$

In the example being considered, the $[Ac^-]$ is found as follows:

$$25 \times 0.1 = 2.5 \text{ mmoles of NaOH added.}$$

Since the number of millimoles of acetate ion formed is equal to the number of millimoles of sodium hydroxide added, there are 2.5 millimoles of acetate ion present in the solution. The total volume of the solution at the equivalence point is the sum of 25 ml. of NaOH added and the 25 ml. of the original acetic acid, this being 50 ml. Therefore,

$$[Ac^-] = \frac{2.5}{50} = 0.05\ M$$

Substituting in equation 5.45,

$$pH = \tfrac{1}{2}(14) + \tfrac{1}{2}(4.74) + \tfrac{1}{2}\log(5 \times 10^{-2})$$

$$pH = 7 + 2.37 - 0.65 = 8.72$$

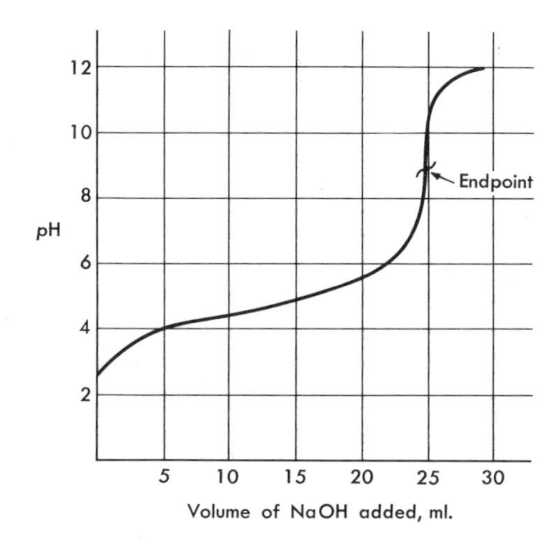

Fig. 5.3. Titration curve of 25 ml. of 0.1 *M* acetic acid titrated with 0.1 *M* sodium hydroxide.

STEP IV. After the equivalence point has been passed, the calculation of pH is made directly from the concentration of the hydroxyl ion that was added. In the example under consideration,

$$10 \times 0.1 = 1.0 \text{ mmole of } OH^- \text{ added beyond the equivalence point.}$$

The total volume of solution is

$$50 + 10 = 60 \text{ ml.}$$

The hydroxyl ion concentration is

$$[OH^-] = \tfrac{1}{60} = 1.67 \times 10^{-2}$$
$$pOH = -\log (1.67 \times 10^{-2}) = 1.78$$
$$pH = (14 - 1.78) = 12.22$$

The titration curve can be obtained experimentally by following the change in pH as the standard base is added. If pH versus ml. of standard base added is plotted, a curve such as shown in Figure 5.3 will be obtained. From the graph the pH at the equivalence point is approximately 8.73.

Weak Acid-Weak Base

The titration of a weak acid with a weak base has little practical value because there is no sharp inflection at the equivalence point. Titrations of this type are seldom performed in volumetric analysis. If such a titration is necessary, the pH at the equivalence point can be approximated by the use of the following equation:

$$[H^+] = \sqrt{\frac{K_w K_a}{K_b}} \qquad (5.46)$$

Anion of Weak Acid-Strong Acid Titration

According to the Brönsted-Lowry theory of acids and bases, the anion of a weak acid is a strong base because of its strong affinity for the proton. Due to this high proton affinity, it will react extensively with the hydrogen ion provided by a strong acid. This makes the titration of the anion of a weak acid with a strong acid possible. An example of this type of titration is the reaction of sodium carbonate with hydrochloric acid. The pH of the solution at the point at which the following reaction is complete is approximately 8.3.

$$CO_3^{=} + H^+ \rightleftharpoons HCO_3^- \qquad (5.47)$$

When all of the bicarbonate ion formed in this reaction has reacted with the hydrogen ion of the hydrochloric acid, according to the equation

$$HCO_3^- + H^+ \rightleftharpoons CO_2 + H_2O \qquad (5.48)$$

the pH of the solution is approximately 4.0. It can be seen that the amount of acid required for the reaction represented in equation 5.47 is the same as that required to complete the reaction shown by equation 5.48.

If the change in pH during the addition of the standard acid is followed, and a graph of pH versus milliliters of acid added is plotted, a curve is obtained that shows two inflection points. Figure 5.4(c) illustrates a titration curve obtained as a result of the titration of 0.1 M sodium carbonate and 0.1 M hydrochloric acid. The volume required to reach the first inflection point is the same as the volume required from the first inflection point to the second inflection point. The value of the ionization constants of carbonic acid can be calculated from this type of titration curve.

In the same manner, the ionization constants of phosphoric acid can be determined by the titration of sodium phosphate with hydrochloric acid.

Mixed Alkali Determination

Components of certain alkaline mixtures composed of sodium hydroxide, sodium carbonate, and sodium bicarbonate can be determined by using a double indicator titration or by preparing a titration curve from the change in pH of the solution during the addition of standard acid solution.

Although mixtures of sodium bicarbonate and sodium hydroxide can occur in the dry state, on dissolution the following reaction occurs:

$$HCO_3^- + OH^- \rightleftharpoons H_2O + CO_3^{=}$$

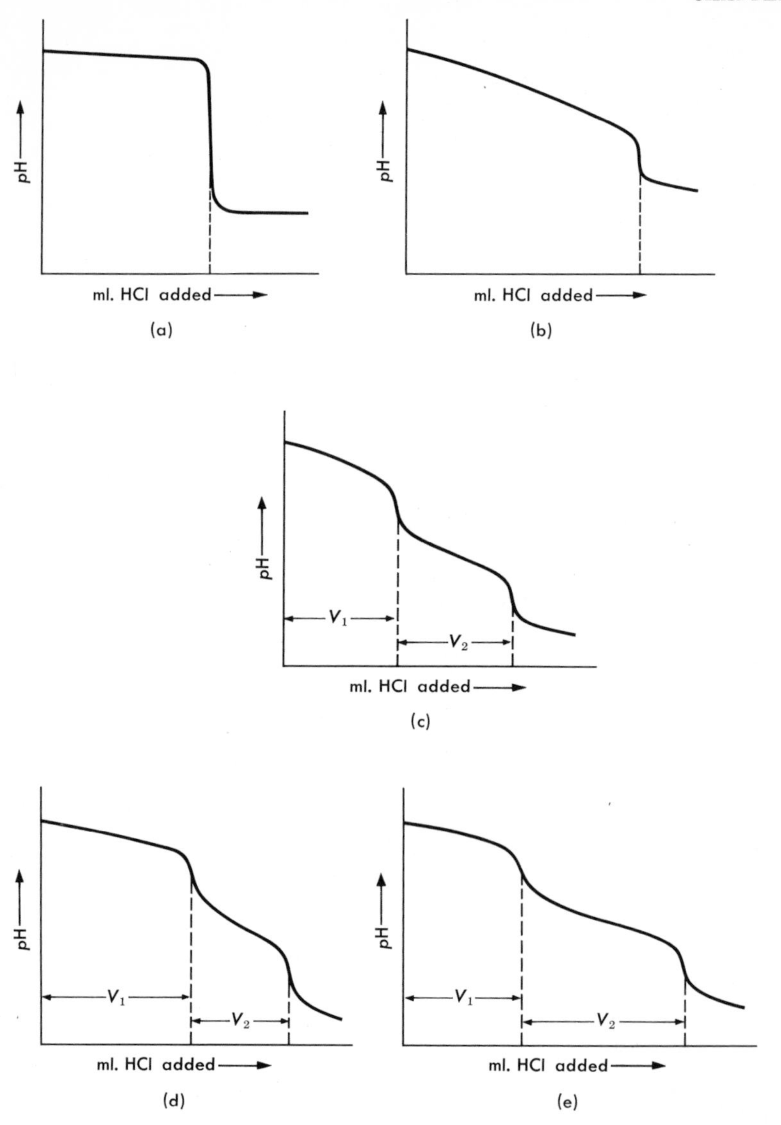

Fig. 5.4. Titration of various alkaline materials with HCl: (a) NaOH, (b) $NaHCO_3$, (c) Na_2CO_3, (d) NaOH and Na_2CO_3, (e) Na_2CO_3 and $NaHCO_3$.

The solution appears to be a mixture of sodium carbonate and sodium hydroxide, or of sodium carbonate and sodium bicarbonate, depending on which original component, sodium hydroxide or sodium bicarbonate, was present in the larger amount. The remaining possibilities of mixtures of two of the three components are all possible in solution.

Double indicator titrations using phenolphthalein and methyl orange are possible, since each of the pure components upon reaction with hydrochloric acid causes one or the other to change color at the point of neutralization. Sodium carbonate is alkaline to phenolphthalein and on titration with hydrochloric acid the indicator is decolorized at a pH that corresponds to completion of the reaction shown in equation 5.47. If, at this point, methyl orange is added to the solution, the indicator will be in the alkaline form (yellow) and on titration with hydrochloric acid it will change to pink (acid form) at a pH which corresponds to completion of the reaction represented by equation 5.48.

By titrating to the color change of methyl orange from yellow to pink, the total alkalinity in the sample can be determined.

With pure sodium hydroxide, phenolphthalein is in the pink form and on titration with hydrochloric acid, one drop of acid beyond the equivalence point will cause the pink color to disappear and the pH of the solution to drop from 9 to about 3.5. At this pH value methyl orange will also be in the acid form (pink). Therefore either indicator will require substantially the same volume of standard hydrochloric acid to neutralize a given volume of sodium hydroxide solution, before it changes color.

Pure sodium bicarbonate solution will cause phenolphthalein to be colorless (acid form), but methyl orange will be in the basic form (yellow), and on titration with standard hydrochloric acid will change to the acid form (pink) at a pH required for completion of the reaction shown by equation 5.48.

In addition to the pure components, two mixtures can be encountered: sodium hydroxide and sodium carbonate, sodium carbonate and sodium bicarbonate. By titrating the sample of the alkali mixture using two indicators, phenolphthalein and methyl orange, successively, the analyst can, from the observation of the color change of each indicator and the volume of standard hydrochloric acid required to cause each color change, determine the identity of the components of the mixture and the amount of each component that is present. The shape of the titration curve, obtained by following the change in pH during the addition of the standard acid, can be used for qualitative and quantitative determination of the mixture. Figure 5.4 illustrates the titration curves obtained for the pure components and for the compatible mixtures of the pure alkali components.

To illustrate the application of the double indicator titration, the following general stoichiometry is given.

Figure 5.4c. Pure sodium carbonate titrated with standard hydrochloric acid.
Let V_1 = volume added to decolorize phenolphthalein.

$$CO_3^{=} + H^+ \rightleftharpoons HCO_3^-$$

V_2 = volume added to change color of methyl orange.

$$HCO_3^- + H^+ \rightleftharpoons CO_2 + H_2O$$

From the equations listed, it can be seen that $V_1 = V_2$ if the solution contains only pure sodium carbonate. The percentage of sodium carbonate in the sample is calculated as

$$\% \, Na_2CO_3 = \frac{(V_1 + V_2) \times N_{HCl} \times \text{meq. wt. } Na_2CO_3 \times 100}{W_s}$$

where $(V_1 + V_2)$ is the total volume of acid added and W_s is the weight of the sample in milligrams. When the total volume of acid is used, the milliequivalent weight of sodium carbonate is $\frac{Na_2CO_3}{2} = 53$.

Figure 5.4d. A mixture of sodium hydroxide and sodium carbonate titrated with standard hydrochloric acid.

Let V_1 = volume added to decolorize phenolphthalein.

$$OH^- + H^+ \rightleftharpoons H_2O$$
$$CO_3^= + H \rightleftharpoons HCO_3^-$$

V_2 = volume added to change the color of methyl orange.

$$HCO_3^- + H^+ \rightleftharpoons H_2O + CO_2$$

From the three chemical equations shown here, V_1 must be greater than V_2 for this mixture to have been present in solution.

The amount of sodium carbonate can be calculated from V_2, since it is a measure of the amount of sodium carbonate in the solution. The volume of acid required to react completely with the sodium carbonate present is twice the volume required to change the color of the methyl orange after the phenolphthalein endpoint $(2V_2)$. Thus, the

$$\% \, Na_2CO_3 = \frac{2V_2 \times N_{HCl} \times \text{meq. wt. } Na_2CO_3 \times 100}{W_s}$$

where the milliequivalent weight of the sodium carbonate is $\frac{Na_2CO_3}{2} = 53$.

The amount of sodium hydroxide present is found by determining the volume of standard acid required for complete neutralization. The volume of acid used for the sodium hydroxide is the volume of acid required to decolorize the phenolphthalein minus the volume of additional acid required to change the color of methyl orange. This can be expressed as $(V_1 - V_2)$. The percentage of sodium hydroxide can be found from the relationship

$$\% \, NaOH = \frac{(V_1 - V_2) \times N_{HCl} \times \text{meq. wt. NaOH} \times 100}{W_s}$$

where the milliequivalent weight of sodium hydroxide is $\frac{NaOH}{1} = 40$.

Figure 5.4e. A mixture of sodium carbonate and sodium bicarbonate titrated with standard hydrochloric acid.

Let V_1 = volume required to decolorize phenolphthalein.

$$CO_3^{=} + H^+ \rightleftharpoons HCO_3$$

V_2 = volume added to change the color of methyl orange.

$$^*HCO_3^- + H^+ \rightleftharpoons H_2O + CO_2$$
$$HCO_3^- + H^+ \rightleftharpoons H_2O + CO_2$$

where the starred (*) equation indicates the reaction of the bicarbonate generated from the carbonate ion, and the unstarred equation represents the reaction of the bicarbonate ion that comes from the sodium bicarbonate in the original mixture. For the solution to contain a mixture of sodium carbonate and sodium bicarbonate V_2 must be greater than V_1.

In this case a measure of the amount of sodium carbonate present is given by the volume of standard hydrochloric acid required to decolorize the phenolphthalein. The volume of acid required for the complete reaction with the sodium carbonate present is twice the volume required to decolorize phenolphthalein ($2V_1$).

The percentage of sodium carbonate is calculated from the relationship

$$\% \text{ Na}_2\text{CO}_3 = \frac{2V_1 \times N_{\text{HCl}} \times \text{meq. wt. Na}_2\text{CO}_3 \times 100}{W_s}$$

where the milliequivalent weight of sodium carbonate is $\frac{\text{Na}_2\text{CO}_3}{2} = 53.$

The amount of sodium bicarbonate present is represented by the additional volume of standard hydrochloric acid required to change the color of methyl orange minus the volume required to decolorize phenolphthalein ($V_2 - V_1$).

The percentage of sodium bicarbonate present can be found by the relationship

$$\% \text{ NaHCO}_3 = \frac{(V_2 - V_1) \times N_{\text{HCl}} \times \text{meq. wt. NaHCO}_3 \times 100}{W_s}$$

where the milliequivalent weight of sodium bicarbonate is $\frac{\text{NaHCO}_3}{1} = 84.$

The volume relationships in a mixed alkali titration, such as has been described above, can be summarized in tabular form (see Table 5.5). These relationships are important to the analyst since they indicate the qualitative composition of the mixture.

To illustrate the application of the above stoichiometric relationships, the following example is given.

TABLE 5.5

Volume Relationships in Mixed Alkali Titrations

COMPONENT	VOLUME TO PHENOLPHTHALEIN ENDPOINT	ADDITIONAL VOLUME TO METHYL ORANGE ENDPOINT
$CO_3^{=}$	V_1	$V_2\ (V_1 = V_2)$
HCO_3^-	0	V_2
OH^-	V_1	0
$CO_3^{=}$; HCO_3^-	V_1	$V_2\ (V_2 > V_1)$
$CO_3^{=}$; OH^-	V_1	$V_2\ (V_1 > V_2)$

EXAMPLE I. A sample of material contains for its active components $NaHCO_3$, Na_2CO_3, NaOH, or possible mixtures of these. A 1.000 gram sample is titrated with 1.038 N HCl. A volume of 17.96 ml. was required to decolorize phenolphthalein. Methyl orange was then added to the solution and an additional 3.21 ml. of the same acid was required to change the color of the solution from yellow to pink. Which components were present? Calculate the percentage of each component present.

Solution:

To determine the components that are present, an approximate titration curve should be drawn from the data given in the problem. The region of inflection should be labeled according to the reactions that are completed in each region. Such a curve is shown below.

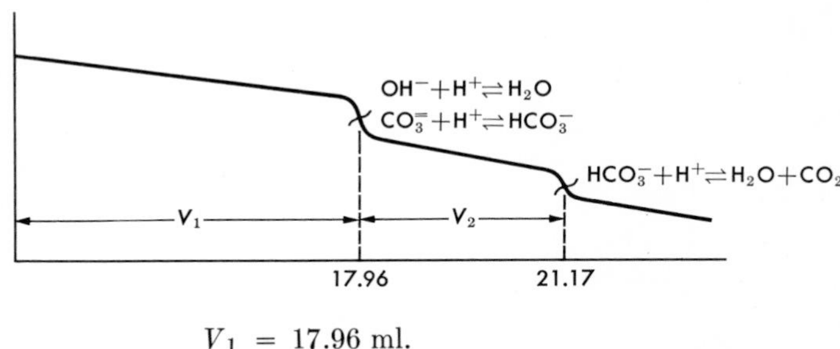

$$V_1 = 17.96 \text{ ml.}$$
$$V_2 = (21.17 - 17.96) = 3.21 \text{ ml.}$$

Since $V_1 > V_2$, sodium carbonate and sodium hydroxide are the active components of the mixture. Since V_2 is a measure of the sodium carbonate present, the percentage of this component can be calculated as follows:

$$\%\ Na_2CO_3 = 2V_2 \times N_{HCl} \times \frac{Na_2CO_3}{2} \times \frac{100}{W_s}$$

$$\%\ Na_2CO_3 = 2 \times 3.21 \times 1.038 \times \frac{106}{2} \times \frac{100}{1000} = 35.3\%$$

The volume of acid that reacted with the sodium hydroxide is $(V_1 - V_2)$, since the volume of the acid required to react with the sodium carbonate to form sodium bicarbonate is the same as the volume of acid required to transform the sodium bicarbonate to carbon dioxide and water.

$$\% \text{ NaOH} = (V_1 - V_2) \times N_{\text{HCl}} \times \frac{\text{NaOH}}{1} \times \frac{100}{W_s}$$

$$\% \text{ NaOH} = 14.75 \times 1.038 \times \frac{40}{1} \times \frac{100}{1000} = 61.2\%$$

References

1. Clark and Lubs, *J. Bacteriol.*, **2,** 1, 109, 191 (1917).

2. Clark, *The Determination of Hydrogen Ions,* 3rd ed., The Williams and Wilkins Company, Baltimore, 1928.

3. Kolthoff and Furman, *Indicators, Their Use in Quantitative Analysis and in Colorimetric Determination of Hydrogen Ion Concentration,* John Wiley and Sons, Inc., New York, 1926.

Laboratory Experiment 2

Determination of Strength of Glacial Acetic Acid

Discussion

A typical neutralization process can be represented by the analysis of a soluble acid or an acid salt. Among the many examples that can be used to illustrate these analytical procedures are the determination of the strength of an acid such as glacial acetic acid and the determination of the acidity of potassium acid phthalate in terms of replaceable hydrogen.

In both cases a standard solution of sodium hydroxide is used to determine the total acidity of the substance. The use of different indicators in the titration of glacial acetic acid with sodium hydroxide illustrates the necessity of using an indicator that changes within a range of *p*H values that encompasses the *p*H at the equivalence point.

Reagents

0.1 *N* NaOH

prepared by dissolving 4.0 grams sodium hydroxide in distilled water and diluting to one liter. Store the solution in a rubber stoppered bottle.

$KHC_8H_4O_4$

potassium acid phthalate, analytical reagent grade.

Phenolphthalein indicator solution

prepared by dissolving 0.5 gram phenolphthalein in 100 ml. of 95% ethyl alcohol.

Methyl orange indicator solution
prepared by dissolving 0.1 gram methyl orange powder in 100 ml. distilled water.

Methyl red indicator solution
prepared by dissolving 0.1 gram methyl red powder in 60 ml. of ethyl alcohol and diluting to 100 ml. with distilled water.

Thymol blue indicator solution
prepared by placing 0.1 gram thymol blue powder in an agate mortar and grinding with 2.15 ml. of 0.1 *N* sodium hydroxide. Dilute the mixture to 100 ml. with distilled water.

Procedure

STANDARDIZATION OF SODIUM HYDROXIDE

Place about 4 to 5 grams of analytical reagent grade potassium acid phthalate (KHP) in a clean weighing bottle and dry in an oven set at 100°–105°C for about one hour. Cool in a desiccator. Weigh accurately to the nearest tenth of a milligram a sample of about 1.0 gram of the dried KHP into each of three 250 ml. beakers.

Add 50 ml. of distilled water to each beaker and stir until the sample has all dissolved. Add 2–3 drops of phenolphthalein indicator solution to each beaker. Titrate the solution in one beaker with 0.1 *N* sodium hydroxide until the appearance of the first permanent pink color. Each of the remaining samples is titrated in the same manner.

From the data obtained, calculate the normality of the sodium hydroxide.

DETERMINING THE STRENGTH OF GLACIAL ACETIC ACID

Weigh a dry stoppered 25 ml. flask. Introduce 2 to 2.5 grams acetic acid into the flask, being careful the acid does not touch the neck of the flask. Reweigh the flask and contents. After the weight has been determined, add 10 to 15 ml. of distilled water and transfer the solution quantitatively to a 500 ml. volumetric flask. Wash the 25 ml. flask with several portions of distilled water, placing the washings in the 500 ml. volumetric flask each time. After the 25 ml. flask has been thoroughly washed, dilute the solution in the 500 ml. volumetric flask to the mark with distilled water at the same temperature as the solution. After thorough mixing, remove from the stock solution a 25 ml. aliquot portion into each of three 250 ml. beakers using a 25 ml. transfer pipet. Titrate each of the samples, using the standard 0.1 *N* sodium hydroxide with phenolphthalein as the indicator.

Titrate a 25 ml. aliquot sample of the acetic acid solution with standard 0.1 *N* sodium hydroxide using each of the following indicators: methyl red, methyl orange, and thymol blue. Record the volume for each titration.

From the data obtained from the phenolphthalein titration, calculate the percentage of acetic acid in the sample. How many equivalents per milliliter does it contain if the density is 1.05 grams per milliliter?

Which of the indicators used gives a sharp color change at the endpoint? Explain the differences in volume of standard sodium hydroxide added, if any are observed, in terms of the suitability of the indicator and color change of the indicator.

Laboratory Experiment 3

Determination of Replaceable Hydrogen in Potassium Acid Phthalate

Reagents

0.1 *N* NaOH

prepared and standardized according to procedure listed in Experiment 2 on page 75.

$KHC_8H_4O_4$

potassium hydrogen phthalate analytical reagent grade.

Phenolphthalein indicator solution

prepared by dissolving 0.5 gram phenolphthalein in 100 ml. of 95% ethyl alcohol.

Procedure

Into three 250 ml. beakers weigh to the nearest milligram triplicate samples of 1.0 to 1.5 grams each of the unknown sample previously dried for one hour at 100–105°C. Add 100 ml. of distilled water to each and stir until the solid is completely dissolved. Add 4–6 drops of phenolphthalein indicator solution to each beaker. Titrate each sample with standard sodium hydroxide solution to the appearance of the first permanent pink color.

From the volume of the sodium hydroxide added and the weight of the sample, calculate the acidity in terms of percent replaceable hydrogen.

Laboratory Experiment 4

Determination of the Total Alkalinity of Soda Ash

Discussion

Soda ash is the term given to impure sodium carbonate. The total alkalinity can be determined by titration with standard hydrochloric acid using methyl orange or methyl purple as an indicator. It is very common to report the total alkalinity in terms of percent sodium oxide.

Reagents

0.1 *N* HCl

prepared by adding 8.5 ml. of concentrated hydrochloric acid to a glass stoppered pyrex bottle containing approximately one liter of distilled water.

Na_2CO_3

sodium carbonate, analytical reagent grade.

Methyl orange indicator solution

prepared by dissolving 0.1 gram of methyl orange in 100 ml. of distilled water.

Procedure

STANDARDIZATION OF HYDROCHLORIC ACID

Place about two grams of analytical reagent grade sodium carbonate in a weighing bottle and dry for one hour in an oven set at 100–105°C. Weigh accurately to the nearest tenth of a milligram triplicate samples of approximately 0.200 gram each into three 250 ml. beakers. Add approximately 100 ml. of distilled water to each beaker. Stir until all of the sodium carbonate is dissolved.

Add three to five drops of methyl orange indicator solution to each beaker. Titrate each solution using 0.1 *N* HCl until the color of the solution turns from yellow to pink. Record the volume of HCl added to each sample.

From the weight of the sodium carbonate used and the volume of hydrochloric acid added, calculate the normality of the acid. Average the values of the normalities obtained and write the average normality on the bottle.

TOTAL ALKALINITY OF SODA ASH

Dry the sample as obtained from the instructor in a weighing bottle for one hour in an oven set at 100–105°C. Weigh accurately to the nearest tenth of a milligram triplicate samples of about 0.500 gram each into three 400 ml. beakers. Add approximately 100 ml. of distilled water to each beaker. Stir until all of the solid goes into solution. Add three to five drops of methyl orange indicator solution to each beaker.

Titrate each sample with standard hydrochloric acid until the color of the solution turns from yellow to pink.

From the volume of the standard hydrochloric acid added, the normality of the acid, and the weight of the sample, calculate the percentage of sodium oxide in the sample.

Laboratory Experiment 5

Determination of a Carbonate Mixture

Discussion

To illustrate the discussion of mixed alkali determinations that has been presented on pages 69–75, the titration of a carbonate mixture with hydrochloric acid can be used. Rather than using a double indicator to determine the endpoints in the reaction, the reaction will be followed by observing the change in *p*H as the titrant is added in small increments. From the volume of the titrant added to reach each inflection point, the components of the carbonate mixture as well as the percent of each component in the mixture can be determined. It is necessary to proceed cautiously using as small an increment as possible in the regions where the *p*H of the solution is changing rapidly. By doing this the inflection region of the curve is well defined and the endpoint of the reaction can be determined very readily within the limits of experimental error.

A curve *p*H *vs.* ml. of hydrochloric acid added is plotted and from this curve the volume of hydrochloric acid used to each endpoint is recorded. The shape of the curve will give information as to the composition of the mixture, and the volumes of acid found will be used in the quantitative calculations of the composition of the mixture.

Apparatus

*p*H meter equipped with glass and calomel electrodes; magnetic stirrer or stirring motor.

Reagents

0.1 N HCl

prepared by adding about 8.5 ml. of concentrated hydrochloric acid to a glass stoppered bottle containing approximately one liter of distilled water.

Na_2CO_3

sodium carbonate, analytical reagent grade.

Procedure

STANDARDIZATION OF HYDROCHLORIC ACID

Place about two grams of analytical reagent sodium carbonate in a weighing bottle and dry for one hour in an oven set at 100°–105°C. Weigh accurately to the nearest tenth of a milligram duplicate samples of approximately 0.2000 gram each into two 400 ml. beakers. Add approximately 100 ml. of distilled water to each beaker. Stir until all of the sodium carbonate has dissolved.

Place the beaker on the magnetic stirrer and insert the bar magnet into the solution. Insert the electrodes of the pH meter into the solution. Fill the buret with 0.1 N HCl.

Place the pH meter in operation according to the instructions furnished by the instructor.

Titrate the sodium carbonate solution with 0.1 N HCl solution recording the pH after each addition of the titrant. At the beginning of the titration, increments as large as 1 ml. may be added until the pH begins to change rapidly; then the size of the increments should be much smaller, as little as 0.05 ml. near the centers of the two regions of inflection. Continue the titration until the pH of the solution reaches a value of 3.0.

Using the data obtained, plot a curve of pH versus milliliters of titrant added for each sample. Determine the volume of acid used at each inflection point. Compare these two volumes. From the total volume of acid used, calculate the normality of the acid.

DETERMINING THE COMPONENTS OF A CARBONATE MIXTURE

Dry the sample as obtained from the instructor in a weighing bottle for one hour in an oven set at 100°–105°C. Weigh accurately to the nearest tenth of a milligram duplicate samples of about 0.2500 gram each into two 400 ml. beakers. Add approximately 100 ml. of distilled water to each beaker. Stir until all of the solid goes into solution.

Titrate each sample in the same manner as in the standardization procedure for hydrochloric acid. Record the pH after each addition of titrant. In this titration, care should be taken in choosing increments so that the first inflection region will not be missed.

Plot a curve of pH versus milliliters of titrant added for each sample. The components of the mixture are determined from the shape of the curve. Using the volume obtained from each inflection point, calculate and report the percentage of each component in the mixture.

Laboratory Experiment 6

Determination of the pK_a of an Indicator

Discussion

One method used to determine the pK_a of an indicator is to measure the absorption spectra of the indicator in solutions of various pH values at a given wavelength using a spectrophotometer.

It is necessary to obtain a complete absorption spectrum over the visible range of the spectrum (370–600 mμ) to determine the wavelength that gives the greatest change in absorbance due to change in pH. This can be accomplished by following the absorption spectrum of the indicator in (1) acid solution, (2) neutral solution, and (3) basic solution. After the spectrum of each solution has been plotted, a wavelength can be selected where the difference in absorption between the acidic solution and the basic solution of the indicator is the greatest. By showing a third solution (neutral solution), the isosbestic point may be determined. The isosbestic point is the wavelength at which there is no change in absorbance with change in pH.

Once the values for the absorbance of a series of solutions of known pH at the selected wavelength are known, then the pH is plotted versus the absorbance values and the pK_a of the indicator can be determined. Equation 5.24 states that

$$pH = pK_a + \log \frac{[HIn]}{[In]}$$

Therefore the pH will equal the pK_a of the indicator when the [HIn] = [In]. This can be assumed to be the halfway point between the absorbance value in the acidic solution and the absorbance value in basic solution. The intersection of the value of the absorbance at the halfway point and the curve locates the value of the pK_a of the indicator.

It is suggested that the directions for the operation of the spectrophotometer to be used be read and understood before beginning the laboratory work necessary to obtain the data for calculation of the pK_a. If the spectrophotometer to be used is a Bausch and Lomb Spectronic 20, then the instructions for its operation are found in Experiment 27 on page 268. These should be studied before beginning the laboratory experiment.

Apparatus

Bausch and Lomb Spectronic 20 or similar spectrophotometer; 5 cuvettes; pH meter equipped with calomel and glass electrodes.

Reagents

0.1 *M* NaOH solution

prepared by dissolving 4.0 grams reagent grade sodium hydroxide in water and diluting to one liter in a liter volumetric flask.

0.1 *M* potassium acid phthalate solution

prepared by dissolving 20.42 grams reagent grade potassium acid phthalate in water and diluting to one liter in a liter volumetric flask.

0.05% solution of bromcresol green indicator

prepared by rubbing 100 mg. of the indicator powder in an agate mortar with 2.9 ml. of 0.05 *M* sodium hydroxide and, after the indicator has gone into solution, diluting with water to 200 ml.

HCl

concentrated, analytical reagent grade.

5 *M* NaOH

prepared by dissolving 2.0 grams sodium hydroxide and diluting to 10 ml. with distilled water.

Procedure

Turn on the spectrophotometer and allow it to warm up for the specified time. In the case of the Bausch and Lomb Spectronic 20 the time is 15 minutes.

A. ABSORPTION SPECTRA OF BROMCRESOL GREEN

(1) Into a clean 25 ml. volumetric flask pipet 1 ml. of bromcresol green solution. Add about 10 ml. of distilled water. Add 5 drops of concentrated HCl and dilute to the mark with distilled water. Thoroughly mix the solution by inverting the stoppered flask several times. Rinse a clean cuvette with this solution. Place about 5 ml. of this solution in the cuvette. This sample will be used to obtain an absorption spectrum of the bromcresol green. Measure the *p*H of the solution by using the remainder of the 25 ml. portion with a *p*H meter. Record the *p*H of the solution.

Measure the percent transmittance, $\%T$, of this solution from 370 mμ to 600 mμ at 10 mμ intervals. Plot the $\%T$ *vs.* λ (mμ) using rectangular coordinate paper. Record the color of the solution.

Calculate the absorbance, A, using the relationship $A = 2 - \log \%T$. Plot A *vs.* λ (mμ) using a second piece of graph paper. Both graphs should be plotted as the data are obtained.

(2) Into a second clean 25 ml. volumetric flask pipet 1 ml. of the bromcresol green solution. Add about 5 ml. of distilled water. Pipet 10 ml. of 0.1 *M* potassium acid phthalate solution into the flask. Dilute to the mark with distilled water. Thoroughly mix the solution by inverting the stoppered flask several times. Rinse a clean cuvette with this solution. Place about 5 ml. of this solution in the cuvette. Measure the *p*H of the solution by using the remainder of the 25 ml. portion with a *p*H meter. Record the *p*H of the solution.

Measure the $\%T$ of this solution from 370 mμ to 600 mμ at 10 mμ intervals. Plot the $\%T$ *vs.* λ (mμ) on the same piece of graph paper used in plotting $\%T$ in A-1. Record the color of the solution.

Calculate the absorbance, A, in the same manner as in A-1 and plot A *vs.* λ (mμ) on the same piece of graph paper as in A-1.

(3) Into the third clean 25 ml. volumetric flask pipet 1 ml. of the bromcresol green solution. Add about 10 ml. distilled water and 10 drops 5 *M* NaOH. Dilute to the mark with distilled water. Thoroughly mix the solution by inverting the stoppered flask several times. Rinse a clean cuvette with this solution. Place about 5 ml. of this solution in the cuvette. Measure the *p*H of the solution by using the remainder of the 25 ml. portion with a *p*H meter. Record the *p*H of the solution.

Measure the $\%T$ of this solution from 370 mμ to 600 mμ at 10 mμ intervals. Plot the $\%T$ *vs.* λ (mμ) on the same piece of graph paper used in plotting $\%T$ in A-1. Record the color of the solution.

Calculate the absorbance, A, in the same manner as in A-1 and plot A *vs.* λ (mμ) on the same piece of graph paper as in A-1.

The three curves will intersect each other in a point called the *isosbestic point.*

B. ABSORPTION AT SELECTED WAVELENGTHS BY THE BROMCRESOL GREEN SOLUTION

(1) From the graph, prepared in Part A, of A *vs.* λ (mμ), select two values for λ, one to the left of the isosbestic point and one to the right of the isosbestic point, at which to make the remaining absorbance measurements. The values of λ, the wavelength, are selected where the acidic and basic forms of the bromcresol green show a maximum difference in their value of absorbance, A.

(2) Pipet into a clean 25 ml. volumetric flask the quantities of the three materials listed for each lettered set below, and dilute to the mark with distilled water. Thoroughly mix each of the solutions by inverting the stoppered flasks several times. Measure the $\%T$ of each of the solutions at the two values of λ, the wavelength, selected in Part B-1. Measure the *p*H of each solution, using a *p*H meter. Record the *p*H of each solution. Record the color of each solution. Calculate the absorbance, A, in the same manner as in A-1.

	ML. BROMCRESOL GREEN	ML. 0.1 *M* KHP	ML. 0.1 *M* NAOH
(a)	1.0	10.0	1.0
(b)	1.0	10.0	3.0
(c)	1.0	10.0	5.0
(d)	1.0	10.0	7.0
(e)	1.0	10.0	9.0
(f)	1.0	10.0	10.0

C. DETERMINATION OF pK_a

(1) Using the absorbance, A, obtained at the selected wavelengths (λ) in Part A and the data obtained in Part B, plot the absorbance A *vs.* *p*H at each of the two values of λ selected. A smooth curve is drawn through the points for each value of λ. The midpoint of each curve is the point where the concentration of the acidic form equals the concentration of the basic form. It is at

this point that the pH equals the pK_a. Determine the pK_a of the indicator from each curve. Compare the value of the pK_a obtained with the one in the literature.

(2) Define the term isosbestic point.

Problems*

1. Assuming complete neutralization in each case, find the equivalent weight of the following acids and bases:

(a) Ag_2O
(b) $Ba(OH)_2$
(c) NH_3
(d) SO_3
(e) Na_2CO_3
(f) $H_2C_2O_4 \cdot 2H_2O$
(g) Fe_2O_3
(h) $KHC_2O_4 \cdot H_2C_2O_4 \cdot 2H_2O$
(i) $NaHCO_3$
(j) $KHC_4H_4O_6$

2. What weight of formic acid, $HCHO_2$, is required to prepare (a) one liter of 0.04 M solution, (b) 300 ml. of a 0.025 N solution? *Ans. (a) 1.84 grams/liter; (b) 0.345 gram*

3. How many grams of potassium tetroxalate ($KHC_2O_4 \cdot H_2C_2O_4 \cdot 2H_2O$) must be dissolved in water and diluted to 600 ml. to make a 0.125 N solution to be used as an acid? *Ans. 6.35 grams*

4. If 65 ml. of hydrochloric acid (sp.gr. 1.100, containing 20.01% hydrochloric acid by weight) has been diluted to 700 ml. what is the normality of the acid solution? *Ans. 0.56 N*

5. What is the normality of a solution as an acid if 12 grams KHC_2O_4, 5 grams $H_2C_2O_4 \cdot 2H_2O$ and 25 grams $KHC_2O_4 \cdot H_2C_2O_4 \cdot 2H_2O$ are dissolved and the solution diluted to exactly one liter? *Ans. 0.47 N*

6. What volumes of 2.5 N and 4.0 N hydrochloric acid must be mixed to make a liter of 3.0 N acid? *Ans. 2.5 N, 0.67 liter; 4.0 N, 0.31 liter*

7. How many ml. of 0.1 N NaOH must be added to a liter of 0.0545 N NaOH solution to make the resulting solution 0.065 N? *Ans. 300 ml.*

8. Calculate the normality of the hydrochloric acid and sodium hydroxide solutions, given the following:

$$1.00 \text{ ml. HCl} \approx 0.95 \text{ ml. NaOH}$$
$$26.30 \text{ ml. HCl} \approx 0.2120 \text{ grams } Na_2CO_3$$

Ans. HCl, 0.152 N; NaOH, 0.160 N

---

* Answers that are given for the problems have been calculated to slide rule accuracy.

9. Calculate the normality of a solution of NaOH from the following data:

weight of sample KHP = 1.5625 grams
volume NaOH used = 50.00 ml.
volume HCl used = 1.20 ml.
1.00 ml. HCl ≎ 0.0225 gram $CaCO_3$

Ans. 0.165 N

10. What is the percentage purity of Na_2CO_3 in a sample of soda ash calculated from the following data?

weight of sample = 1.7200 grams
volume HCl used = 49.50 ml.
volume NaOH used = 1.62 ml.
normality NaOH = 0.2780
1.00 ml. HCl ≎ 0.95 ml. NaOH

Ans. 38.9%

11. A sample of oxalic acid is to be analyzed by titrating it with a solution of 0.100 *N* NaOH. What weight of sample should be taken so that each milliliter of NaOH will represent 1 percent of $H_2C_2O_4 \cdot 2H_2O$? *Ans. 0.630 gram*

12. What weight of soda ash must be taken for analysis so that the volume of 0.100 *N* HCl will equal the percentage of Na_2O in the sample? *Ans. 0.310 gram*

13. A mixture of pure $BaCO_3$ and pure $CaCO_3$ weighs 0.500 gram. The mixture is titrated with HCl, requiring 12.90 ml. What is the percentage of calcium in the mixture if

30.40 ml. HCl ≎ 45.60 ml. NaOH
2.00 ml. NaOH ≎ 0.0746 gram $NaHC_2O_4$

Ans. 11.6%

14. In the analysis of soda ash, what is the normality of the acid if 0.500 gram is titrated with the volume of acid that is twice the percentage of sodium carbonate in the sample? *Ans. 0.047 N*

15. What is the hydrogen ion concentration of a solution when: (a) *p*OH = 6.25, (b) pH = 3.50? *Ans. (a)* 1.78×10^{-8}, *(b)* 3.16×10^{-4}

16. What is the *p*H of a solution whose hydrogen ion concentration is 2.6×10^{-4} moles per liter? *Ans. 3.58*

17. Benzoic acid, C_6H_5COOH, has an ionization constant of 6.6×10^{-5}. What percent of the acid is ionized in a 0.01 *M* solution? *Ans. 8.3%*

18. If 15 ml. of 0.250 *N* acetic acid solution is diluted to 400 ml. and titrated with 0.150 *N* sodium hydroxide, what will be the *p*H (a) before the addition of sodium hydroxide, (b) after the solution has been half neutralized, and (c) at

the equivalence point? (K_i $HC_2H_3O_2$ = 1.8×10^{-5}.) *Ans.* (*a*) *3.4*; (*b*) *4.74*; (*c*) *10.2*

19. A 200 ml. solution containing NH_4OH is titrated with 0.200 *N* HCl; 25 ml. of acid is required to reach the equivalence point. What is the *p*H of the solution (a) at the start of the titration, (b) one third of the way to the equivalence point, and (c) at the equivalence point? (K_i NH_4OH = 1.75×10^{-5}.) *Ans.* (*a*) *10.8*; (*b*) *9.5*; (*c*) *5.4*

20. If 400 ml. of 0.15 *N* ammonium hydroxide is titrated with 0.1200 *N* hydrochloric acid, calculate the *p*H of the solution when (a) 0.0 ml., (b) 25 ml., (c) 40 ml., (d) 50 ml., and (e) 51 ml. of acid have been added. *Ans.* (*a*) *11.2*; (*b*) *9.2*; (*c*) *8.6*; (*d*) *5.2*; (*e*) *1.9*

21. Calculate the *p*H of each of the following solutions:

(a) 0.25 *M* in H_3PO_4 and 0.15 *M* in KH_2PO_4
(b) 0.10 *M* in KH_2PO_4 and 0.02 *M* in K_2HPO_4
(c) 0.10 *M* H_3PO_4
(d) 0.10 *N* NaH_2PO_4

Ans. (*a*) *1.7*; (*b*) *6.0*; (*c*) *1.5*; (*d*) *4.0*

22. A sample of sodium carbonate containing NaOH and inert matter weighs 1.1520 grams. It is titrated with 0.2500 *N* HCl, using phenolphthalein in cold solution, and becomes colorless after the addition of 46.24 ml. After the addition of methyl orange, 23.12 ml. of the acid is needed to complete the neutralization. What is the percentage of NaOH and of Na_2CO_3? *Ans.* *NaOH, 20%*; *Na_2CO_3, 53%*

23. A solution of alkali is prepared from NaOH known to be contaminated with Na_2CO_3. With phenolphthalein in the cold, 36.20 ml. of the alkali is required to neutralize 50.00 ml. of 0.500 *N* HCl. With methyl orange as the indicator 35.62 ml. of the alkali is required for the same amount of acid. How many grams of Na_2CO_3 and NaOH are contained in each milliliter of the alkali solution? *Ans.* *Na_2CO_3, 0.002 gram*; *NaOH, 0.027 gram*

24. A sample is known to contain either NaOH or $NaHCO_3$ or Na_2CO_3 or possible mixtures of these. A 1.000 gram sample requires 35.50 ml. of 0.500 *N* HCl with methyl orange as an indicator. The same weight of sample requires 30.25 ml. of the acid with phenolphthalein as an indicator. Calculate the percentage of each component in the mixture. *Ans.* *Na_2CO_3, 27.8%*; *NaOH, 50%*

25. A sample contains NaOH, Na_2CO_3, $NaHCO_3$, or possible mixtures of these. To a sample weighing 1.000 gram dissolved in water is added phenolphthalein as an indicator. The solution is titrated in the cold with 0.075 *N* acid, of which 13.86 ml. is required. Methyl orange is added and an additional 16.35 ml. of the same acid is required. Determine the constituents present and calculate the percentage of each. *Ans.* *Na_2CO_3, 11.1%*; *$NaHCO_3$, 1.57%*

CHAPTER 6

Principles of Oxidation-Reduction Methods

Oxidation-reduction (redox) methods of analysis involve substances that are capable of participating in an oxidation-reduction reaction. These methods are among the most widely used analytical volumetric methods because of their applicability to the determination of many substances which cannot be satisfactorily analyzed by other types of volumetric methods.

Definitions

A substance that is capable of accepting electrons is classed as an **oxidizing agent.** A **reducing agent** is a substance that will give up electrons. To illustrate this conjugate system, the following general equation can be used.

$$\text{Red} \rightleftharpoons \text{Ox} + ne$$

where Red is the reducing agent (reductant) and Ox is the conjugate oxidizing agent (oxidant).

In terms of the transfer of electrons, the process of **oxidation** is defined as the loss of electrons and **reduction** as the gain of electrons. In accordance with these definitions, the oxidizing agent is itself reduced and the reducing agent is itself oxidized when an oxidation-reduction reaction occurs.

For example,

$$Fe^{++} \rightleftharpoons Fe^{+++} + 1e \qquad \text{(oxidation)}$$
$$Sn^{++} \rightleftharpoons Sn^{++++} + 2e \qquad \text{(oxidation)}$$

Both Fe^{++} and Sn^{++} are known to be good reducing agents.

On the other hand, Ag^{+} can be easily reduced according to the reaction

$$Ag^{+} + 1e \rightleftharpoons Ag^{\circ} \qquad \text{(reduction)}$$

It is well known that potassium permanganate ($KMnO_4$), a strong oxidizing agent in acid solution, is reduced as shown by the reaction

$$MnO_4^{-} + 8H^{+} + 5e \rightleftharpoons Mn^{++} + 4H_2O \qquad \text{(reduction)}$$

The number of electrons that are transferred per mole of substance involved in the oxidation-reduction reaction is important in stoichiometric considerations. The relative ease with which these electrons are given up or taken on is a significant factor in determining the degree of completion of the redox reaction. Substances that have a strong electron affinity, that is, a strong tendency to acquire electrons, are classed as strong oxidizing agents. Substances which exhibit a strong tendency to lose electrons, and which are thus easily oxidized, are classed as strong reducing agents. Oxidizing agents and reducing agents can be arranged in tabular form according to their relative strength. Such an arrangement is shown in Appendix IV.

A redox system consists of a set of substances among which a redox reaction can occur. A redox reaction is a chemical reaction in which the oxidizing agent is reduced and the reducing agent oxidized. The general equation used to express such a reaction is given as

$$\text{oxidant}_1 + \text{reductant}_2 \rightleftharpoons \text{oxidant}_2 + \text{reductant}_1$$

For this reaction, the number of equivalents of oxidant used up must equal the number of equivalents of reductant consumed when the equivalence point has been reached.

Gram Equivalent Weight of Oxidant or Reductant

In an earlier chapter (page 44), the number of equivalents represented by a certain weight of a substance was defined as the weight of the substance divided by the gram equivalent weight of that substance. To determine the number of equivalents of either a reducing agent or an oxidizing agent requires that the gram equivalent weight of the substance be known or calculated. The gram equivalent weight of an oxidizing or reducing agent is defined as that weight (in grams) which is numerically equal to the molecular weight of the substance divided by the number of electrons transferred. This can be expressed by the following relationship:

$$\text{Gr. eq. wt. A} = \frac{\text{M.W. of A}}{\text{no. of electrons transferred}}$$

The gram equivalent weight of potassium permanganate when used in acid solution is $\frac{KMnO_4}{5} = \frac{158.04}{5} = 31.61$ gr. This calculation is based upon the number of electrons gained in the reduction of the permanganate ion in acid solution, shown by the half-reaction

$$MnO_4^- + 8H^+ + 5e \rightleftharpoons Mn^{++} + 4H_2O$$

TABLE 6.1
Common Oxidizing Agents and Reducing Agents

FORMULA	HALF-REACTION	EQ. WT.
$KMnO_4$	$MnO_4^- + 8H^+ + 5e \rightarrow Mn^{++} + 4H_2O$	$\frac{KMnO_4}{5}$
$K_2Cr_2O_7$	$Cr_2O_7^{=} + 14H^+ + 6e \rightarrow 2Cr^{+++} + 7H_2O$	$\frac{K_2Cr_2O_7}{6}$
KIO_3	$IO_3^- + 6H^+ + 6e \rightarrow I^- + 3H_2O$	$\frac{KIO_3}{6}$
$Ce(SO_4)_2$	$Ce^{++++} + 1e \rightarrow Ce^{+++}$	$\frac{Ce(SO_4)_2}{1}$
I_2	$I_2 + 2e \rightarrow 2I^-$	$\frac{I_2}{2}$
H_2O_2	$H_2O_2 + 2H^+ + 2e \rightarrow 2H_2O$	$\frac{H_2O_2}{2}$
$Na_2C_2O_4$	$C_2O_4^{=} \rightarrow 2CO_2 + 2e$	$\frac{Na_2C_2O_4}{2}$
$Fe(NH_4)_2(SO_4)_2$	$Fe^{++} \rightarrow Fe^{+++} + 1e$	$\frac{Fe(NH_4)_2(SO_4)_2}{1}$
As_2O_3	$AsO_3^{\equiv} + H_2O \rightarrow AsO_4^{\equiv} + 2H^+ + 2e$	$\frac{As_2O_3}{4}$
$SnCl_2$	$Sn^{++} \rightarrow Sn^{++++} + 2e$	$\frac{SnCl_2}{2}$
H_2O_2	$H_2O_2 \rightarrow O_2 + 2H^+ + 2e$	$\frac{H_2O_2}{2}$
$Na_2S_2O_3$	$2S_2O_3^{=} \rightarrow S_4O_6^{=} + 2e$	$\frac{Na_2S_2O_3}{1}$

This balanced half-reaction shows that there are five electrons gained by each permanganate ion. Table 6.1 gives several common oxidizing and reducing agents with their balanced ionic half-reactions and a symbolic representation of their gram equivalent weights.

Balancing Oxidation-Reduction Equations

Two methods are in common use for balancing oxidation-reduction equations. One is the **change in oxidation number method** and the other is the **ion-electron method.** The former depends on determining the change in oxidation number of the oxidizing and the reducing agents. To complete the balancing of the equation with respect to those reactants and products that have not entered into the redox reaction, the process of balancing by inspection is used.

In the ion-electron method, those ion species that take part in the oxidation half-reaction are written in a partial equation. In like manner, those ion species that take part in the reduction half-reaction are written as a second partial equation. Each partial equation is separately balanced. Then the partial equations are combined by addition, using such coefficients for them as are necessary to make the total number of electrons gained equal to the total number of electrons lost. Only those ionic species that take part in the reaction are shown in the final balanced equation. Those species that do not take part are not shown. Such ions can be classed as "spectator ions."

Both methods of balancing redox equations are extensively discussed in textbooks of general chemistry and physical chemistry. It is necessary here to review only the method that will be used in this book. In the opinion of the author, the ion-electron method seems to satisfy the needs of analytical chemists better; therefore it will be used in preference to the change in oxidation number method.

To illustrate the application of the ion-electron method, the reaction of potassium permanganate and iron(II) sulfate in acid solution will be used. The skeleton partial equation for the oxidation of the reductant is written:

$$Fe^{++} \rightleftharpoons Fe^{+++}$$

The expression is balanced with respect to atoms but not for charge. To balance the charge, one electron must be added to the right side or subtracted from the left side of the incomplete reaction. The author's preference is to add one electron to the right side of the equation, giving the balanced ionic half-reaction

$$Fe^{++} \rightleftharpoons Fe^{+++} + 1e$$

The skeleton equation for the reduction of the oxidant is written next.

$$MnO_4^- \rightleftharpoons Mn^{++}$$

The equation is not balanced with respect to number and kinds of atoms or charges. Since the reaction takes place in acid solution, H^+ can be considered to be a reactant. The reaction of H^+ and the oxygen furnished by the MnO_4^- will result in the formation of water; thus the reaction that is balanced with respect to the number and kind of atoms is

$$MnO_4^- + 8H^+ \rightleftharpoons Mn^{++} + 4H_2O$$

The charges must now be balanced. The net charge on the left side of the arrow is $+7$ $(-1 + 8)$, that on the right side of the arrow is $+2$. To balance the charges on either side of the arrow, five electrons ($5e$) must be added to the left side, giving the balanced ionic half-reaction

$$MnO_4^- + 8H^+ + 5e \rightleftharpoons Mn^{++} + 4H_2O$$

The two half-reactions are added, multiplying each half-reaction by the appropriate coefficient so that the electrons gained equal the electrons lost. In this example, it is apparent that the half-reaction containing the iron must be multiplied by 5 to balance the electrons needed in the reduction of the MnO_4^-.

$$5\,[Fe^{++} \rightleftharpoons Fe^{+++} + 1e]$$

$$\frac{MnO_4^- + 8H^+ + 5e \rightleftharpoons Mn^{++} + 4H_2O}{5Fe^{++} + MnO_4^- + 8H^+ \rightleftharpoons 5Fe^{+++} + Mn^{++} + 4H_2O}$$

The reaction of arsenic(III) oxide and iodine can be used as another illustration. The oxide is dissolved in sodium hydroxide, reacting as shown by the equation

$$As_2O_3 + 6OH^- \rightleftharpoons 2AsO_3^{\equiv} + 3H_2O$$

The incomplete half-reaction for the oxidation of the $AsO_3^{\equiv}$ is written as

$$AsO_3^{\equiv} + H_2O \rightleftharpoons AsO_4^{\equiv} + 2H^+$$

The equation is balanced with respect to kind and number of atoms but not according to charge. The net charge on the left of the arrow is -3 while the net charge to the right of the arrow is -1. By adding two electrons ($2e$) to the right side of the arrow the charges are balanced, giving the balanced half-reaction

$$AsO_3^{\equiv} + H_2O \rightleftharpoons AsO_4^{\equiv} + 2H^+ + 2e$$

The incomplete half-reaction for the reduction of iodine is represented by

$$I_2 \rightleftharpoons 2I^-$$

This is balanced with respect to kind and number of atoms but not according to charge. The net charge on the right side of the arrow is -2, whereas there is zero charge on the left side of the arrow. By adding two electrons ($2e$) to the left side of the equation, the balanced equation for the half-reaction is

$$I_2 + 2e \rightleftharpoons 2I^-$$

To obtain the balanced ionic equation, the two half-reactions are added as shown:

$$AsO_3^{\equiv} + H_2O \rightleftharpoons AsO_4^{\equiv} + 2H^+ + 2e$$

$$\frac{I_2 + 2e \rightleftharpoons 2I^-}{AsO_3^{\equiv} + H_2O + I_2 \rightleftharpoons AsO_4^{\equiv} + 2H^+ + 2I^-}$$

PROCESSES INVOLVING PERMANGANATE

Potassium permanganate is a common, very powerful oxidizing agent that can be used to determine many cations and anions, such as iron(II), tin(II), oxalate, nitrite, sulfite, and Hg(II), by direct titration. In acid solution the purple permanganate ion is reduced to the almost colorless manganese(II) ion. The need for an indicator is eliminated since one drop of permanganate solution beyond the endpoint will color the solution. The pink color can be used to signal the equivalence point of the reaction.

The most significant disadvantage in the use of permanganate solutions is that they have a tendency to decompose. This tendency is greater in acid solutions than in neutral solutions. Therefore, standard solutions of potassium permanganate have to be restandardized at regular intervals to eliminate errors as a result of change in normality.

Permanganate titrations can be used in the indirect determination of oxidizing agents as well as in the direct titration of reducing agents. An example of this type of process is the determination of the oxidizing power of a pyrolusite ore (see page 103). A measured amount of reducing agent, sodium oxalate, is added in excess to the pyrolusite sample and after the reaction is complete, the excess reducing agent is titrated, using a standard solution of potassium permanganate. The one requirement for this type of reaction is that the permanganate does not react in any way with the products of the preceding reaction.

Standardization of Permanganate Solutions

To standardize potassium permanganate solutions, either of two common reducing agents is generally used. These are iron(II) salts or sodium oxalate. The ionic half-reactions and the net reaction of permanganate with each in acid solution are represented as follows:

$$MnO_4^- + 8H^+ + 5e \rightleftharpoons Mn^{++} + 4H_2O$$

$$5\,[Fe^{++} \rightleftharpoons Fe^{+++} + 1e]$$

$$\overline{MnO_4^- + 5Fe^{++} + 8H^+ \rightleftharpoons Mn^{++} + 5Fe^{+++} + 4H_2O}$$

$$2\,[MnO_4^- + 8H^+ + 5e \rightleftharpoons Mn^{++} + 4H_2O]$$

$$5\,[C_2O_4^= \rightleftharpoons 2CO_2 + 2e]$$

$$\overline{2MnO_4^- + 16H^+ + 5C_2O_4^= \rightleftharpoons 2Mn^{++} + 8H_2O + 10CO_2}$$

Unless otherwise specified, a standard potassium permanganate solution has been standardized by reaction with either of these two reducing agents in acid solution. The equivalent weight of the potassium permanganate in these two reactions is $\frac{KMnO_4}{5}\cdot$ There are five equivalents per mole.

When permanganate is used as a titrating solution against a reducing agent, each drop of permanganate falling into the solution causes local coloration that disappears immediately on stirring. The coloration remains for a longer period of time as the endpoint is approached. Careful titration technique at this point eliminates the necessity of a back titrating solution.

When hydrochloric acid is used in the dissolution of a sample, the chloride ion may interfere in the final titration of the substance. If such a condition occurs, as for example, in the determination of iron in a limonite ore, the addition of Zimmerman-Reinhardt reagent will remove the interference provided by the chloride ion by decreasing the potential of the permanganate-manganese(II) half-cell to a value that is lower than that of the Cl^{-}-Cl_2 half-cell. This solution is called "preventive solution" or "manganese(II) sulfate titrating solution" by some authors. The use of this titrating solution is illustrated in the laboratory exercise on page 105.

The stoichiometry of the permanganate process can be explained by using the following illustrative examples.

EXAMPLE I. A $KMnO_4$ solution has an "iron titer" of 11.16 mg. What is the normality of the $KMnO_4$ solution?

Solution:

$$MnO_4^- + 8H^+ + 5e \rightleftharpoons Mn^{++} + 4H_2O$$

$$Fe^{++} \rightleftharpoons Fe^{+++} + 1e$$

$$\text{meq. wt. of Fe} = \frac{\text{Fe}}{1} = 55.85$$

"Iron titer" = 11.16 mg., which is to say that 1 ml. of $KMnO_4$ solution will oxidize 11.16 mg. of iron from Fe^{++} to Fe^{+++}.

$$\text{Normality } KMnO_4 = \frac{11.16}{1 \times 55.85} = 0.200\ N$$

EXAMPLE II. What is the percent MnO_2 in a sample of pyrolusite if to a 500.0 mg. sample is added 750.0 mg. sodium oxalate and 50.0 ml. of 6 N H_2SO_4, and the excess sodium oxalate is titrated with 30.00 ml. of 0.100 N $KMnO_4$ solution?

Solution:

The number of milliequivalents of sodium oxalate added is

$$\frac{750.0}{\frac{Na_2C_2O_4}{2}} = 11.19 \text{ meq. added}$$

The number of milliequivalents of sodium oxalate that was added in excess is equal to the number of milliequivalents of $KMnO_4$. This is given by

$$30.00 \times 0.100 = 3.00 \text{ meq.}$$

The number of milliequivalents of sodium oxalate that reacted with the MnO_2 is

$$11.19 - 3.00 = 8.19 \text{ meq.}$$

The percentage of MnO_2 is determined as follows:

$$8.19 \times \frac{MnO_2}{2} \times \frac{100}{500} = 71.08\%$$

PROCESSES INVOLVING DICHROMATE

Potassium dichromate, although not as strong an oxidizing agent in acid solution as potassium permanganate, is commonly used as an oxidizing agent. It has several advantages over potassium permanganate. The principal ones are that standard solutions of dichromate are stable at high temperatures, and iron(II) salts can be oxidized in cold dilute hydrochloric acid solution without the chloride ion being appreciably oxidized. Potassium dichromate is available in such a high state of purity and stability that standard solutions can be prepared directly.

There is a decided disadvantage in comparison with potassium permanganate in that an indicator is needed to signal the appearance of the equivalence point. The indicator can be either an internal or an external indicator. The internal indicator is much less tedious to use than the external indicator. Potassium dichromate solutions are very useful in potentiometric titrations, where indicators are not necessary (see page 138).

Redox Indicators

A soluble organic substance that can exist in two states of oxidation, with both forms capable of being present together in equilibrium and one having a different color from the other, can be used as a **redox indicator.** To be useful in a specific reaction the electrode potential for the half-reaction involving the two forms must be of a value that is near the potential at the equivalence point of the two substances involved in the titration. Furthermore, the indicator must not react in any manner—other than that of being converted from one form to the other—with the substances present in solution or those that may be added to the solution being titrated.

Redox indicators can be of two types, internal and external.

(1) Internal indicators are those that are introduced into the solution being titrated. The color change is observed during the addition of the titrant. An example of an internal indicator is the sodium salt of diphenylamine sulfonate in its use in the titration of iron(II) ions by dichromate. The color change is from colorless to purple. This color change can be seen even in the presence of the green chromium(III) ions that are formed as a result of the reduction of the dichromate ion.

(2) External indicators are those indicators which cannot be used within the solution being titrated. In this case, drops of the indicator are placed on a white spot plate and the titration is done in the regular way until near the estimated endpoint. Then a drop of the solution is removed from the beaker and placed in contact with the drop of indicator solution on the spot plate. The color formed indicates whether the endpoint of the reaction has been reached. The titration is continued until a single drop of the solution gives the required color with the indicator.

There are two rather evident conditions which must be met in the use of external indicators. The first is that the analyst must have a fairly accurate estimate of the quantity of the substance to be determined in the sample. The second condition is that the removal of small portions of the solution to test with the indicator must not introduce a significant error through loss of the substance being determined. Unless the first condition is met, however, the second is not likely to be. If dilute solutions are used and an estimate can be made of the amount of the substance in the sample, the error is usually small. A method which uses an external indicator can be very satisfactory in checking the quality of a product in a routine manner. For instance, in the determination of iron(II) in the presence of iron(III), using dichromate as the oxidant, potassium ferricyanide can be used as an external indicator, since it forms a deep blue precipitate with the iron(II) ions but not with the iron(III) ions.

Standard Solutions of Potassium Dichromate

(1) *Direct Method of Preparation.* Standard solutions of potassium dichromate can be prepared directly by weighing primary standard quality potassium dichromate, dissolving it in water, and making the solution up to a definite volume in a volumetric flask. The normality can then be calculated from the weight, the equivalent weight of potassium dichromate, and the volume of the solution.

(2) *Indirect Method of Preparation.* Solutions of potassium dichromate can be prepared to the approximate normality desired, then standardized using iron(II) sulfate or iron wire of known purity.

In general, the direct method is used since potassium dichromate of a very high purity is readily available.

Dichromate Process

The ionic half-reaction illustrating the reduction of dichromate in acid solution is

$$Cr_2O_7^{=} + 14H^+ + 6e \rightleftharpoons 2Cr^{+++} + 7H_2O$$

From this reaction, the equivalent weight of potassium dichromate is $\frac{K_2Cr_2O_7}{6} = \frac{294.22}{6} = 49.04$, since there are six electrons required to balance the half-reaction with respect to charge. This reaction also emphasizes the effect of the hydrogen ion concentration of the solution. Titrations involving the use of potassium dichromate must be carried out in solutions that are 1 N to 2 N in acid.

Potassium dichromate solutions can be used for volumetric titrations of iron(II) solutions directly, and for many other reducing agents indirectly. Excess reducing agent, such as standard iron(II) sulfate, can be added to an oxidizing agent and the excess titrated using standard dichromate solution.

An example of an indirect titration is furnished by the determination of nitrate in a sample. The nitrate is treated with a known excess of iron(II) sulfate; in the presence of ammonium molybdate catalyst and high concentration of hydrochloric acid, the nitrate ion is reduced to nitric oxide (NO), and an equivalent amount of iron(II) ion is oxidized. After being cooled and the acid content partially neutralized, the solution can be titrated with standard dichromate solution, using diphenylamine sodium sulfonate as the indicator.

Stoichiometry

The following examples illustrate the stoichiometric calculations used in the dichromate process.

EXAMPLE I. In the standardization of a potassium dichromate solution against iron wire that is 98.50% pure, 41.25 ml. of the solution was used. The weight of iron used was 0.2000 gram. Calculate the normality of the potassium dichromate.

Solution:

The number of milliequivalents of Fe used can be calculated as follows:

$$\text{meq. Fe} = \frac{200.0 \times 0.9850}{\frac{\text{Fe}}{1}} = 3.53$$

The meq. Fe = meq. $K_2Cr_2O_7$, therefore the normality of the $K_2Cr_2O_7$ solution can be calculated from

$$V \times N = \text{meq. } K_2Cr_2O_7 = \text{meq. Fe}$$
$$41.25 \times N = 3.53$$
$$N = 0.0855$$

EXAMPLE II. A sample of limonite weighing 0.6170 gram was taken for analysis of iron, using potassium dichromate. 47.50 ml. of dichromate solution (1.000 ml. $K_2Cr_2O_7 \approx 6.300$ mg. Fe) was added. The excess dichromate was titrated with 2.80 ml. of a standard iron(II) sulfate solution (1.000 ml. $FeSO_4 \approx 1.035$ ml. $K_2Cr_2O_7$). Calculate the percentage of iron expressed as Fe_2O_3 in the sample.

Solution:

The normality of the $K_2Cr_2O_7$ solution is calculated as follows:

$$N_{K_2Cr_2O_7} = \frac{6.30}{55.85 \times 1} = 0.1128$$

The volume of $K_2Cr_2O_7$ in excess over that required for the sample can be obtained by

$$\frac{1.000}{1.035} = \frac{2.80}{V_x}$$
$$V_x = 3.73 \text{ ml. } K_2Cr_2O_7 \text{ in excess}$$

The volume of $K_2Cr_2O_7$ solution that reacted with the iron(II) in the sample is

$$(47.50 - 3.73) = 43.77 \text{ ml.}$$

Since all the iron in the limonite ore was originally converted to the reduced form, iron(II), then the percentage of Fe as Fe_2O_3 is determined as follows:

$$\% \, Fe_2O_3 = 43.77 \times 0.1128 \times \frac{159.7}{2} \times \frac{100}{617} = 63.9\%$$

PROCESSES INVOLVING CERIUM(IV)

Cerium(IV) is a very powerful oxidizing agent. Like dichromate solution, cerium(IV) solutions are very stable at high temperatures. They do not oxidize chloride ion at ordinary temperatures—an advantage over potassium permanganate. They have only one possible oxidation number change and that is from +4 to +3. Although the cerium(IV) ion has a yellow color, it is only in the titration of an oxidizable substance whose solution is clear that this color can be used as an indicator. In most cases an indicator is needed. Titration of iron(II) ions can be accomplished using Ferroin (orthophenanthroline-iron(II) complex) as an indicator.

Cerium(IV) Methods

Cerium(IV) is reduced to the colorless cerium(III) ion according to the following ionic half-reaction:

$$Ce^{++++} + 1e \rightleftharpoons Ce^{+++}$$

The equivalent weight of cerium(IV) sulfate is $\frac{Ce(SO_4)_2}{1} = 332.25$. The cerium(IV) solution is usually prepared from a weighed amount of the salt of cerium(IV) ammonium sulfate ($Ce(SO_4)_2 \cdot 2(NH_4)_2SO_4 \cdot 2H_2O$) dissolved in dilute sulfuric acid and made up to a specified volume, using a volumetric flask.

Cerium(IV) solutions, like potassium dichromate solutions, are commonly used in potentiometric titrations, where indicators are not necessary and where stability and strong oxidizing ability are important requirements.

PROCESSES INVOLVING IODINE

From the value of the electromotive force of the iodide-iodine half-cell, it can be seen that this redox half-reaction lies intermediate between those of strong oxidizing agents and those of strong reducing agents. Iodide ion will react quantitatively with many strong oxidizing agents, since it can be oxidized rather easily. Yet iodine can be reduced readily enough to react with many strong reducing agents. As a result of this dual character, the volumetric methods using the iodide-iodine redox system can be divided into two types: direct methods, where a standard solution of iodine is used as an oxidizing agent; and indirect methods, where the iodide ion is quantitatively oxidized to iodine and the liberated iodine titrated with a standard reducing agent.

Direct Methods

Volumetric methods that use a standard iodine solution as a direct oxidizing agent are called **iodimetric methods.** Standard iodine solutions can be used to titrate directly such reducing agents as hydrogen sulfide, sulfite ion, arsenic(III) salts, and tin(II) salts. The following reaction illustrates the use of standard iodine solution as a direct oxidizing agent with the reducing agent arsenic(III) solution.

$$AsO_3^{\equiv} + I_2 + H_2O \rightleftharpoons AsO_4^{\equiv} + 2I^- + 2H^+$$

Because of the lower value of the potential of the iodide-iodine half-reaction, the number of substances that can be titrated directly with iodine is less than the number that can be titrated by standard permanganate solution.

Indirect Methods

In acid solution practically all oxidizing agents will oxidize iodide ion to iodine quantitatively. The iodine formed in the reaction can then be titrated by means of a standard reducing agent, sodium thiosulfate solution. This type of indirect titration is given the general term **iodometry.**

Iodometric methods have a wide acceptance because of the following facts.

(1) Potassium iodide, KI, is readily available in a high state of purity.

(2) A good indicator, starch, is available to signal the equivalence point in the reaction. Starch turns blue-black in the presence of free iodine and excess iodide ion. Therefore, when the blue-black color disappears, the iodine has been completely reduced to the iodide ion.

(3) Iodometric reactions are rapid and quantitative.

(4) A precise reducing agent, sodium thiosulfate ($Na_2S_2O_3$), is available to react with the iodine.

The amount of iodine liberated in each reaction of iodide ion with an oxidizing agent is a measure of quantity of the oxidizing agent originally present in the solution. The amount of standard sodium thiosulfate solution required to titrate the liberated iodine is equivalent to the amount of oxidizing agent present in the original solution. This fact can be seen from the following equations:

$$Cr_2O_7^{=} + 6I^- + 14H^+ \rightarrow 3I_2 + 2Cr^{+++} + 7H_2O$$

$$3I_2 + 6S_2O_3^{=} \rightarrow 6I^- + 3S_4O_6^{=}$$

As a general rule the equivalent weight of an oxidizing agent can be found by dividing its molecular weight by the number of gram-atoms of iodine liberated per mole of oxidant.

Iodometric methods can be used for the quantitative determination of strong oxidizing agents such as potassium dichromate, potassium permanganate, hydrogen peroxide, manganese(IV) oxide, copper(II) ion, and bromine(V) ion.

Indicators

The appearance of the color of free iodine in solution can be used as an indicator in direct (iodimetric) methods. This is useful only when the solution is colorless before the appearance of the iodine color.

Free iodine is soluble in organic solvents, such as chloroform and carbon tetrachloride, imparting a red-violet color to the solution. This property can be used to detect small amounts of iodine normally invisible in aqueous solution, by concentrating the iodine in a small volume of organic solvent, the color of which will be visible. It is important that the mixture be shaken well near the endpoint in order to equilibrate the iodine between the aqueous and organic phases.

To mark the disappearance of iodine in the indirect (iodometric) methods, starch can be used as the indicator. When starch is heated in water, various decomposition products are formed, among which is β-amyl pectin which will form a deep, blue-black complex with iodine. The sensitivity of the indicator is increased by the presence of iodide ion in solution.

If the starch indicator solution is added in the presence of a large concentration of iodine, the disappearance of the blue-black color is very gradual. For use in indirect methods, the indicator is added at a point when nearly all of the iodine has been reduced to iodide ion, causing the disappearance of the blue-black color to be more rapid. As an indicator for the direct method, the starch solution can be added at the beginning of the titration since it will be used to signal the appearance of free iodine by the formation of the blue-black starch iodine complex.

Starch indicator solution must be freshly prepared because, when it stands, decomposition takes place and its sensitivity is decreased. A preservative such as a small amount of mercury(II) iodide can be added to inhibit the decomposition of the solution.

Preparation and Standardization of Solutions

Iodine, although generally not used as a primary standard, can be used in the preparation of standard solutions provided precautions are taken. The main disadvantage is the fact that iodine has an appreciable vapor pressure at room temperature, which makes accurate weighing difficult. It is more common practice to prepare a solution of iodine of the approximate concentration required, and then to standardize it against a standard reducing agent.

Free iodine is only slightly soluble in water. Its solubility can be increased by having an excess of iodide ion present. It is very likely that this increase in solubility results from the reaction between iodine and excess iodide ion to form the triiodide complex, as shown by the equation.

$$I_2 + I^- \rightarrow I_3^-$$

The excess iodide ion does not interfere with the chemical reaction nor affect the stoichiometric considerations.

To prepare a solution of iodine, the required weight of iodine and three or four times its own weight of potassium iodide, together with a small amount of water, are placed in a mortar and ground together (triturated). Water is added in small amounts and the mixture triturated until all of the solid material has gone into solution. The solution is transferred to a volumetric flask and diluted to the required volume with water. After a thorough mixing, the iodine solution is allowed to stand, preferably overnight, before standardization. The solution is standardized against a standard sodium thiosulfate solution or against solid arsenic(III) oxide.

Solutions of sodium thiosulfate are made up to an approximate normality by dissolving the solid in water that has been previously boiled to remove carbon dioxide. The solution is standardized by taking a known amount of oxidizing agent, treating it with excess iodide ion, and then titrating the liberated iodine with the sodium thiosulfate solution. Oxidizing agents such as potassium dichromate, potassium bromate, potassium iodate, and metallic copper (as copper(II) ion) can be used. It is a good practice to standardize the sodium thiosulfate against the same kind of oxidizing agent which it will later be used to determine. For example, if sodium thiosulfate is to be used mainly for the determination of copper, it should be standardized against pure copper.

Iodometric and Iodimetric Processes

Both iodometric and iodimetric processes depend on the following reversible reaction:

$$2I^- \rightleftharpoons I_2 + 2e$$

From this equation, the equivalent weight of iodine is the molecular weight of iodine divided by two $\frac{I_2}{2}$ or $\frac{I}{1} = 126.91$.

The fundamental reaction of the redox system using iodine and sodium thiosulfate can be expressed in terms of two half-reactions:

$$I_2 + 2e \rightarrow 2I^-$$

$$2S_2O_3^= \rightarrow S_4O_6^= + 2e$$

$$I_2 + 2S_2O_3^= \rightarrow 2I^- + S_4O_6^=$$

This reaction proceeds quantitatively in neutral or slightly acid solution. In strongly alkaline or acid solutions the oxidation of sodium thiosulfate does not proceed by a single reaction. In the former, the thiosulfate ion is oxidized to sulfate ion as well as to the tetrathionate ion. In the latter, the thiosulfuric acid formed undergoes an internal oxidation-reduction reaction to sulfurous acid and sulfur. Both these reactions lead to errors since the equivalency as a reducing agent in either case is not the same as for thiosulfate.

The control of the *p*H of the reaction mixture is important. The influence of *p*H is not as great below *p*H 8–9. In many cases the liberated iodine is titrated in acid solution employed for the reaction of a strong oxidizing agent and iodide ion. In these cases, the titration of the liberated iodine must be completed quickly to eliminate undue exposure to the atmosphere since an acid medium constitutes an optimum condition for atmospheric oxidation of the iodide ion.

Although the iodide-iodine half-reaction is influenced only in a small way by hydrogen ion concentration, those oxidizing agents that contain oxygen show a great dependence on hydrogen ion concentration. It is possible then to modify the reaction between oxidizing agents of this type and iodide ion by changes in *p*H. In some cases, it is possible to make a redox reaction quantitative in either direction by changes in *p*H. For instance, in solutions that are strongly acidic, arsenic(V) ion will quantitatively oxidize iodide ion. On the other hand, if the hydrogen ion concentration is low (*p*H 8–9), the arsenic(III) ion is quantitatively oxidized by iodine. This is the reverse of the reaction that occurs in solutions of high acidity.

The reaction involving copper(II) ion and iodide takes place because the copper(I) ion formed as a result of the reduction of copper (II) ion is removed from solution as solid copper(I) iodide.

The following are several sources of error in iodine methods of analysis:

(1) *The loss of iodine by volatilization from the solution.* This can be decreased by having a large excess of iodide ion in solution to keep the iodine tied up in the triiodide complex (I_3^-). It is apparent that titrations using iodimetric or

iodometric methods are made from cold solution in order to keep the loss of iodine by volatilization to a minimum.

(2) *The atmospheric oxidation of iodide ion in acid solution.* In acid solution, prompt titration of the liberated iodine is necessary in order to prevent the oxidation by atmospheric oxygen, of significant amounts of iodide ion present in the solution.

(3) *Starch solution not freshly prepared or prepared from cold water.* In either case the indicator will not function properly. The endpoint will not be visible to the analyst.

Karl Fischer Determination of Water

The Karl Fischer reagent reacts quantitatively with water in a nonaqueous medium. It can be used to titrate the moisture in a sample directly or by a back titration of excess Karl Fischer reagent, using a standard water-in-methanol solution.

The reagent contains iodine, sulfur dioxide, and pyridine, dissolved in methanol. The water reacts with the Karl Fischer reagent causing the iodine to be reduced by the sulfur dioxide according to the equations

$$I_2 + SO_2 + 3C_5H_5N + H_2O \rightarrow 2(C_5H_5N{\cdot}HI) + C_5H_5NOSO_2$$
$$(C_5H_5NOSO_2) + CH_3OH \rightarrow C_5H_5N{\cdot}(HCH_3SO_4)$$

Rather than the pyridinium sulfate being formed, it is more probable that the methyl ester is formed in a stepwise reaction as shown above.

The appearance of the color of free iodine can be used as an indication of the completion of the removal of water from the sample. This is not as sensitive an indication of the removal of water as the more commonly used potentiometric method of detecting the endpoint (see page 107).

Karl Fischer reagent is used extensively to determine water in nonaqueous media and especially to determine water in organic reagents.

Stoichiometry

The following examples can be used to illustrate the stoichiometric considerations in the methods which involve use of the iodine-iodide half-reaction.

EXAMPLE I. A 0.300 gram sample of As_2O_3 was dissolved in sodium hydroxide, buffered with sodium bicarbonate, and required exactly 50.00 ml. of the standard iodine solution for oxidation. Calculate the normality of the iodine solution.

Solution:

The number of milliequivalents of As_2O_3 are calculated as follows:

$$\text{meq. } As_2O_3 = \frac{300.0}{\frac{197.82}{4}} = 6.07$$

Since the meq. As_2O_3 are equivalent to the meq. I_2, the normality of the iodine solution is

$$50.00 \times N_{I_2} = 6.07$$
$$N = 0.1214$$

EXAMPLE II. Excess potassium iodide is added to a solution containing 239.3 mg. of potassium dichromate, and the liberated iodine requires 48.80 ml. of standard thiosulfate solution for reduction. What is the normality of the thiosulfate solution?

Solution:

According to the equation

$$Cr_2O_7^{=} + 6I^- + 14H^+ \rightarrow 2Cr^{+++} + 3I_2 + 7H_2O$$

potassium dichromate liberates 6 milliequivalents of iodine per mole of dichromate, and the liberated iodine is titrated with sodium thiosulfate according to the equation

$$2S_2O_3^{=} + I_2 \rightarrow S_4O_6^{=} + 2I^-$$

Thus 6 milligram equivalents of sodium thiosulfate will be required to react with the iodine; therefore one millimole of dichromate will require 6 milliequivalents of thiosulfate ion.

$$48.80 \times N_{Na_2S_2O_3} = \frac{\frac{239.3}{294.2}}{6}$$
$$N = 0.100$$

EXAMPLE III. In a sample of an alloy weighing 1.000 gram, the tin was reduced to tin(II) chloride which required 39.75 ml. of 0.1200 N iodine solution for titration. Calculate the percentage of tin in the alloy.

Solution:

The number of milliequivalents of iodine is equivalent to the number of milliequivalents of tin(II). They can be calculated as follows:

$$\text{meq. } I_2 = 39.75 \times 0.1200 = 4.77$$

The percentage of the tin in the alloy is

$$\% \text{ Sn} = 4.77 \times \frac{118.7}{2} \times \frac{100}{1000} = 28.1\%$$

Laboratory Experiment 7

Determination of the Oxidizing Power of Pyrolusite

Discussion

As suggested on page 92, an illustration of the indirect determination of oxidizing agents using standard potassium permanganate solution is the determination of the oxidizing power of a pyrolusite ore. The active oxidizing agent in an ore of this type is manganese(IV) oxide (MnO_2). The oxidizing agent is reduced with a known excess of a reducing agent, for example sodium oxalate, and then the excess reducing agent is titrated with standard permanganate in acid solution. From the amount of the reducing agent added and the volume of standard potassium permanganate solution used the oxidizing power of the ore can be calculated. It is common to express this oxidizing power as the percent "available oxygen."

Reagents

6 *N* H_2SO_4
: prepared by adding 20 ml. of concentrated sulfuric acid to 100 ml. distilled water.

$KMnO_4$
: potassium permanganate, analytical reagent grade.

$Na_2C_2O_4$
: sodium oxalate, analytical reagent grade.

Procedure

PREPARATION OF 0.1 *N* $KMnO_4$

Prepare a solution of approximately 0.1 *N* $KMnO_4$ by dissolving 3.3 grams reagent grade $KMnO_4$ in approximately one liter of distilled water in a 1500 ml. beaker. Warm and stir the solution until all of the crystals have dissolved. Heat the solution to just below boiling and keep it at this temperature for about an hour. Cover the solution with a watch glass and allow it to stand until cool, preferably overnight. Filter the solution using a glass wool plug in a suction filter system; the filtering removes the manganese dioxide initially present in the permanganate and those reduction products formed by the action of the permanganate with oxidizable materials in the water.

STANDARDIZATION OF $KMnO_4$

Dry about 5 grams of analytical reagent grade $Na_2C_2O_4$ for one hour in a weighing bottle kept in an oven set at 100–105°C. Into 400 ml. beakers weigh to the nearest tenth of a milligram from a weighing bottle, triplicate samples of the dry $Na_2C_2O_4$ of about 0.2500 gram each. Add 200 ml. of water and 30 ml. of 6 *N* H_2SO_4, and stir until the $Na_2C_2O_4$ has dissolved. Using a thermometer as a stirring rod, warm the solution until the temperature is brought to 80–90°C. At this point remove from the heat and titrate with the prepared potassium permanganate solution, stirring constantly until a pink coloration appears and lasts for 30 seconds. The oxidation by permanganate in acid solution proceeds slowly until there are enough manganese(II) ions formed to catalyze the subsequent oxidation. After this, the reaction then proceeds in a relatively rapid manner.

From the data obtained, calculate the normality of the permanganate solution as an oxidizing agent. The oxalate is oxidized according to the net reaction

$$2MnO_4^- + 5C_2O_4^= + 16H^+ \rightarrow 10CO_2 + 2Mn^{++} + 8H_2O$$

DETERMINATION OF THE OXIDIZING POWER OF PYROLUSITE

Dry the finely ground sample of the pyrolusite for 1 hour in an oven set at 100–105°C. Weigh to the nearest tenth of a milligram triplicate samples of the dried powdered pyrolusite of about 0.5000 gram each into 400 ml. beakers. Into the same beakers weigh to the nearest tenth of a milligram one gram of the previously dried $Na_2C_2O_4$. Add 25 ml. of distilled water and 50 ml. of 6 *N* H_2SO_4 to each beaker. Cover the beakers and warm the solutions gently until the evolution of CO_2 ceases and the residues are free from black particles. Do not let the solutions evaporate to any extent. Dilute the solutions to about 250 ml., heat to a temperature of 80–90°C and, while hot, titrate the excess oxalate with standard permanganate until a pink coloration appears and lasts for 30 seconds.

From the data obtained, calculate the oxidizing power of pyrolusite in terms of percentage MnO_2 as well as percentage "available oxygen."

Laboratory Experiment 8

Determination of Iron in Limonite Ore

Discussion

Since most ores of iron contain iron in both the +2 and +3 oxidation state, it is necessary, after bringing the sample of the ore into solution, to convert the iron to one oxidation state before making the determination. In this procedure, using potassium permanganate as the final reactant, the iron is all reduced to the +2 oxidation state by the addition of the reducing agent $SnCl_2$. After the destruction of the excess $SnCl_2$ by the addition of $HgCl_2$, as shown by the equation

$$2HgCl_2 + Sn^{++} + 4Cl^- \rightarrow Hg_2Cl_2 + SnCl_6^=$$

a white precipitate appears. The presence of a dark or grey precipitate indicates that an excess of $SnCl_2$ has been added. The secondary reaction,

$$Sn^{++} + Hg_2Cl_2 + 4Cl^- \rightarrow 2Hg + SnCl_6^=$$

indicates the presence of finely divided elemental mercury. The mercury can react with the standard permanganate solution, making the iron determination of no value.

To prevent the oxidation of the chloride ion by permanganate ion, Zimmerman-Reinhardt reagent is added. The components of this solution, $MnSO_4 \cdot H_2O$, H_3PO_4, H_2SO_4 are all in large concentration. The purpose of the three components is to prevent the oxidation of the chloride ion. In part this is accomplished by having a large concentration of manganese(II) ions which causes the potential of the MnO_4^--Mn^{++} half-cell to be lower than that of the Cl^--Cl_2 half-cell. The phosphoric acid reacts with the iron(III) ions as fast as they are generated to form a colorless complex; by thus removing the iron(III) ions from solution, the potential of the Fe^{+++}-Fe^{++} half-cell is lowered, which favors the oxidation of iron(II). Replacement of colored iron(III) ions by the colorless complex also makes the pink color at the endpoint easier to detect. Sulfuric acid furnishes the hydrogen ion concentration necessary for the oxidation to take place.

The solution is then titrated with standard oxidizing agent, potassium permanganate, to a permanent pink color.

Reagents

6 *N* HCl

prepared by mixing equal volumes of concentrated hydrochloric acid and distilled water.

1 *N* $SnCl_2$

prepared by dissolving 1.15 grams $SnCl_2 \cdot 2H_2O$ in a mixture of 1.7 ml. concentrated HCl and 5 ml. of distilled water, and diluting with distilled water to 10 ml.

0.2 *N* $HgCl_2$

prepared by dissolving 6.25 grams $HgCl_2$ in distilled water and diluting to 250 ml. with distilled water.

0.1 *N* $KMnO_4$

Standard potassium permanganate solution prepared in the manner described on page 104.

Zimmerman-Reinhardt reagent

prepared by dissolving 6.7 grams $MnSO_4 \cdot H_2O$ in a mixture made by pouring 13.8 ml. of 85% H_3PO_4 and 13.0 ml. of concentrated H_2SO_4 into 50 ml. of distilled water. Dilute to 100 ml. with distilled water.

Procedure

Into 250 ml. beakers weigh to the nearest tenth of a milligram three samples, of about 0.3000 gram each, of the ore which has been previously dried in an oven set at 100–105°C. Add 20 ml. of 6 *N* HCl to each beaker. Cover each of the beakers with a watch glass and heat to just below boiling. Continue heating until all of the sample is dissolved or until all that remains is a white residue, which indicates that all of the sample has been dissolved and that which remains is a siliceous material.

Keeping the solution hot, add dropwise a solution of 0.1 *N* $SnCl_2$ until all of the iron(III) ions have just been reduced to iron(II) ions. The disappearance of the yellow color signals the completion of this reduction. Two drops of the $SnCl_2$ solution are added in excess.

Cool the solution completely, and add rapidly without much delay 30 ml. of 0.2 *N* $HgCl_2$ solution. A white opalescent precipitate should form. If there is no precipitate, insufficient $SnCl_2$ solution has been added; if the precipitate is grey or dark colored, too much $SnCl_2$ has been added. In either case the sample should be discarded.

Allow the solution to stand for 5 minutes. At the end of the waiting period, dilute to 400 ml. with cold distilled water, add 25 ml. of Zimmerman-Reinhardt reagent, and titrate the cold solution at once with standard permanganate solution to a pink color that remains for 30 seconds while the solution is stirred.

From the data obtained, calculate and report the percentage iron, Fe, in the sample.

Laboratory Experiment 9

Karl Fischer Titration of Water

Discussion

The Karl Fischer reagent solution reacts quantitatively with water. It can be used to titrate the moisture in a sample directly or by back titration of the excess Karl Fischer reagent, using a standard water-in-methanol solution.

The titration must be conducted in an atmosphere as dry as possible since atmospheric water will cause erroneous results. Therefore, the reagent bottle, burets, and the sample beaker must be protected from atmospheric moisture by suitable drying media.

The endpoint of the titration is determined when one drop causes the titrimeter eye to open and remain open for 10 seconds. The timing of the endpoint is best accomplished by the use of a stop watch.

The volume of Karl Fischer reagent required to reach the endpoint in the titration of a known volume of standard water-in-methanol solution is recorded. The titer of the reagent can be calculated from the following relationship:

$$\text{ml. standard} \times \frac{\text{mg. } H_2O \text{ per ml. standard}}{\text{ml. Karl Fischer reagent added}} = KF$$

$$KF = \text{mg. } H_2O \text{ per ml. Karl Fischer reagent}$$

The solution in the sample beaker contains no water, and samples are added to the solution for measurement. If it is necessary to have this anhydrous solution stand for any length of time, a drop of Karl Fischer reagent is added and the solution is checked to see that it is still at the endpoint before addition of the new sample.

Apparatus

Fisher titrimeter — Karl Fischer assembly

Reagents

Karl Fischer reagent
Water-in-methanol standard solution (1 mg. water per ml.)

Procedure

A. Place the Karl Fischer assembly of the Fisher titrimeter in operation according to the directions given by the instructor.

B. Fill the dry titrating beaker, containing a plastic-covered stirring magnet, with sufficient water-in-methanol solution to contact the platinum wires of the two platinum electrodes. The volume should be accurately recorded. Turn the titrimeter switch to CAL position. Set the main titrimeter dial to 0.5 volt. Null the eye (just open position) using the *eye control* knob.

C. Start the magnetic stirrer, being careful that the stirrer bar does not hit the lower tips of the electrodes. Set the main dial at 0.35 volt. Turn the *control switch* to POL position.

D. Titrate, using Karl Fischer reagent, until one drop causes the eye to open and remain open for 10 seconds. Use a stopwatch to time the endpoint. This is the critical point in the titration—to be sure that one drop causes the eye to remain open for 10 seconds. Record the volume of Karl Fischer reagent added.

E. To the sample beaker, add a 5 ml. aliquot of the unknown solution.

F. Titrate the unknown solution with Karl Fischer reagent in the same manner as was done in the standardization according to steps C and D. Record the volume of Karl Fischer reagent added.

Calculations

(1) From the data obtained in step D, calculate the Karl Fischer titer.

(2) Using the following relationship and the data obtained in step F, calculate the mg. water per ml. of unknown solution.

$$\text{mg. } H_2O \text{ per ml.} = \frac{V_f \times KF}{\text{vol. of sample}}$$

Laboratory Experiment 10

Determination of Percentage Composition of Hydrogen Peroxide

Discussion

In acid solution, potassium permanganate will oxidize hydrogen peroxide according to the reaction

$$5H_2O_2 + 2MnO_4^- + 6H^+ \rightarrow 5O_2 + 2Mn^{++} + 8H_2O$$

The percentage composition of hydrogen peroxide can be determined by titration with standard potassium permanganate solution.

Reagents

0.1 *N* $KMnO_4$ solution
prepared and standardized according to the procedure listed in Experiment 7, page 104.

H_2SO_4
sulfuric acid, analytical reagent grade.

Procedure

Weigh to the nearest tenth of a milligram a clean dry 10 ml. volumetric flask. Record the weight. Add about 2.0 to 2.5 ml. of hydrogen peroxide to the flask being careful that none of the solution adheres to the side of the flask or to the stopper of the flask. Reweigh the flask to the nearest tenth of a milligram and record the weight.

Rinse the sample into a 400 ml. beaker containing 50 ml. of distilled water to which has been added 3 ml. of concentrated sulfuric acid. Titrate the solution immediately with standard 0.1 *N* potassium permanganate solution.

Repeat this procedure for two more samples of hydrogen peroxide solution. From the data obtained calculate the percentage of hydrogen peroxide in each sample. Report the average value of the percentage composition of hydrogen peroxide.

Laboratory Experiment 11

Determination of Calcium from Acid-Soluble Calcium Carbonate

Discussion

Calcium may be determined volumetrically in acid solution using standard potassium permanganate solution. The calcium ion in the unknown carbonate ore is precipitated from an ammoniacal, neutral, or buffered acetic acid solution as calcium oxalate according to the reaction

$$Ca^{++} + C_2O_4^{=} + H_2O \rightarrow CaC_2O_4 \cdot H_2O$$

The precipitate is filtered, washed to remove the excess oxalate ion and dissolved in dilute sulfuric acid. The resulting oxalic acid is titrated with standard potassium permanganate solution. The oxalate ion on titration with standard potassium permanganate in acid solution gives up two electrons on oxidation; therefore the equivalent weight of oxalic acid is $\frac{H_2C_2O_4}{2}$. Since each calcium ion is associated with one oxalate ion, the equivalent weight of calcium in this case is $\frac{Ca}{2}$.

A common means of reporting the amount of calcium in a sample is to report it in terms of percent calcium oxide (CaO).

Reagents

0.1 *N* $KMnO_4$
: prepared and standardized according to the procedure listed in Experiment 7, page 104.

3% $(NH_4)_2C_2O_4$
: prepared by dissolving 3 grams of analytical reagent grade ammonium oxalate in distilled water and diluting to 100 ml.

6 *N* NH_4OH
: prepared by diluting 40 ml. of concentrated NH_4OH to 100 ml. with distilled water.

Methyl red indicator solution
: prepared by dissolving 0.1 gram of methyl red in 60 ml. of ethyl alcohol and diluting to 100 ml. with distilled water.

3.6 *N* H_2SO_4
: prepared by adding 25 ml. of concentrated sulfuric acid to 225 ml. of distilled water in a 400 ml. beaker. Allow the solution to cool and store in a 500 ml. glass stoppered pyrex bottle.

HCl
: concentrated hydrochloric acid, analytical reagent grade.

Procedure

Place 3–5 grams of the unknown sample in a weighing bottle and dry for one hour in an oven set at 100–105°C. Cool in a desiccator to room temperature.

Into three 400 ml. beakers, weigh to the nearest tenth of a milligram triplicate samples of about 0.5000 gram each. To each beaker add 20 ml. of distilled water. Cover each beaker with a watch glass. Slide the watch glass aside and add

5 ml. of concentrated hydrochloric acid to each beaker being careful that no material is lost due to splattering from the rapid release of carbon dioxide. If the sample has not dissolved completely after the reaction has ceased, warm the covered beaker until all of the solid has gone into solution. Rinse off the watch glass into the beaker; wash down the sides of the beaker using a jet of distilled water. Dilute to about 200 ml. with distilled water and heat to boiling.

Add slowly with stirring to each beaker, the volume of 3% ammonium oxalate solution calculated to be sufficient to precipitate the calcium ion in the sample if it is assumed that the unknown is pure calcium carbonate.

Add 3–5 drops of methyl red indicator solution to each beaker. Add dropwise, from a buret or a dropper, 6 *N* NH_4OH to each solution accompanied by vigorous agitation until the color of the solution just turns yellow indicating it is alkaline. Keep the solution hot for one hour. If magnesium is known not to be present, the solution can stand until the next laboratory period. If magnesium is known to be present, it must be filtered at the end of the hour.

Filter the solution through ashless filter paper. Wash the precipitate by decantation with cold water two or three times and then quantitatively transfer the precipitate to the filter paper. Wash the precipitate on the paper with several small portions of cold water until the last washings upon the addition of calcium chloride solution show no test for the oxalate ion.

Place in a 400 ml. beaker 50 ml. of 3.6 *N* H_2SO_4. Remove the filter from the funnel and place it in the beaker. Heat the solution to boiling while breaking up the filter paper with a stirring rod. The solution is titrated immediately with 0.1 *N* potassium permanganate solution until the appearance of a pink color that remains for 30 seconds.

Using each of the remaining two samples consecutively, repeat the procedure for the solution and titration of the calcium oxalate precipitate.

From the volume of the standard potassium permanganate used and the weight of the sample, calculate the percentage of calcium oxide in each sample. Report the average value of the percentage of calcium oxide found.

Laboratory Experiment 12

Determination of Copper in Copper Ore

Discussion

The basic reaction in the determination of copper using the iodimetric method can be represented by the equation

$$2Cu^{++} + 4I^- \rightarrow 2CuI + I_2$$

This is a rapid quantitative reaction in slightly acid solution if there is a large excess of iodide ion present and if the copper is present as a simple rather than as a complex ion. The iodine that is liberated can be titrated in the usual manner with standard sodium thiosulfate.

Iron interferes since iron(III) ions will oxidize iodine. Since the iron will be found as iron(III) salts as a result of dissolution of the ore, a means of preventing this interference is necessary. This can be accomplished by converting the iron(III) ion to a soluble, slightly dissociated fluoride complex, $FeF_6^{\equiv}$, using ammonium bifluoride. At a *p*H of 3.0–4.0 the iron in this form is not reduced by iodide ion. The *p*H must be regulated very carefully so that the iodide ion will be completely reduced by copper with no reaction by the iron(III) ion.

If arsenic and antimony are present, they will provide no interference at this *p*H if they are in the higher state of oxidation.

Reagents

0.1 *N* $Na_2S_2O_3$

prepared by dissolving 25 grams of analytical reagent grade $Na_2S_2O_3 \cdot 5H_2O$ in one liter of freshly boiled distilled water. Add about 0.2 gram of sodium carbonate as a preservative. Cool and store in a clean pyrex glass stoppered bottle.

Cu

copper metal, electrolytic grade, foil.

KI

potassium iodide, analytical reagent grade.

KCNS

potassium thiocyanate, analytical reagent grade.

HNO_3

concentrated nitric acid, analytical reagent grade.

1:1 HNO_3

prepared by mixing equal volumes of concentrated nitric acid and distilled water.

6 *N* NH_4OH

prepared by diluting 40 ml. of concentrated ammonium hydroxide to 100 ml. with distilled water.

6 *N* $HC_2H_3O_2$

prepared by diluting 35 ml. of concentrated acetic acid to 100 ml. with distilled water.

Starch indicator solution

prepared by adding 50 ml. of boiling distilled water to 0.5 gram of soluble starch. Boil for 2–3 minutes, cool, and decant into a glass stoppered bottle.

$Br_2 \cdot H_2O$

prepared by saturating 100 ml. of distilled water with liquid bromine.

Procedure

STANDARDIZATION OF SODIUM THIOSULFATE

Weigh to the nearest tenth of a milligram triplicate samples of 0.2000–0.2500 gram each of electrolytic copper foil and transfer to 250 ml. beakers. Add 5 ml. of concentrated nitric acid and 25 ml. of distilled water to each beaker. Cover and warm until the solution is complete. Heat the solution until all the oxides of nitrogen are expelled. Add 5 ml. of saturated bromine water and heat until all of the bromine is expelled. (This requires two to three minutes of boiling.) Cool the solutions to room temperature. To one of the solutions add 6 N NH_4OH dropwise until the blue color of the $Cu(NH_3)_4^{++}$ ion appears or a blue green precipitate of $Cu(OH)_2$ forms and remains on stirring. In the case of the copper ammonia complex formation, boil gently for three to five minutes to remove the excess ammonium hydroxide. Add 20 ml. of 6 N $HC_2H_3O_2$. Cool the solution and add 3 grams of potassium iodide stirring until all of the solid is dissolved.

Titrate the solution immediately with 0.1 N $Na_2S_2O_3$ until the color of the liberated iodine has nearly disappeared (the color of the solution is a light tan). Add 5 ml. of starch indicator solution, about 2 grams of KCNS and continue to titrate the solution until the blue-black color of the starch-iodo complex disappears and remains so for 15 seconds.

Each of the remaining solutions is treated in the same manner one at a time.

From the data obtained calculate the normality of the sodium thiosulfate solution.

DETERMINATION OF COPPER IN A COPPER ORE

Into each of three 250 ml. beakers weigh to the nearest tenth of a milligram triplicate samples of 0.3500–0.5000 gram each of the finely ground ore that has been previously dried for an hour at 100–105°C. Add 10 ml. of concentrated nitric acid to each beaker and heat gently until all of the copper has been brought into solution. A white siliceous residue will remain. Evaporate the solution to about 5 ml., dilute to about 25 ml. with distilled water, and boil the solution to expel the oxides of nitrogen and to dissolve the soluble salts that may have come out of solution. If the residue remaining in the beaker is light colored and small it may be left in the solution. If not, it may be filtered off and the filter paper washed with hot 0.6 N HNO_3.

To each solution add a few drops of Fe(III) solution to insure that iron is present in the solution. To one solution add 6 N NH_4OH dropwise until the iron(III) ion has been precipitated and the solution has a faint odor of ammonium hydroxide after blowing over the top of the solution. Add 2.0 grams of ammonium bifluoride which has been weighed to the nearest tenth of a gram on a trip balance. (**Do not weigh on an analytical balance.**) Stir to dissolve the iron(III) hydroxide that has been precipitated previously.

Add 3 grams of potassium iodide to the solution and stir to dissolve all the solid. Titrate the liberated iodine immediately with standard sodium thiosulfate until the color of the solution is a very light tan. Add 5 ml. of freshly prepared starch indicator solution and titrate until the blue-black color has nearly disappeared. Add 2 grams of KCNS and titrate dropwise with standard sodium thiosulfate until the color has just disappeared leaving a suspension of CuI that is a creamy white color.

Each of the remaining solutions is treated in the same manner one at a time.

From the data obtained and the value of the blank, if any, calculate the percentage of copper in the ore.

BLANK DETERMINATION

Potassium iodide may contain appreciable amounts of potassium iodate which in acid solution will react with potassium iodide and liberate iodine according to the equation

$$IO_3^- + 5I^- + 6H^+ \rightarrow 3I_2 + 3H_2O$$

The liberated iodine would react with sodium thiosulfate causing the normality of the thiosulfate solution to be low. To determine the amount of sodium thiosulfate solution that is used to reduce the iodine liberated, the following procedure can be used.

Prepare a solution of 3 grams of potassium iodide dissolved in distilled water and acidify the solution with sulfuric acid. Add 5 ml. of starch solution and if a blue-black color appears, determine the volume of 0.1 *N* sodium thiosulfate necessary to cause the color to disappear. Record the volume required since this volume must be subtracted from the volume required in the standardization and the copper determination.

Problems

1. Using the ion-electron method, balance the following oxidation-reduction equations.

(a) $MnO_4^- + I^- + H^+ = Mn^{++} + I_2 + H_2O$

(b) $Cr_2O_7^= + Fe^{++} + H^+ = Cr^{+++} + Fe^{+++} + H_2O$

(c) $IO_3^- + I^- + H^+ = I_2 + H_2O$

(d) $AsO_3^{\equiv} + I_2 + H_2O = AsO_4^{\equiv} + I^- + H^+$

(e) $MnO_4^- + C_2O_4^= + H^+ = Mn^{++} + CO_2 + H_2O$

(f) $MnO_4^- + Fe^{++} + H^+ = MnO_2 + Fe^{+++} + H_2O$

2. Write the balanced ion half-reactions and the overall balanced ionic equation for the reaction that takes place when the following oxidizing and reducing agents are mixed.

(a) Cu^{++} and I^-

(b) I_2 and $S_2O_3^=$

(c) Mn^{++} and MnO_4^- (neutral solution)
(d) Cu and HNO_3 (concentrated)

3. Write the complete and balanced equations for the half-cell reactions indicated by the following changes.

(a) $HNO_2 \rightarrow NO_3^-$ (acid solution)
(b) $Zn \rightarrow ZnO_2^=$ (basic solution)
(c) $Br_2 \rightarrow BrO_3^-$ (acid solution)
(d) $PH_3 \rightarrow P$ (basic solution)
(e) $CrO_4^= \rightarrow Cr^{+++}$ (acid solution)

4. Using the equation written in problem 2, give the equivalent weight of the following: (a) Cu, (b) I_2, (c) $Na_2S_2O_3$, (d) $KMnO_4$ (acid solution).

5. Fifty milliliters of iron(II) ammonium sulfate solution contains 1.750 grams of pure $FeSO_4(NH_4)_2SO_4{\cdot}6H_2O$. What is the normality of this solution? What is the molarity of the solution? What volume of a solution containing 0.2940 gram of $K_2Cr_2O_7$ will be required to react with 10.00 ml. of the iron(II) ammonium sulfate solution? *Ans. 0.089 N; 0.089 M; 0.15 ml.*

6. A solution of nitric acid is 2.00 *N* as an acid. How many milliliters of water must be added to 25 ml. of the acid to make it 2.00 *N* as an oxidizing agent? Assume reduction of HNO_3 to NO. *Ans. 50 ml.*

7. Calculate the normality as an acid and as a reducing agent of a solution prepared by dissolving a mixture of 15.00 grams $H_2C_2O_4{\cdot}2H_2O$, 5.00 grams KHC_2O_4 and 10 grams $KHC_2O_4{\cdot}H_2C_2O_4{\cdot}2H_2O$ in water and diluting it to exactly 500 ml. with water. *Ans. 0.40 N as acid; 0.48 N as redox*

8. A solution of potassium permanganate contains 3.0240 grams of $KMnO_4$ per 500 ml. of solution. What is the normality of the solution as an oxidizing agent in acid solution? What is the value of 1.00 ml. of this solution in terms of (a) Fe, (b) Fe_2O_3, (c) $Na_2C_2O_4$, and (d) KHC_2O_4? *Ans. 0.19 N, all units mg.; (a) 10.6; (b) 15.1; (c) 12.7; (d) 12.1*

9. A solution of $KHC_2O_4{\cdot}H_2C_2O_4{\cdot}2H_2O$ is 0.150 *N* as an acid. What is the normality of this solution as a reducing agent? *Ans. 0.20 N*

10. Calculate the normality as a reducing agent of a solution prepared by dissolving 10 grams KHC_2O_4 in exactly 750 ml. of water. What weight of K_2CrO_4 will react with 25.00 ml. of the KHC_2O_4 solution in the presence of sulfuric acid? *Ans. 0.21 N; 0.257 gram*

11. If 0.2650 gram of iron wire that is 99.50% pure is dissolved in acid, reduced to iron(II), and requires 42.53 ml. of $KMnO_4$ solution for the titration, calculate the normality of the permanganate solution. *Ans. 0.11 N*

12. A solution contains 2.5325 grams $KMnO_4$ per 600 ml. of solution. What is the normality of the solution? Calculate the value of 1.00 ml. of the solution in terms of (a) Fe_2O_3, (b) $Na_2C_2O_4$, (c) Fe, (d) FeO. *Ans. 0.13 N; (a) 10.6; (b) 8.7; (c) 7.2; (d) 9.3. All units mg.*

13. To a 0.250 gram sample of limonite ore is added 25.00 ml. of $KMnO_4$ solution (1.00 ml. ≎ 5.31 mg. Fe). The excess permanganate solution is titrated using 3.00 ml. of $FeSO_4$ solution (1.00 ml. ≎ 9.2 mg. FeO). What is the percentage of iron in the sample? *Ans. 44.5%*

14. How many grams of $KMnO_4$ are contained in 500 ml. of solution if a certain volume of it will oxidize a weight of potassium tetroxalate requiring one half that volume of a 0.15 N NaOH solution for neutralization? *Ans. 15.8 grams*

15. A sample of pyrolusite weighing 0.500 gram is treated with 0.475 gram $Na_2C_2O_4$ and 15 ml. of 6 N H_2SO_4. The resulting solution is titrated with 20.95 ml. of standard potassium permanganate solution (1.00 ml. ≎ 30.4 mg. $FeSO_4 \cdot 7H_2O$). What is the oxidizing power in terms of percentage available oxygen? *Ans. 15.1%*

16. In the analysis of a 250.0 mg. sample of pyrolusite, 55.0 ml. of iron(II) ammonium sulfate was used, and after the reaction was complete, 12.40 ml. of $KMnO_4$ was required for the excess iron(II). The original iron(II) solution contained 39.2 mg. of the pure hydrated crystals per ml. Twenty (20.00) ml. of the $KMnO_4$ will oxidize 15.00 ml. of KHC_2O_4 solution which is 0.100 N as an acid. What is the percentage of Mn in the pyrolusite? *Ans. 39.5%*

17. In analysis of iron ore containing 65.0% Fe_2O_3, a sample weighing 0.400 gram is taken and the iron is reduced to iron(II) and then oxidized with 0.15 N potassium permanganate. Calculate the volume that would be required. *Ans. 21.8 ml.*

18. In the analysis of a sample of limonite by $K_2Cr_2O_7$ solution (1.00 ml. ≎ 11.17 mg. Fe), what weight of sample should be taken so that the percentage of FeO will be found by multiplying the buret reading by 3? How many milligrams of $K_2Cr_2O_7$ are in each milliliter of the above dichromate solution? *Ans. 0.479 gram; 9.8 mg./ml.*

19. From the following data, calculate the percentage of iron in a sample of limonite.

1.00 ml. $K_2Cr_2O_7$ ≎ 5.585 mg. Fe
dichromate solution used = 46.83 ml.
iron(II) solution used = 2.37 ml.
weight of sample = 0.7235 gram
1.00 ml. iron(II) solution ≎ 1.032 ml. $K_2Cr_2O_7$ *Ans. 34.2%*

20. What weight of $K_2Cr_2O_7$ is required to prepare the following solutions:

(a) 300 ml. of 0.15 N solution
(b) 500 ml. of a solution each ml. of which is equivalent to 11.17 mg. Fe

Ans. (a) 2.21 grams; (b) 9.8 mg./ml.

21. A 0.500 gram sample of iron ore is dissolved in acid, reduced, and titrated with 0.1025 N $K_2Cr_2O_7$, requiring 39.62 ml. of solution. Calculate the per-

centage of iron and the percentage of Fe_2O_3 in the ore. *Ans. Fe, 45.2%; Fe_2O_3, 64.5%*

22. In the analysis of a 1.000 gram sample of chromite ore which contains 5.97% Cr_2O_3, what weight of hydrated iron(II) ammonium sulfate will have to be added so that the excess iron(II) ion will require 30.00 ml. of 0.095 *N* $K_2Cr_2O_7$? *Ans. 2.96 grams*

23. A 0.6520 gram sample of a cerium(IV) compound of 97.8% purity is titrated with 32.60 ml. of 0.05 *N* iron(II) solution. Calculate the equivalent weight of the cerium(IV) compound. *Ans. 391*

24. Calculate the normality of an iodine solution containing 6.25 grams of iodine in 350 ml. solution. *Ans. 0.141 N*

25. A solution of arsenite is prepared by dissolving 0.2650 gram pure As_2O_3. This solution requires 34.85 ml. of iodine solution for titration. What is the normality of the iodine solution? *Ans. 0.154 N*

26. What is the value of 1.00 ml. of 0.05 *N* sodium thiosulfate solution in terms of (a) Cu and (b) Cu_2O? *Ans. (a) 3.18 mg; (b) 3.57 mg.*

27. What is the normality of a thiosulfate solution if 23.45 ml. are required to titrate the iodine liberated by 0.01862 gram of copper? *Ans. 0.0125 N*

28. Pure $K_2Cr_2O_7$ weighing 332.1 mg. was boiled with an excess of concentrated HCl. The liberated chlorine was passed into a solution of KI. The iodine liberated was titrated with 66.79 ml. of sodium thiosulfate solution. Calculate the normality of the thiosulfate solution. *Ans. 0.101 N*

29. A sample of impure potassium iodide weighing 0.500 gram is treated with 0.194 gram of pure $K_2Cr_2O_7$ and the solution is boiled to expel the liberated iodine. The solution is treated with excess potassium iodide and the liberated iodine is titrated with 9.85 ml. of 0.100 *N* $Na_2S_2O_3$. What is the percentage purity of the sample of KI? *Ans. 99.2%*

30. Given a thiosulfate solution (1.00 ml. $\approx$ 8.35 mg. $KBrO_3$). Calculate the weight of copper ore to be taken for analysis so that the percentage of copper(I) sulfide may be found by dividing the buret reading by 2. *Ans. 4.77 grams*

31. What weight of pyrolusite containing 87.47% MnO_2 will oxidize the same amount of oxalic acid as would 35.60 ml. of a permanganate solution, of which 1.00 ml. will liberate 0.0350 gram of I_2 from KI? *Ans. 0.487 gram*

32. The copper in a 2.70 gram sample of copper ore is treated in solution with excess KI and the liberated I_2 treated with 19.80 ml. $Na_2S_2O_3$ (1.00 ml. $\approx$ 7.23 mg. $KBrO_3$). What is the purity of the ore in terms of Cu_2O? *Ans. 13.6%*

33. An excess of potassium iodide is added to a solution of potassium dichromate, and the liberated iodine is titrated with 46.70 ml. of 0.150 *N* sodium thiosulfate solution. How many grams of $K_2Cr_2O_7$ are contained in the dichromate solution? *Ans. 0.344 gram*

CHAPTER 7

Electromotive Force Measurements

Redox processes, when defined in terms of electron transfer, are very closely associated with the transfer of electricity. Oxidation-reduction reactions can be made to proceed by the application of an electric current. In a reverse manner an electric current can be obtained from an oxidation-reduction reaction.

The electrolysis of molten sodium chloride is an example of the use of an electric current to bring about an oxidation-reduction reaction. At the anode, negative chloride ions are oxidized to free chlorine gas, and the positive sodium ion is reduced to sodium metal at the cathode.

The energy that is associated with oxidation-reduction reactions can be converted into electrical energy thus making it available to do work. To illustrate this type of conversion, a galvanic cell composed of a platinum electrode inserted in an iron(II) sulfate solution and a platinum electrode inserted in a cerium(IV) sulfate solution, the two solutions being connected by a salt bridge (U-tube filled with an electrolyte such as potassium sulfate), will be used. The cell can be represented as follows:

$$Pt \mid Fe^{++}, Fe^{+++} \parallel Ce^{++++}, Ce^{+++} \mid Pt$$

The value of the electromotive force (*emf*) of galvanic cells depends on the concentrations of the substances taking part in the electrode reaction, the temperature, and the total pressure. A complete dependence on the concentration factor is a characteristic of analytical applications. Thus the emf of the cell described above is a function of the concentration of the Fe^{++}, Fe^{+++}, Ce^{++++}, Ce^{+++} ions that are present in solution.

The combination of the two solutions with a salt bridge is known as a **cell.** Each solution and its electrode is termed a **half-cell.**

Conventions

There have been for years two different sign conventions for electrode potentials. In various physical chemistry textbooks one or the other will be found in use exclusively. For the want of a better classification they have been termed the **European convention** and the **American convention;** the latter is sometimes referred to as the **Lewis-Randall convention,** named after its founders.

It is generally believed that the two conventions differ only in sign. This is not strictly the case, but rather, it is a basic difference in meaning. This difference can be shown by using the Fe, Fe^{++} electrode reaction according to the reaction

$$Fe = Fe^{++} + 2e$$

The value of the *emf*, when the Fe^{++} is at unit activity, known as the **standard electrode potential,** is assigned according to the European convention as -0.44 volt with respect to the standard hydrogen electrode. If the American convention is used the value would be taken as $+0.44$ volt. It appears that there is just a difference in sign. Consider the same electrode with the half reaction

$$Fe^{++} + 2e = Fe$$

where the standard potential would be -0.44 volt according to the European convention, but according to the American convention this value would be -0.44 volt rather than $+0.44$ volt. It is apparent that if the reaction is expressed as an oxidation reaction, the standard electrode potential of this half-cell is positive according to the American convention and if the reaction is expressed as a reduction reaction, the standard electrode potential of this half-cell is negative according to the same convention. In the use of the European convention the sign does not change and as a result it is an invariant quantity. This is not true of the value as determined by the American convention.

The basic difference in the conventions is the difference between the *emf* of an electrode and the emf of the half-reaction. The potential of the Fe, Fe^{++} electrode measured with respect to the standard hydrogen electrode will be the same -0.44 volt, regardless of whether the reaction is written as an oxidation or a reduction. From the thermodynamic standpoint, the spontaneous reaction of Fe to Fe^{++} in the presence of an oxidizing agent requires that the change in free energy, ΔG, be negative. If the reaction with the standard redox system, H^+, H_2, proceeds spontaneously as written

$$Fe + 2H^+ = Fe^{++} + H_2$$

(as it does in this case), then ΔG for the reaction must be negative. Since

$$\Delta G = -nFE^\circ \tag{7.1}$$

the value of E° must be positive. Therefore, when the half-reaction for the Fe, Fe^{++} half-cell is expressed as an oxidation reaction, the corresponding potential must be given a positive sign. If the reaction is expressed as a reduction reaction, a negative sign is required, in which case ΔG will have a positive value, indicating that the corresponding reaction with the standard redox system will not proceed spontaneously.

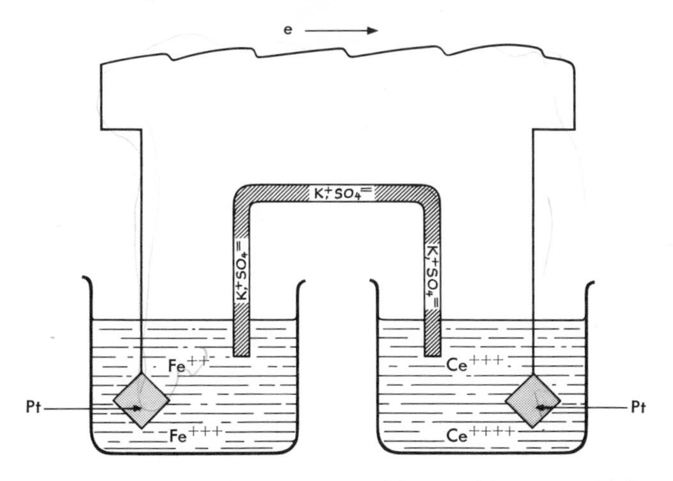

Fig. 7.1. Diagrammatic sketch of cell Fe^{++}, Fe^{+++} and Ce^{+++}, Ce^{++++}.

The European convention refers to the experimentally observed potential of the electrode with respect to the standard hydrogen electrode; whereas the American convention is concerned with the tendency of the reaction to proceed in the direction dictated by the thermodynamic considerations of the reaction.

To resolve this problem, it has been suggested that the term **electrode potential** be used when using the European convention and the term **electromotive force of the half-cell** be used when referring to the American convention.

With reference to Figure 7.1, the diagrammatic sketch of the cell

$$Pt \mid Fe^{++}, Fe^{+++} \parallel Ce^{++++}, Ce^{+++} \mid Pt$$

the conventions that will be used in this textbook can be illustrated.

The anode is described as the electrode at which oxidation takes place. The cathode is the electrode at which reduction takes place. The electrons will flow through the external circuit from the anode to the cathode. In the case of the cell shown in Figure 7.1, when the cell discharges spontaneously, the electrons will pass through the wire connecting the two electrodes, from the electrode dipping in the Fe^{++}, Fe^{+++} solution to the electrode dipping in the solution of Ce^{+++}, Ce^{++++}.

The standard potential, E°, of the cell can be found by the following:

$$E^\circ_{\text{cell}} = E^\circ_{\text{right elect.}} - E^\circ_{\text{left elect.}}$$

With all the components of the cell at unit activity, the standard potential of the diagramed cell is

$$E^\circ = 1.61 - 0.77 = +0.84 \text{ volt.}$$

This indicates that the electron flow through the outer wire is from left to right. Thus the reaction at the left hand electrode is

$$Fe^{++} = Fe^{+++} + 1e$$

The reaction at the right hand electrode is

$$Ce^{++++} + 1e = Ce^{+++}$$

If the standard potential, $E°$, of the cell is positive when the oxidation reaction takes place at the left hand electrode and the reduction reaction takes place at the right hand electrode, then the overall reaction will proceed spontaneously as written.

Those electrode potentials that are given a positive sign are those electrodes that are more positive than the standard hydrogen electrode. Those that are given a negative sign are negative with respect to the standard hydrogen electrode. In the electrochemical series of elements, those electrodes above hydrogen are thus given a negative sign and those below hydrogen are given a positive sign. When the series is set up in this manner, the half-reaction of each electrode is written as a standard reduction reaction. The electrode half-reactions listed in Appendix IV are given as reduction reactions.

Electrode Potential Measurements

The electrode potential, ideally, should be the emf that is generated by a single half-cell. It is not possible to measure the potential of a single electrode absolutely; however, the potential of a single electrode can be measured with reference to an arbitrary standard electrode. If the half-cell to be used as a standard has its potential arbitrarily set at 0.00 volt, then the potential difference measured between the standard electrode and the electrode whose potential is desired will be the value of the electrode potential of the latter. For example, in the reaction

$$Cu^{++} + H_2 \rightarrow Cu^0 + 2H^+$$

the two half-reactions are

$$H_2 = 2H^+ + 2e \qquad Cu^{++} + 2e = Cu^0$$

The measurement of the absolute potential associated with either half-reaction is a difficult one. However, since chemical reactions involve the difference in *emf* between two half-reactions, values of absolute potentials become unnecessary. If the hydrogen gas, hydrogen ion half-cell is chosen as a reference electrode, the potentials of other electrodes can be determined and expressed with reference to that standard.

The equation for the half-cell of the hydrogen electrode, and its standard potential, $E°$, are

$$2H^+ + 2e = H_2 \qquad E° = 0.00 \tag{7.2}$$

The conditions for the standard potential to be zero are that the hydrogen gas be at one atmosphere pressure and the hydrogen ion concentration at unit activity.

It has been shown that the overall potential of a cell is the difference between the potential of the two electrodes. If E_1° is the potential of the electrode to be measured and E_H° is the potential of the standard hydrogen electrode, then the overall potential of the cell can be shown to be

$$E_{cell}^\circ = E_1^\circ - E_H^\circ \tag{7.3}$$

Since $E_H^\circ = 0.00$, then the overall potential of the cell is equal to the potential of the electrode being measured against the standard hydrogen electrode.

The overall potential of a cell made up of two half-cells, each of which has been measured against the standard hydrogen electrode, can be calculated as follows:

$$E_1^\circ = E_1^\circ - E_H^\circ \qquad E_2^\circ = E_2^\circ - E_H^\circ$$

$$E_{cell}^\circ = (E_1^\circ - E_H^\circ) - (E_2^\circ - E_H^\circ) = E_1^\circ - E_2^\circ$$

The potential of the cell made up of the Cu^{++}, Cu^0 electrode and the standard hydrogen electrode is +0.337 volt. If this cell is set up according to the conventions adopted in this text, the cell diagrammatically is shown as

$$\text{Pt} \mid H_2 \text{ (1 atmos.)}, H^+ (a = 1) \parallel Cu^{++} (a = 1) \mid Cu$$

The positive value of the overall potential of the cell indicates that the electrons pass through the external wire from left to right.

To calculate the value of the electromotive force of an oxidation-reduction reaction, it is necessary to determine the difference between the electrode potentials of the two half-reactions involved. To accomplish this it is necessary that all of the half-cells be written either as oxidations or reductions. When the difference is obtained, the sign of the overall potential of the cell will determine whether the reaction will proceed spontaneously in the direction as written or whether the reverse reaction is the direction of spontaneous reaction. There are several steps that, if followed, will help solve the problem of sign and its application to the direction of spontaneous chemical reaction.

(1) Each ionic half-reaction is written as a reduction reaction. The electrons will always appear on the left hand side of the arrow. (Oxidant + ne = Reductant)

(2) The standard electrode potential, $E°$, is written as a reduction potential along with each half-reaction.

(3) Each half-reaction is multiplied by the correct coefficient so that the electrons transferred in the two half-reactions will be equal. The values of the

standard potential are **not** multiplied by these coefficients. The value of $E°$ of any half-cell is independent of any other half-cell with which it may be combined.

(4) The second half-reaction is subtracted from the first. The reactants are transposed to whatever side of the equation is necessary to remove negative signs in the final chemical equation for the redox reaction. The values of $E°$ of each cell are subtracted in the same manner as the ionic half-reactions.

(5) The sign of the overall standard potential of the cell determines the direction of spontaneous reaction. If the sign of the overall standard potential of the cell is positive (+), the reaction proceeds spontaneously from left to right as written. If the sign of the overall standard potential of the cell is negative (−), the reaction proceeds spontaneously from right to left as written.

To illustrate these steps, the following example is given.

$$\mathrm{Pt} \mid \mathrm{Fe^{++}, Fe^{+++}} \parallel \mathrm{Ce^{++++}, Ce^{+++}} \mid \mathrm{Pt}$$

$$\begin{array}{llll}
(1) & \mathrm{Fe^{+++}} + 1e = \mathrm{Fe^{++}} & & E_1^\circ = +0.77 \\
(2) & \mathrm{Ce^{++++}} + 1e = \mathrm{Ce^{+++}} & & E_2^\circ = +1.61 \\
\hline
(1) \text{ minus } (2) & \mathrm{Fe^{+++}} - \mathrm{Ce^{++++}} = \mathrm{Fe^{++}} - \mathrm{Ce^{+++}} & & E_{1-2}^\circ = -0.84 \\
 & \mathrm{Fe^{+++}} + \mathrm{Ce^{+++}} \overset{\longleftarrow}{=} \mathrm{Fe^{++}} + \mathrm{Ce^{++++}} & & E_{1-2}^\circ = -0.84
\end{array}$$

The reaction will proceed spontaneously from right to left as written, since the sign of the overall potential of the cell is negative.

To show that there is no preference in the order of writing down the half-reactions, the same cell half-reactions can be written

$$\begin{array}{llll}
(1) & \mathrm{Ce^{++++}} + 1e = \mathrm{Ce^{+++}} & & E_1^\circ = +1.61 \\
(2) & \mathrm{Fe^{+++}} + 1e = \mathrm{Fe^{++}} & & E_2^\circ = +0.77 \\
\hline
(1) \text{ minus } (2) & \mathrm{Ce^{++++}} + \mathrm{Fe^{++}} \underset{\longrightarrow}{=} \mathrm{Ce^{+++}} + \mathrm{Fe^{+++}} & & E_{1-2}^\circ = +0.84
\end{array}$$

The reaction will proceed spontaneously from left to right as written, since the sign of the overall standard potential is positive. In both cases the direction of the spontaneous reaction is the same.

The oxidation of iron(II) by dichromate can be written as follows:

$$\begin{array}{ll}
(1) & \mathrm{Cr_2O_7^{=}} + 14\mathrm{H^+} + 6e = 2\mathrm{Cr^{+++}} + 7\mathrm{H_2O} \\
(2) & 6\,[\mathrm{Fe^{+++}} + 1e = \mathrm{Fe^{++}}] \\
\hline
(1) \text{ minus } (2) & \mathrm{Cr_2O_7^{=}} + 14\mathrm{H^+} + 6\mathrm{Fe^{++}} \underset{\longrightarrow}{=} 2\mathrm{Cr^{+++}} + 6\mathrm{Fe^{+++}} + 7\mathrm{H_2O}
\end{array}$$

$$\begin{array}{l}
E_1^\circ = +1.33 \\
E_2^\circ = +0.77 \\
\hline
E_{1-2}^\circ = +0.56
\end{array}$$

The reaction proceeds from left to right, as written, since the overall potential is positive.

In both cases all reactants and products are at unit activity. In general, analytical chemists prefer to use molarity rather than activity because this simplifies the calculations involved. Therefore the standard electrode potential, $E°$, will be used when the concentration of all reactants and products is one molar.

Relation of Electrode Potential to Concentration

In most chemical reactions involving redox potentials, the concentrations of the components are normally not one molar. It is possible to calculate the potentials of these cells even though the components are not at unit concentration.

In 1889, Nernst presented a fundamental equation for the potential of the electrode with relation to concentration of the components of the half-cell and the temperature of the cell. This equation, usually called the Nernst equation, is as follows:

$$E = E° - \frac{RT}{nF} \ln \frac{a_{\text{red}}}{a_{\text{ox}}} \tag{7.4}$$

where E is the overall potential of the half-cell, $E°$ is the standard electrode potential expressed as a reduction potential, R is the universal gas constant, T the absolute temperature, n is the number of electrons transferred in the half-cell reaction, F is the value of the faraday. If the pertinent values of R = 8.3144 joules/°K, F = 96,493 coulombs, T = 298°K, and the conversion value of 2.303 to transfer from natural logarithms to common logarithms are used; and if a, the activity, is replaced by molar concentration, the Nernst equation becomes

$$E = E° - \frac{0.0591}{n} \log \frac{[\text{red}]}{[\text{ox}]} \tag{7.5}$$

Molar concentrations can be used here since analytical calculations in this particular field require a precision of only one or two significant figures. Since the precision of the analysis is determined by the volume measurement in the titration rather than by the *emf* measurement, the use of activities and activity coefficients is not required.

To illustrate the application of the Nernst equation to the calculation of the overall potential of a redox system, the following examples are given.

EXAMPLE I. Calculate the overall *emf* at 25°C of the following cell.

Pt | Ce^{+++} (0.10 M), Ce^{++++} (0.001 M) || Fe^{++} (0.01 M), Fe^{+++} (1.0 M) | Pt

Solution:

(1) $Ce^{++++} + 1e = Ce^{+++}$ $\qquad E_1^\circ = +1.61$

$$E_1 = E_1^\circ - \frac{0.0591}{1} \log \frac{[Ce^{+++}]}{[Ce^{++++}]}$$

$$E_1 = +1.61 - \frac{0.0591}{1} \log \frac{0.10}{0.001}$$

$$E_1 = 1.61 - 0.12 = 1.49$$

(2) $Fe^{+++} + 1e = Fe^{++}$ $\qquad E_2^\circ = +0.77$

$$E_2 = E_2^\circ - \frac{0.0591}{1} \log \frac{[Fe^{++}]}{[Fe^{+++}]}$$

$$E_2 = +0.77 - 0.0591 \log \frac{0.01}{1.0}$$

$$E_2 = 0.77 - (-0.12) = 0.89$$

$$\begin{array}{llr}
(1) & Ce^{++++} + 1e = Ce^{+++} & E_1 = +1.49 \\
(2) & Fe^{+++} + 1e = Fe^{++} & E_2 = +0.89 \\
\hline
(1)\ \text{minus}\ (2) & Ce^{++++} + Fe^{++} \underset{\longrightarrow}{=} Ce^{+++} + Fe^{+++} & E_{1-2} = +0.60
\end{array}$$

The positive sign indicates that the reaction shown proceeds spontaneously from left to right with a cell potential of +0.60 volt.

EXAMPLE II. Calculate the *emf* obtainable from the following cell. Write the equation for the spontaneous reaction.

$$\text{Pt} \left| \begin{array}{ll} Mn^{++} & (0.10\ M) \\ H^{+} & (0.05\ M) \\ MnO_4^{-} & (0.05\ M) \end{array} \right\| \begin{array}{ll} Sn^{++} & (0.05\ M) \\ & \\ Sn^{++++} & (0.025\ M) \end{array} \right| \text{Pt}$$

Solution:

(1) $MnO_4^{-} + 8H^{+} + 5e = Mn^{++} + 4H_2O$ $\qquad E_1^\circ = +1.52$

$$E_1 = E_1^\circ - \frac{0.0591}{5} \log \frac{[Mn^{++}][H_2O]^4}{[MnO_4^{-}][H^{+}]^8}$$

$$E_1 = 1.52 - \frac{0.0591}{5} \log \frac{0.1}{(0.05)(0.05)^8}$$

$$E_1 = 1.52 - 0.15 = 1.37$$

(2) $Sn^{++++} + 2e = Sn^{++}$ $\qquad E_2^\circ = +0.15$

$$E_2 = E_2^\circ - \frac{0.0591}{2} \log \frac{[Sn^{++}]}{[Sn^{++++}]}$$

$$E_2 = 0.15 - \frac{0.0591}{2} \log \frac{0.05}{0.025}$$

$$E_2 = 0.15 - 0.009 = 0.14$$

$$
\begin{array}{lrcl}
(1) & 2\,[MnO_4^- + 8H^+ + 5e & = & Mn^{++} + 4H_2O] \\
(2) & 5\,[Sn^{++++} + 2e & = & Sn^{++}] \\
\hline
(1)\text{ minus }(2) & 2MnO_4^- + 16H^+ + 5Sn^{++} & \underset{\longrightarrow}{=} & 2Mn^{++} + 8H_2O + 5Sn^{++++}
\end{array}
$$

$$
\begin{aligned}
E_1 &= +1.37 \\
E_2 &= +0.14 \\
\hline
E_{1-2} &= +1.23
\end{aligned}
$$

The reaction proceeds spontaneously from left to right as written.

Equilibrium Constants from Half-Cell Potentials

From the two basic equations

$$\Delta G^\circ = -nFE^\circ \tag{7.6}$$

and

$$\Delta G^\circ = -RT \ln K_{eq} \tag{7.7}$$

the expression for the equilibrium constant, K_{eq}, can be related to the standard cell potential as follows:

$$E^\circ_{\text{cell}} = \frac{RT}{nF} \ln K_{eq} \tag{7.8}$$

The similarity of this equation and the Nernst equation is shown by the following:

$$E_1 = E_1^\circ - \frac{0.0591}{n} \log \frac{[\text{red}_1]}{[\text{ox}_1]}$$

$$E_2 = E_2^\circ - \frac{0.0591}{n} \log \frac{[\text{red}_2]}{[\text{ox}_2]}$$

At equilibrium, $E_1 = E_2$, then

$$
\begin{aligned}
E_1^\circ - E_2^\circ &= \frac{0.0591}{n} \log \frac{[\text{red}_1]}{[\text{ox}_1]} - \frac{0.0591}{n} \log \frac{[\text{red}_2]}{[\text{ox}_2]} \\
&= \frac{0.0591}{n} \log \frac{[\text{red}_1][\text{ox}_2]}{[\text{ox}_1][\text{red}_2]} = \frac{0.0591}{n} \log \frac{[\text{prod}]}{[\text{react}]}
\end{aligned}
$$

Since the $\frac{[\text{prod}]}{[\text{react}]} = K_{eq}$ and $(E_1^\circ - E_2^\circ) = E^\circ_{\text{cell}}$, then

$$E^\circ_{\text{cell}} = \frac{0.0591}{n} \log K_{eq} \tag{7.9}$$

In the calculation of equilibrium constants, activities rather than molar concentrations must be used to obtain precisely accurate results. As an example of a calculation of a simple equilibrium constant, the reduction of permanganate ion by iodide ion can be used. The overall reaction is expressed as

$$10I^- + 2MnO_4^- + 16H^+ = 5I_2 + 2Mn^{++} + 8H_2O$$

The two half-cell reactions that are used to obtain the overall equation are

$$\begin{array}{rcll} 2\,[MnO_4^- + 8H^+ + 5e & = & Mn^{++} + 4H_2O] & E^\circ = +1.52 \\ 5\,[I_2 + 2e & = & 2I^-] & E^\circ = +0.54 \\ \hline 2MnO_4^- + 16H^+ + 10I^- & = & 2Mn^{++} + 8H_2O + 5I_2 & E^\circ_{cell} = +0.98 \end{array}$$

$$0.98 = \frac{0.0591}{10} \log K_{eq}$$

$$\log K_{eq} = \frac{9.8}{0.0591} = 169$$

$$K_{eq} = 10^{169}$$

Since the solubility product constant, K_{sp}, is a special case of the equilibrium constant, it is possible to calculate the solubility product constants of relatively insoluble substances, using standard cell potentials. For example, the solubility product constant of silver chloride can be calculated from the reaction

$$AgCl \rightarrow Ag^+ + Cl^-$$

The two half-reactions that can be used to obtain the above overall reaction are

$$\begin{array}{rcll} AgCl + 1e & = & Ag + Cl^- & E^\circ = 0.224 \\ Ag^+ + 1e & = & Ag & E^\circ = 0.800 \\ \hline AgCl + Ag & = & Ag + Ag^+ + Cl^- & E^\circ_{cell} = -0.576 \\ AgCl & = & Ag^+ + Cl^- & E^\circ_{cell} = -0.576 \end{array}$$

$$-0.576 = \frac{0.0591}{1} \log K_{sp}$$

$$\log K_{sp} = \frac{-0.576}{0.0591} = -9.81$$

$$K_{sp} = 10^{-9.81} = 1.54 \times 10^{-10}$$

Since the concentration of the AgCl in a saturated solution is constant, then the solubility product constant of silver chloride is 1.54×10^{-10}.

Extent of Oxidation-Reduction Reactions

All reversible reactions proceed in one direction or the other until equilibrium conditions are reached; therefore, to determine the extent to which a reaction can proceed it is only necessary to express the reaction as two half-cell reactions, and then to set the two electrode potentials equal. The potential of the cell decreases steadily until the equilibrium is reached and at this point the potential of one half-cell equals the potential of the other, and the overall value of the potential of the two cells is zero.

To illustrate the calculations involved in determining the extent to which oxidation-reduction reactions take place, the following example is given.

EXAMPLE I. When excess metallic aluminum is added to a solution that is 0.60 M in Cu(II) ions, what is the theoretical concentration of Cu(II) ions after equilibrium is reached ($2Al + 3Cu^{++} \rightarrow 2Al^{+++} + 3Cu$)? Experiment shows that the reaction listed is practically complete.

Solution:

$$[Al^{+++}] = 0.40\ M \text{ since 3 moles of Cu gives 2 moles of Al}$$

$$[Cu^{++}] = X \text{ Molar}$$

$$Cu^{++} + 2e = Cu \qquad E^\circ = +0.344$$

$$Al^{+++} + 3e = Al \qquad E^\circ = -1.67$$

$$E_{Al} = -1.67 - \frac{0.0591}{3} \log \frac{1}{0.4}$$

$$E_{Cu} = +0.344 - \frac{0.0591}{2} \log \frac{1}{X}$$

At equilibrium $E_{Al} = E_{Cu}$; therefore,

$$-1.67 - \frac{0.0591}{3} \log \frac{1}{0.4} = 0.344 - \frac{0.0591}{2} \log \frac{1}{X}$$

$$\log X = -67$$

$$X = 1 \times 10^{-67} \text{ moles Cu(II) ions per liter at equilibrium}$$

Problems

1. Calculate the potentials of the following half-cells.

(a) Fe^{++} (0.01 M) $=$ Fe^{+++} (0.25 M) $+ 1e$ *Ans.* *−0.85v*

(b) Pb^{++} (0.025 M) $+ 2H_2O = PbO_2 + 4H^+$ (0.05 M) $+ 2e$
Ans. *−1.24v*

(c) Mn^{++} (0.10 M) $+ 4H_2O = MnO_4^-$ (0.03 M) $+ 8H^+$ (0.1 M) $+ 5e$

(d) $Cu = Cu^{++}$ (0.5 M) $+ 2e$

(e) $Hg = Hg^{++}$ (0.01 M) $+ 2e$

2. What is the *emf* of the following cell?

oxidation reduction

$$Ag \mid Ag^+ (0.30\ M) \parallel Ag^+ (0.005\ M) \mid Ag$$

What is the direction of the flow of electrons through the wire connecting the electrodes as written? *Ans.* *−0.107v; left to right*

3. Calculate the *emf* obtainable from the following cell.

$$\text{Pt} \mid \text{Fe}^{++}\ (0.20\ M),\ \text{Fe}^{+++}\ (0.35\ M) \parallel \text{Cr}^{+++}\ (0.01\ M),\ \text{Cr}_2\text{O}_7^{=}\ (0.5\ M),\ \text{H}^+\ (0.05\ M) \mid \text{Pt}$$

Write the equation for the spontaneous net reaction. *Ans. 0.39v;* $Cr_2O_7^{=} + 6Fe^{++} + 14H^+ = 6Fe^{+++} + 2Cr^{+++} + 7H_2O$

4. Indicate the direction of the following reaction.

$$2\text{Fe}^{++}\ (0.30\ M) + \text{Sn}^{++++}\ (0.01\ M) = 2\text{Fe}^{+++}\ (0.06\ M) + \text{Sn}^{++}\ (0.10\ M)$$

Calculate the *emf* of the cell if the reaction takes place reversibly in a voltaic cell. *Ans. right to left; 0.61v*

5. Calculate the equilibrium constant for each of the following.

(a) $2Br^- + I_2 \rightleftharpoons Br_2 + 2I^-$ *Ans.* 1.25×10^{-18}
(b) $Cu^{++} + 2Ag \rightleftharpoons Cu + 2Ag^+$ *Ans.* 4×10^{-16}

6. Calculate the solubility product of AgI from the following half-reactions.

$$\text{Ag}^+ + 1e = \text{Ag};\quad \text{AgI} + 1e = \text{Ag} + \text{I}^-$$

Ans. 1.5×10^{-16}

7. Which of the following reactions should take place as shown when the ion concentrations are one molar?

(a) $2Fe^{++} + PbO_2 + 4H^+ \rightarrow 2Fe^{+++} + Pb^{++} + 2H_2O$ *Ans. Yes*
(b) $10Cr^{+++} + 6MnO_4^- + 11H_2O \rightarrow 5Cr_2O_7^{=} + 6Mn^{++} + 22H^+$
(c) $2Cl^- + Br_2 \rightarrow 2Br^- + Cl_2$ *Ans. No*
(d) $Zn + 2Cr^{+++} \rightarrow Zn^{++} + 2Cr^{++}$
(e) $Cr_2O_7^{=} + 6Br^- + 14H^+ \rightarrow 3Br_2 + 2Cr^{+++} + 7H_2O$

8. Calculate the *emf* of the following cell and write the balanced ionic equation for the reaction that will proceed spontaneously from left to right.

$$\text{Cu} \mid \text{Cu}^{++}\ (0.010\ M) \parallel \text{Cu}^{++}\ (0.09\ M) \mid \text{Cu}$$

9. What is the direction of the reaction, and the *emf*, if the following reaction takes place reversibly at 25°C in a voltaic cell?

$$2\text{Fe}^{+++}\ (0.25\ M) + 2\text{Cl}^-\ (0.15\ M) = 2\text{Fe}^{++}\ (0.15\ M) + \text{Cl}_2\ (0.25\ M)$$

Ans. right to left; 0.61v

10. A solution which is 0.025 *M* in copper(II) ion is shaken with metallic zinc until equilibrium is reached. What is the concentration of copper(II) ion remaining in the solution?

CHAPTER **8**

Potentiometric Titrimetric Methods

Methods that employ a single measurement of the electromotive force (*emf*) of a galvanic cell, that follow the change in *emf* of an indicator electrode during the titration of a substance using a standard reagent solution, or that measure the change in *p*H are examples of potentiometric titrimetric methods.

In the previous chapter, the relationship between the *emf* of a galvanic cell and the concentration of the components of the cell was discussed. The practical application of this relationship is the potentiometric titration. By setting up one half-cell using the solution to be titrated and another half-cell having a known fixed potential, it is possible to use the overall potential of the cell as a measure of the concentration of the substance being titrated. The potential is measured after each addition of titrant. The value of the *emf* is plotted against the volume of titrant added and a characteristic curve is obtained. Potentiometric methods are used most often in the titration of colored solutions or turbid solutions, where the use of chemical indicators is either unsatisfactory or impossible.

The titrations are generally classified into three distinct types of reactions:

Acid-Base.
Oxidation-Reduction (Redox).
Precipitation and Complex Formation.

Apparatus for Potentiometric Titration

The apparatus necessary for a potentiometric titration consists of an indicator electrode, a reference electrode, and a potential measuring device. A diagrammatic sketch of the arrangement of these components is shown in Figure 8.1.

The **indicator electrode** in a potentiometric titration is the electrode whose potential is dependent on the concentration of the substance being titrated. Indicator electrodes are readily available for redox reactions and acid-base reactions but are limited in their availability for precipitation and complex formation reactions.

A **reference electrode** maintains a constant potential with respect to the solution, regardless of any change in the concentration of any specific ion in the

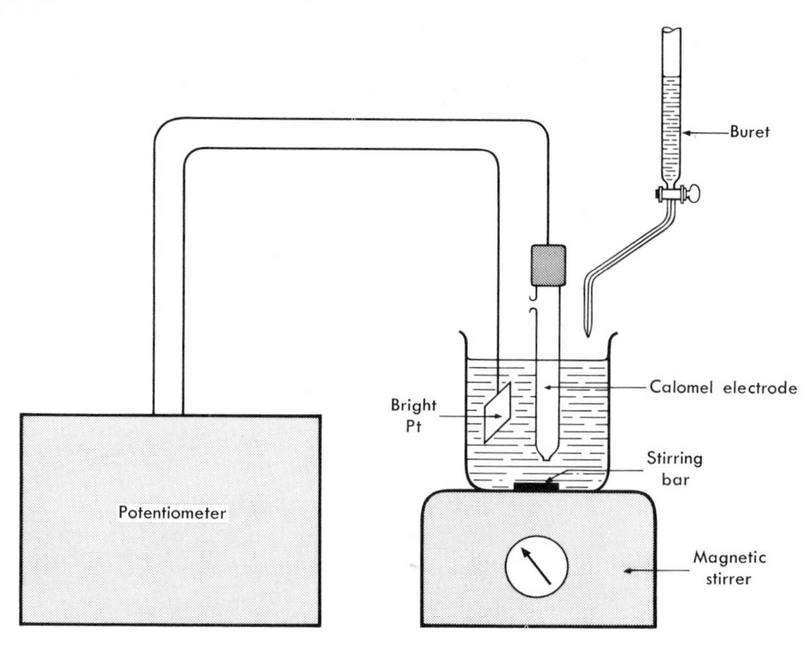

Fig. 8.1. Diagrammatic sketch of apparatus for potentiometric titration.

solution. The standard hydrogen electrode is used as a primary reference electrode. The most commonly used secondary reference electrodes are the calomel electrodes and the mercury(I) sulfate electrode. The potential of the calomel electrode is a function of the concentration of the chloride ion in the cell. Table 8.1 gives the potential of the calomel electrodes of different chloride ion concentration at 25°C.

TABLE 8.1

Standard Potential ($E°$) of Calomel Electrodes for Three Chloride Ion Concentrations

CONCENTRATION OF CHLORIDE ION IN CALOMEL ELECTRODE	$E°$ AT 25°C, VOLT
0.1 Normal	0.3338
1.0 Normal	0.2800
Saturated	0.2415

In Table 8.2 are given some indicator and reference electrodes that can be used in typical reactions. This list is given as a general guide and should not be considered as complete.

The potential measuring meter can be calibrated directly in voltage units or it may be calibrated in pH units (Figure 8.2), since many of the potential measurements are made for pH titrations. There are several types of commercially

Table 8.2

Common Indicator and Reference Electrodes Used in Various Types of Reactions

TYPE OF REACTION	INDICATOR ELECTRODE	REFERENCE ELECTRODE
Acid-Base	Glass	Calomel
Redox		
Inorganic	Platinum	Calomel
Inorganic	Platinum	Tungsten
Iodimetry	Platinum	Tungsten
Precipitation		
Silver ion	Silver	Mercury(I) sulfate
Halogen	Silver or silver-silver chloride	Mercury(I) sulfate
Heavy metal	Heavy metal	Calomel

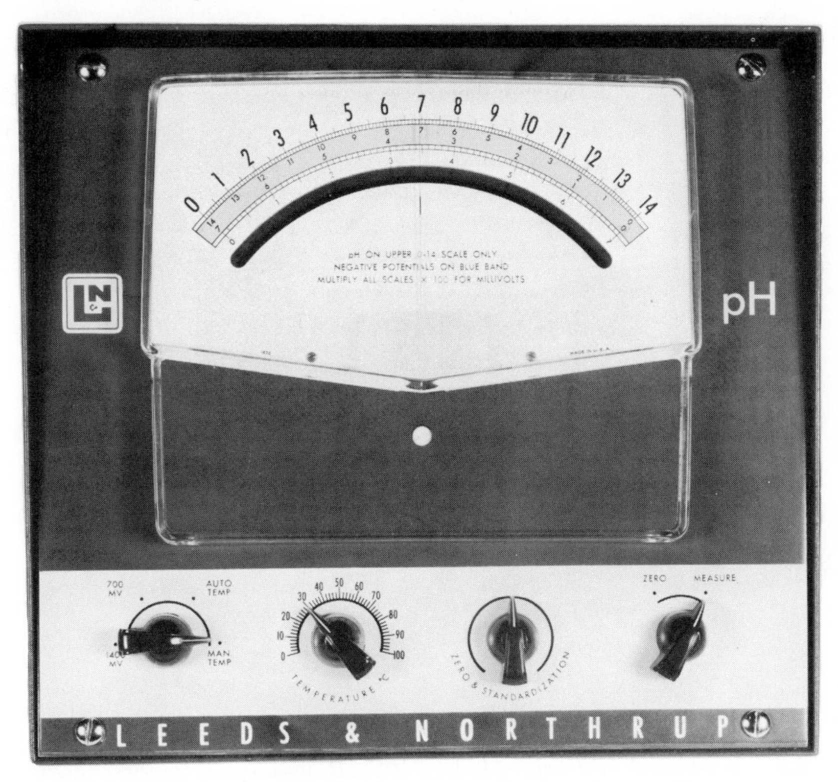

Fig. 8.2. Potential measuring meter calibrated directly in voltage and pH units. *Courtesy Leeds and Northrup Company*

available measuring meters calibrated both in units of pH and voltage (Figures 8.3 and 8.4). In some instruments, instead of a meter an electron ray indicator tube is used. The instrument is so designed that the "magic eye" will close or open above or below a given potential. If the potential at the equivalence point is known or can be estimated, the critical potential of the eye can be adjusted so that the eye will either open or close at the present potential. Instruments are also available that will automatically stop the flow of titrant into the solution when the potential of the equivalence point has been reached (Figure 8.5).

ACID-BASE TITRATIONS

The electrode system used in an acid-base titration is composed of an indicator electrode sensitive to changes in hydrogen ion concentration (*e.g.*, glass electrode), and a calomel electrode as a reference electrode. The potentiometric acid-base titration has few advantages over visual titrations where there is no

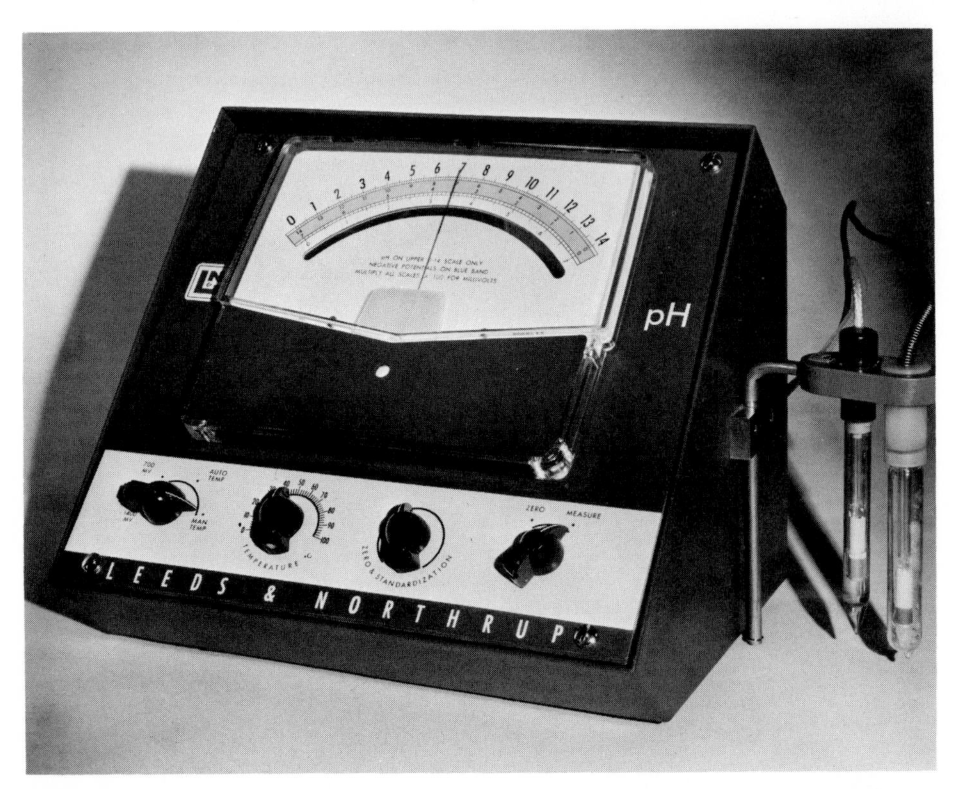

Fig. 8.3. Leeds and Northrup Model 7401 pH indicator. *Courtesy Leeds and Northrup Company*

Fig. 8.4. Beckman Zeromatic pH meter. *Courtesy of Beckman Instruments, Inc., Fullerton, California*

turbidity and no color, or where there are no substances present that would act as interferences with the visual indicator. Where these situations do exist the potentiometric method is indispensable.

Electrode System

The glass electrode consists of a thin-walled glass bulb sealed to a supporting tube. The inside of the bulb may be a silver-silver chloride electrode:

$$\text{Ag, AgCl} \mid \text{HCl } (0.1\ M)$$

The potential of the glass electrode follows the hydrogen electrode exactly over a range of pH from 0 to 10.

The potential of the glass electrode is given by the equation

$$E_g = E_g^\circ + 0.0591\ p\text{H} \tag{8.1}$$

Fig. 8.5. Beckman automatic titrator. *Courtesy of Beckman Instruments, Inc., Fullerton, California*

Even with identical solutions in contact with the glass membrane inside and outside, there is a small residual potential across the membrane. This is called the **asymmetry potential** of the glass electrode. As a result of this asymmetry potential, the standard potential of the glass electrode, E_g°, will vary from electrode to electrode. Thus the pH relationship is determined by standardizing the measuring instrument and its electrode system against a buffer solution of known pH. A diagrammatic sketch of a commercially available glass electrode is given in Figure 8.6.

The reference electrode most commonly used is a saturated calomel electrode that can be prepared in the laboratory or purchased commercially (see Figure 8.7a and b). The half-cell reaction for the electrode reaction of the calomel electrode is

$$Hg_2Cl_2 + 2e = 2Hg + 2Cl^-$$

The calomel and the mercury present are at unit activity because of their presence as a solid and liquid respectively; thus the potential for the half-cell can be calculated from the Nernst equation. At 25°C this relationship is

$$E = E^\circ - \frac{0.0591}{2} \log [Cl^-]^2$$

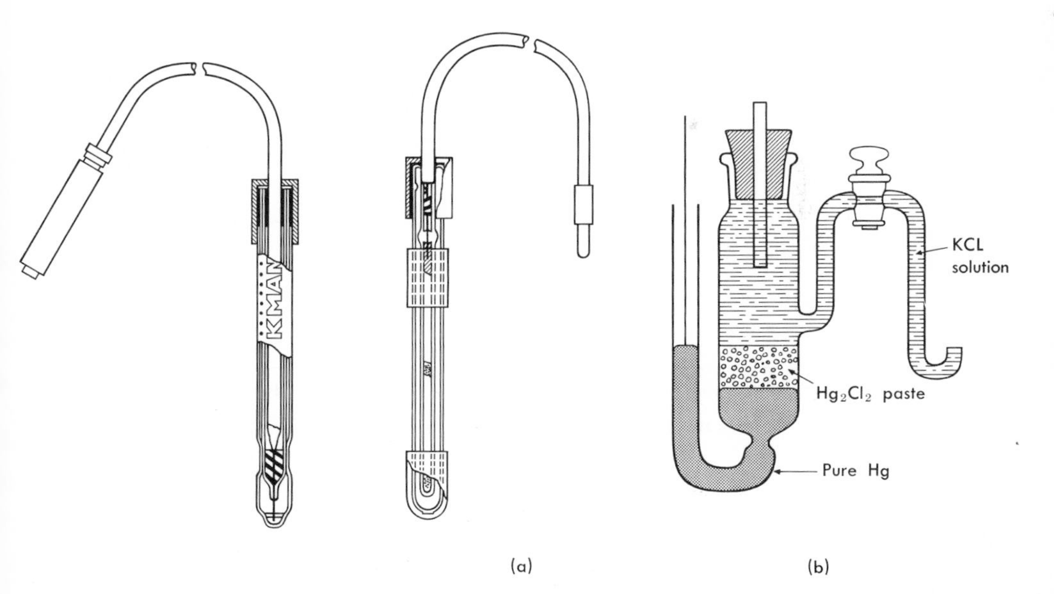

Fig. 8.6. Commerical glass electrode. *Redrawn courtesy of Beckman Instruments, Inc., Fullerton, California*

Fig. 8.7. Two types of calomel electrodes. (**a**) Fiber type calomel reference electrode. (**b**) Laboratory type calomel electrode. *Fiber type electrode redrawn courtesy of Beckman Instruments, Inc., Fullerton, California*

If the concentration of the chloride ion is fixed, the potential of the electrode is also fixed (see Table 8.1, page 132).

Titration Procedure

The titrating solution is added in small increments and the *p*H value is measured and recorded after each addition. These values are plotted versus the volume of titrant added, to give titration curves such as are shown in Figure 8.8. The shape of the curve will depend on the material being titrated. In each case, the equivalence point is at the inflection point in the curve, where the slope is a maximum.

The precision and accuracy of the potentiometric method is as good as that of visual methods. Although it is applicable in more special determinations, it is also subject to error in some cases. Any chemical interference in which the hydrogen ion concentration is affected, such as in the absorption of carbon dioxide from the air, will cause the titration to be worthless.

The glass electrode system has been used frequently in nonaqueous solutions because, in titration, relative values of *p*H are used. The greatest application of potentiometric measurements is in the titration of colored, turbid, or other solutions where visual indicators fail.

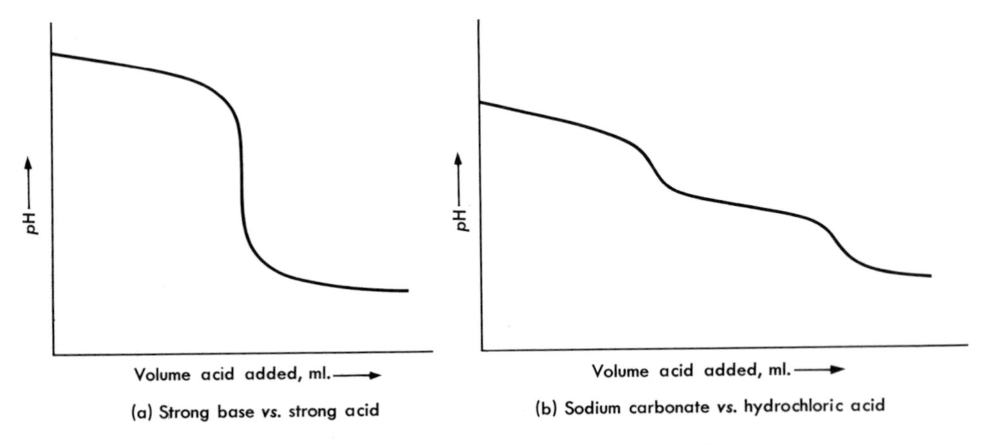

Fig. 8.8. Typical acid-base potentiometric titration curves.

OXIDATION-REDUCTION TITRATIONS

Potentiometric titrations involving oxidation-reduction reactions are very common. A typical example is the potentiometric titration of iron(II) ion with potassium dichromate. The reaction proceeds as follows:

$$6Fe^{++} + Cr_2O_7^{=} + 14H^+ = 2Cr^{+++} + 6Fe^{+++} + 7H_2O \qquad \textbf{(8.2)}$$

Electrode System

The electrode system used in the titration of iron(II) ions with potassium dichromate comprises a bright platinum electrode as an indicator electrode and a calomel electrode as the reference electrode. As is shown in Table 8.2, tungsten can be used as a reference electrode in some inorganic redox reactions.

Mechanics of Titration

If the iron(II) ions are present in the beaker in acid solution at the beginning of the titration and the dichromate ions in the buret, the potential at the platinum electrode is dependent on the ratio of the concentration of iron(II) to iron(III) ions. The potential of the half-cell

$$Pt \mid Fe^{++}, Fe^{+++}$$

is given by the Nernst equation

$$E = E^\circ - \frac{0.0591}{1} \log \frac{[Fe^{++}]}{[Fe^{+++}]} \tag{8.3}$$

As the dichromate ion is added, the ratio $[Fe^{++}]/[Fe^{+++}]$ changes, resulting in a change in *emf* indicated by the change in potential at the platinum electrode. This potential change will continue until the equivalence point is reached. At this point the titration involves the iron(II)-iron(III) and the dichromate-chromium(III)-hydrogen ion equilibrium. The reaction is asymmetrical and consequently the titration curve is not symmetrical around the equivalence point. The potential of the endpoint is much closer to the dichromate-chromium(III) standard potential than to the iron(II)-iron(III) standard potential. The rate of change of the potential at the endpoint is so rapid that no significant error results from using the maximum of $\Delta E/\Delta V$ as the endpoint.

Beyond the equivalence point, the dichromate-chromium(III)-hydrogen ion system controls the potential. This potential can be calculated from the following relation:

$$E = E^\circ - \frac{0.0591}{6} \log \frac{[Cr^{+++}]^2}{[Cr_2O_7^{=}][H^+]^{14}} \tag{8.4}$$

A titration curve can be obtained by plotting the *emf* measured versus the volume of titrant added. A titration curve obtained from the titration of iron(II) ammonium sulfate in sulfuric acid solution with potassium dichromate is shown in Figure 8.9.

The endpoint of the reaction can be determined either graphically or analytically. These methods of endpoint determination are discussed in a later section (see page 142).

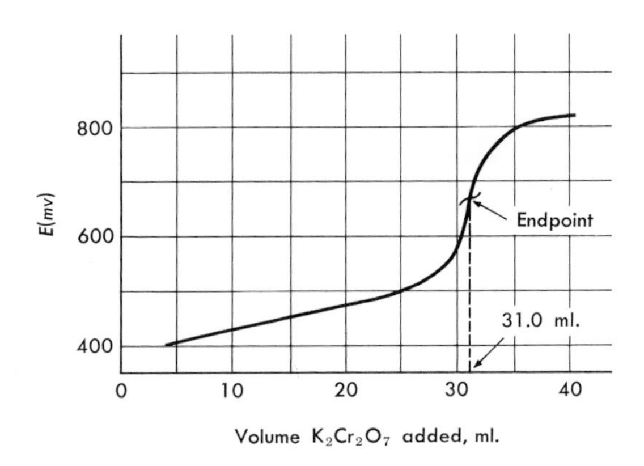

Fig. 8.9. Titration of 1.2209 g. $Fe(NH_4)_2(SO_4)_2 \cdot 6H_2O$ with 0.1001*N* $K_2Cr_2O_7$ in acid solution.

As can be seen from the Nernst equation giving the potential of the dichromate-chromium(III) ion (equation 8.4), the concentration of the hydrogen ion is an important factor in the calculation of the potential of the half-cell and therefore will affect the overall potential read on the measuring potentiometer. As long as the initial hydrogen ion concentration remains constant, the potential change will be determined by the change in the ratio of the products to the reactants in the overall reaction. If, however, the initial hydrogen ion concentration is changed, the curve will be shifted vertically along the potential axis.

The practical result of this shift is that it is not possible to titrate a redox system involving hydrogen ion to a definite potential value, since it is difficult to control the hydrogen ion concentration to the required precision. In the iron(II)-iron(III), dichromate-chromium(III) reaction in acid solution, if the acid is present in large excess, the effect on the potential at the endpoint will be so small that the reaction could be titrated to a given potential. Moreover, the potential is changing so rapidly near the equivalence point that the error in volume due to the small change in the potential as a result of the difference in hydrogen ion content from sample to sample will be well within the experimental error of the titration.

PRECIPITATION AND COMPLEX FORMATION TITRATIONS

In many cases the equivalence point of precipitation reactions and of complex formation reactions can be determined potentiometrically. One example is the titration of a soluble chloride with silver nitrate. Ions such as silver and mercury that form soluble stable complexes (*e.g.*, $Ag(CN)_2^-$, $Hg(CN)_2^-$) can be titrated potentiometrically with the complex-forming compound.

The lack of suitable indicator electrodes has greatly limited the use of potentiometric methods in precipitation and complex formation titrations. Potentiometric methods are of special value in the analysis of a mixture of halides, since it is possible to analyze a mixture of chloride ion and iodide ion without resorting to an indirect method of analysis.

Electrode System

The electrode system used in this type of titration is dependent on the specific reaction. To titrate a halide solution using silver nitrate, the indicator electrode used is a silver electrode, and the reference electrode can either be a calomel electrode or a mercury(I) sulfate electrode. If a calomel electrode is used, a bridge must be employed to keep the unknown chloride from coming in contact with the chloride ion in the calomel electrode. A mercury(I) sulfate reference electrode does not require this precaution. When ions of heavy metals are being titrated, the indicator electrode is made of the heavy metal, and the reference electrode is a calomel electrode.

Mechanics of Titration

To illustrate the potentiometric principle as applied to precipitation reactions, the titration of silver ion with chloride ion can be used. Comprising a silver electrode and a calomel electrode, the cell can be represented as

$$\mathrm{Hg} \mid \mathrm{Hg_2Cl_2}, \mathrm{Cl^-}(1\ M) \parallel \mathrm{Ag^+} \mid \mathrm{Ag}$$

The overall potential of the cell can be obtained from the relation

$$E = 0.515 + 0.0591 \log [\mathrm{Ag^+}] \quad \textbf{(8.5)}$$

The titration curve of the type obtained here shows a sudden inflection at the equivalence point, just as in an acid-base or redox titration. Figure 8.10 shows a curve for the potentiometric titration of chloride ion using a standard solution of silver nitrate.

The value of the solubility product constant of the substance precipitated in the reaction can be determined if the potential at the equivalence point can be measured. On the other hand, if the solubility product is known, then the potential at the equivalence point can be calculated.

At the equivalence point there is one chloride ion present for every silver ion, thus

$$[\mathrm{Ag^+}] = [\mathrm{Cl^-}] = \sqrt{K_{sp}} \quad \textbf{(8.6)}$$

Substituting the $\sqrt{K_{sp}}$ for the $[\mathrm{Ag^+}]$ in equation 8.5, it becomes

$$E = 0.515 + 0.0591 \log \sqrt{K_{sp}} \quad \textbf{(8.7)}$$

This relationship shows the importance of potentiometric titrations in the calculation of physical constants. It emphasizes their application to physical chemistry as well as their analytical value.

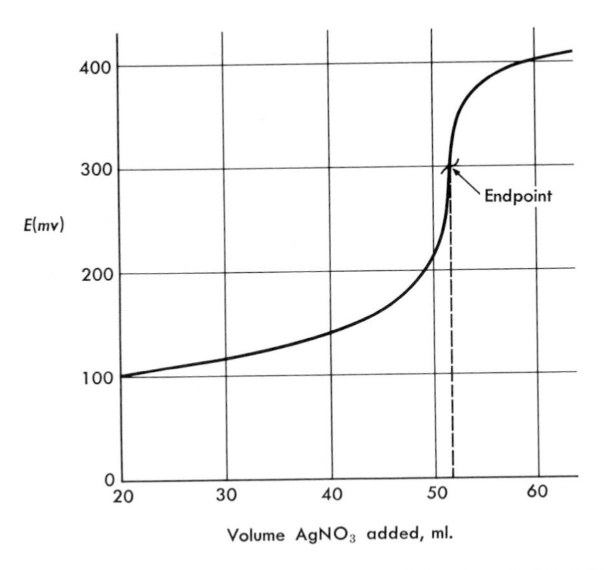

Fig. 8.10. Titration of 25 ml. 0.1032 N KCl with 0.0500 N $AgNO_3$.

TREATMENT OF POTENTIOMETRIC DATA

The data obtained from potentiometric titrations consist of instrument readings, either in units of voltage or pH, that correspond to measured increments of titrant added. The readings are plotted versus the milliliters of titrant added, giving a titration curve from which the endpoint can be determined. Near the equivalence point the potential changes very rapidly with small additions of titrant. The endpoint corresponds to the point where the slope of the titration curve is a maximum. To determine the volume of titrant added at the equivalence point as accurately as possible, either of two methods can be used. They are called the graphical method and the analytical method. To illustrate the use of these methods in the location of the endpoint, the titration of iron(II) with potassium dichromate will be used. The data required for the construction of the titration curve are given in Table 8.3.

These methods may be used with acid-base titrations, using values of pH in a manner similar to the ones illustrated using potential (E) values.

Graphical Method

The potential readings are plotted versus the volume of titrant added, and the titration curve shown in Figure 8.11 is obtained. All of the values are positive regardless of convention because the polarity of the indicator electrode, both when responding to Fe^{++}, Fe^{+++} and to Cr^{+++}, $Cr_2O_7^{=}$, H^+, remains the same (actually positive) toward the reference electrode—in this case the calomel electrode—thus allowing a single positive scale to be used.

TABLE 8.3

Data for the Titration of 1.2209 g. $Fe(NH_4)_2(SO_4)_2 \cdot 6H_2O$ with 0.1001 N $K_2Cr_2O_7$ Solution

VOLUME $K_2Cr_2O_7$ ADDED	E (mv)
5.00	410
10.00	430
15.00	450
20.00	470
25.00	490
30.00	545
30.50	567
30.60	572
30.70	577
30.80	585
30.90	600
31.00	640
31.10	660
31.20	670
31.30	680
31.40	690
31.50	700
32.00	750
34.00	790
40.00	820

The simplest method of determining the endpoint is by visual inspection. A line is drawn vertically through the steep portion of the curve to intersect the horizontal axis. The point of intersection is taken as the volume of the titrant added at the endpoint. This is quite satisfactory for those reactions which show a rather steep curve in the vicinity of the endpoint. The accuracy of the value of the volume decreases as the steepness of the curve decreases.

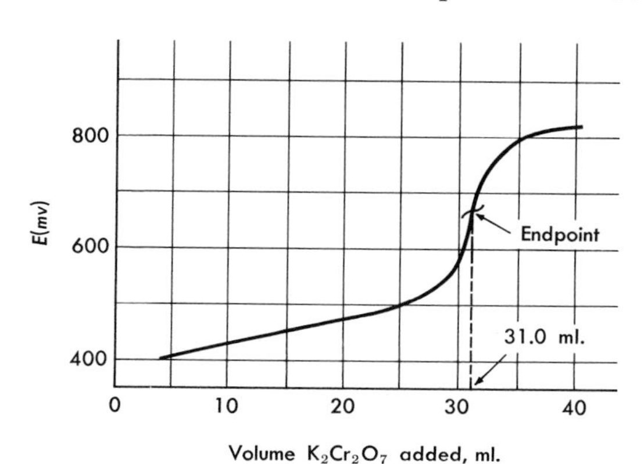

Fig. 8.11. Reproduction of previous titration curve (Fig. 8.9) for easy reference. Titration of 1.2209 g. $Fe(NH_4)_2(SO_4)_2 \cdot 6H_2O$ with 0.1001 N $K_2Cr_2O_7$ solution.

It is not always easy to locate the endpoint by mere visual inspection. A more accurate method of locating the endpoint volume is to use a differential plot in which $\Delta E/\Delta V$ versus volume of titrant is plotted. ΔE is the difference in adjacent values of the potential (E) per unit volume increment ΔV. This curve will rise to a maximum at the endpoint. The values that are taken to construct this curve are those in the vicinity of the endpoint, since these are the only ones that are significant. It is best for the volume to be added in equal increments in the vicinity of the endpoint since this will simplify the calculations. A value of 0.10 ml. was chosen as the unit increment in the example illustrated here.

The data shown in the third column of Table 8.4 are obtained by dividing the difference in adjacent potential values by the difference in volume expressed

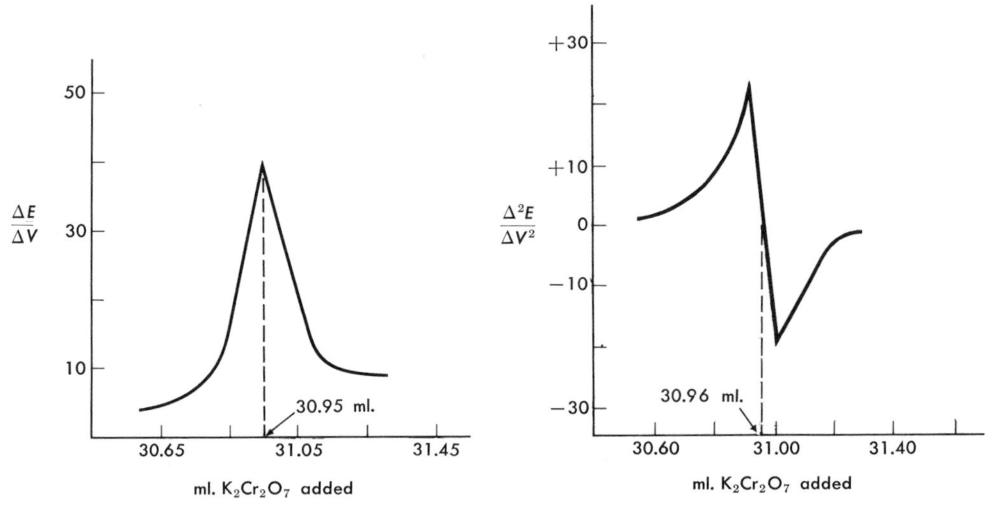

Fig. 8.12. Differential plot, $\Delta E/\Delta V$ *vs.* ml. added.

Fig. 8.13. Differential plot, $\Delta^2E/\Delta V^2$ *vs.* ml. added.

in terms of the unit increment. These values are then plotted versus the midpoint value between the volumes used to obtain $\Delta E/\Delta V$. The differential curve shown in Figure 8.12 results from the data given in Table 8.4.

Very often it is difficult to determine the peak exactly because of the steep slope of the differential curve. The second differential, $\Delta^2E/\Delta V^2$, can be plotted versus ml. of titrant added. Figure 8.13 shows the curve resulting from the data given in the fourth column of Table 8.4. The point where the vertical line connecting the maximum value of $\Delta^2E/\Delta V^2$ to the minimum value of $\Delta^2E/\Delta V^2$ crosses the zero line gives the volume of the titrant added at the endpoint.

TABLE 8.4

Changes in Cell Potential with Volume of Oxidant near Endpoint
1.2209 g. $Fe(NH_4)_2(SO_4)_2 \cdot 6H_2O$ *vs.* 0.1001 *N* $K_2Cr_2O_7$

VOLUME $K_2Cr_2O_7$ ADDED, ml.	E (millivolts)	$\Delta E/\Delta V$ mv./0.1 ml.	$\Delta^2 E/\Delta V^2$
30.50	567		
		5	
30.60	572		0
		5	
30.70	577		3
		8	
30.80	585		7
		15	
30.90	600		25
		40	
31.00	640		−20
		20	
31.10	660		−10
		10	
31.20	670		0
		10	
31.30	680		0
		10	
31.40	690		0
		10	
31.50	700		

Differential plots are very advantageous in the location of the exact volume at the endpoint for reactions which are **unsymmetrical.** Unsymmetrical reactions are those redox reactions for which different numbers of electrons are involved in the two half-reactions, or those acid-base reactions that are not of the strong acid-strong base type.

Analytical Method

A rapid, convenient method of determining the volume at the endpoint in a potentiometric titration without drawing a titration curve is called the **analytical** method. The only potential readings that need be taken are those just before and just after the endpoint. The titrant must be added in equal increments in this region. The second derivative $\Delta^2 E/\Delta V^2$ is calculated, and the endpoint volume is taken as that volume at which $\Delta^2 E/\Delta V^2$ is equal to zero. From Table 8.4 the values near the endpoint are used on the following page to illustrate the use of the analytical method.

VOLUME ADDED	$\Delta^2 E/\Delta V^2$
30.80	7
30.90	25
31.00	−20
31.10	−10

$$V = 30.90 + \left(\frac{25}{45} \times 0.10\right) = 30.96 \text{ ml. endpoint volume.}$$

The size of the increment of titrant, ΔV, to be taken is dependent on the magnitude of the slope at the endpoint. The optimum increment to be taken is learned with experience.

Laboratory Experiment 13

Potentiometric Determination of Iron

Apparatus

*p*H meter equipped with calomel and platinum electrodes or available oxidation-reduction titrator.

Reagents

0.1 *N* $K_2Cr_2O_7$

prepared by weighing to the nearest tenth of a gram about 4.9 grams analytical reagent grade potassium dichromate into a one liter volumetric flask, dissolving in distilled water, and diluting to the mark with distilled water.

$Fe(NH_4)_2(SO_4)_2 \cdot 6H_2O$

iron(II) ammonium sulfate, previously analyzed standard.

H_2SO_4

concentrated sulfuric acid.

Procedure

Into 250 ml. beakers weigh accurately to the nearest milligram two samples of about 1.0–1.5 grams of the $Fe(NH_4)_2(SO_4)_2 \cdot 6H_2O$ that has been previously analyzed. Dissolve each sample in 100 ml. of distilled water and add 10 ml. of concentrated sulfuric acid.

If using a *p*H meter set to measure potential, insert a platinum electrode and a calomel electrode into the solution in one beaker. If not using a *p*H meter, insert the electrodes specified by the manufacturer of the oxidation-reduction titrator that is being used.

With the buret filled with the potassium dichromate solution, begin the titration of the iron(II) salt, recording the value of the potential after each addition. Increments of 2 or 3 ml. may be added initially until the potential begins to change rapidly; then increments of 0.1 ml. each are added until the rate of change of the potential levels off. The titration is continued until about 10 ml. of excess titrant has been added.

Repeat this same procedure using the remaining sample of analyzed iron(II) ammonium sulfate.

Into 400 ml. beakers weigh accurately to the nearest milligram two samples of about 1.0–1.5 grams of the unknown iron(II) compound that has been previously dried for an hour in an oven set at 100–105°C. Dissolve each sample in 100 ml. of distilled water and add 10 ml. of concentrated sulfuric acid. Titrate these two samples in the same manner as was used for the analyzed iron(II) ammonium sulfate samples. Record the value of the potential after each addition of $K_2Cr_2O_7$.

Using the data obtained, plot a curve of potential versus milliliters of titrant added for each of the four samples. In addition, plot curves of $\Delta E/\Delta V$ and Δ^2E/Δ^2V versus milliliters of titrant added for each of the four samples.

Determine the volume of dichromate used for each of the analyzed $Fe(NH_4)_2(SO_4)_2{\cdot}6H_2O$ solutions, and from this volume calculate the normality of the $K_2Cr_2O_7$ solution. Compare this value with the calculated value of the normality of the $K_2Cr_2O_7$ solution as it was prepared.

From the volume of the dichromate used, determine and report the percentage of the iron, Fe, in the unknown iron(II) compound.

In each case, the volume of dichromate solution used and the equivalence potential are obtained from the analytical treatment of the data obtained near the equivalence point.

Laboratory Experiment 14

Potentiometric Analysis of Chloride-Iodide Mixture

Apparatus

*p*H meter equipped with silver and calomel electrodes.

Reagent

0.1 *N* $AgNO_3$ solution

prepared by weighing accurately 8.5 grams of analytical reagent grade silver nitrate into 500 ml. volumetric flask, dissolving in a small amount of distilled water and diluting to the mark with distilled water. The solution is mixed and stored in a dark glass stoppered bottle.

Procedure

Into three 600 ml. beakers weigh to the nearest tenth of a milligram triplicate samples of about 0.500 gram each of the unknown previously dried at 100–105°C. To each beaker add about 300 ml. of distilled water and stir until all of the solid is dissolved.

Using one sample at a time titrate with 0.1 N silver nitrate, taking potential readings after each increment of titrant added. Increments of 2 ml. can be added until the change in potential becomes greater than 25 millivolts for 2 ml. additions; then take readings for each 0.2 ml. increment added.

Repeat the above procedure for each of the two remaining samples.

Plot the value of potential (*mv*) versus ml. of 0.1 N silver nitrate added on rectangular coordinate paper. From the two breaks in the curve, calculate the percent of chloride and iodide in the mixture. The average value of the three values obtained for the percentage of chloride and iodide in the mixture is reported.

CHAPTER 9

Volumetric Precipitation, Complex Formation, and Chelometric Methods

Volumetric precipitation, complex formation, and chelometric methods of analysis are based on the measurement of the quantity of standard solution necessary to react in a precipitation or complex formation reaction with the substance being determined. This can be accomplished by a direct or an indirect titration. Both visual and instrumental methods may be used to detect the endpoint. There are many precipitation and complex formation reactions that would fulfill the requirements set forth for volumetric methods, except that no visual indicator is available to signal the endpoint of the reaction. In many cases, potentiometric, conductimetric, amperometric or turbidimetric methods can be used to mark the endpoint of the reaction.

PRECIPITATION METHODS

Precipitation (precipitimetric) methods are based on the availability of indicators to signal the endpoint of reactions and on reactions that proceed rapidly and sufficiently near to completion to give a sharp endpoint in titration. The standard solution of the precipitating agent may be added to give a direct endpoint, or an excess of the standard solution may be added and the excess measured by titration. Precipitation methods are classified according to the types of compounds formed with the indicators. There are three types of reactions.

(1) Formation of Colored Secondary Precipitates.
(2) Formation of Colored Complex Ions.
(3) Formation of Colored Adsorption Compounds.

Formation of Colored Secondary Precipitates

The endpoint in this type of precipitation reaction is marked by the formation of a colored secondary precipitate. The **Mohr method** for the determination of the chloride ion can be used as an example to illustrate this general type.

In the Mohr method, potassium chromate is added to a neutral solution of the chloride ion before titration with standard silver nitrate solution. The appearance of an orange-red precipitate of silver chromate indicates that the endpoint has been reached. The reactions that occur in this method are

$$Ag^+ + Cl^- \rightarrow AgCl \text{ (white precipitate)}$$
$$2Ag^+ + CrO_4^= \rightarrow Ag_2CrO_4 \text{ (orange-red precipitate)}$$

Since the silver chloride formed is more insoluble than the silver chromate, the formation of the orange-red silver chromate will not take place until the chloride ion concentration has been reduced to a very low value.

The concentration of chromate ion that is required to precipitate the silver chromate at the equivalence point can be calculated from the solubility product constant relationships of Ag_2CrO_4 and AgCl.

The solubility product constant of AgCl is

$$K_{sp} = [Ag^+][Cl^-] = 1 \times 10^{-10}$$

and at the equivalence point

$$[Ag^+] = [Cl^-] = \sqrt{1 \times 10^{-10}} = 1 \times 10^{-5}\ M$$

The solubility product constant of Ag_2CrO_4 is

$$K_{sp} = [Ag^+]^2[CrO_4^=] = 9 \times 10^{-12}$$

the concentration of the chromate ion at the equivalence point for silver chloride is expressed as

$$[CrO_4^=] = \frac{9 \times 10^{-12}}{[1 \times 10^{-5}]^2} = 9 \times 10^{-2} = 0.09\ M$$

At this concentration the color of potassium chromate solution is intensely yellow, making it difficult to determine the appearance of the orange-red color. It is better to use a 0.009 M solution of the chromate ion, even with the sacrifice in accuracy, since it will be much easier to detect the appearance of the orange-red precipitate. If a solution of 0.009 M chromate ion is used, the concentration of the silver ion left in solution when silver chromate starts to precipitate can be calculated as follows:

$$[Ag^+] = \sqrt{\frac{9 \times 10^{-12}}{9 \times 10^{-3}}} = 3.3 \times 10^{-5}\ M$$

In a total volume of 50.00 ml. this corresponds to an excess of 0.05 ml. of silver ion added. The endpoint occurs slightly beyond the stoichiometric point in the chloride precipitation in an amount that can be calculated by running a blank on the indicator in the absence of the chloride ion.

When using the Mohr method for the determination of chloride, it is best to standardize the silver nitrate against potassium chloride under the same conditions as are to be used in the determination of the unknown.

There are several restrictions on the use of the Mohr method. The solution being titrated must be neutral or nearly so. In solutions of pH less than 6, the chromate ion will react with the hydrogen ion according to the equation

$$2CrO_4^{=} + 2H^+ \rightarrow Cr_2O_7^{=} + H_2O$$

Solutions with pH greater than 10 will cause the precipitation of silver oxide. All foreign ions that can be precipitated by silver ions must be absent. The Mohr method cannot be used for the titration of iodide ion because of the adsorption effects of this anion on the silver precipitate.

The main application of the Mohr method is in the determination of chloride ion in drinking water.

Formation of Colored Complex Ions

To illustrate the method where the indicator forms a colored complex ion, the **Volhard method** for the determination of the chloride ion will be used. This is an example of the **indirect method** in precipitation titrations.

A measured amount of standard silver nitrate is added in excess of the amount needed to precipitate the chloride in solution. The precipitated silver chloride is filtered, washed, and the filtrate titrated with standard potassium thiocyanate using iron(III) alum as the indicator.

The resulting reactions are as follows:

$$Ag^+ + Cl^- \rightarrow AgCl \text{ (white precipitate)}$$
$$Ag^+ + CNS^- \rightarrow AgCNS \text{ (white precipitate)}$$
$$CNS^- + Fe^{+++} \rightarrow Fe(CNS)^{++} \text{ (reddish brown color)}$$

If the excess silver ion is titrated in the presence of the silver chloride precipitate, some of the silver chloride is transformed to the less soluble silver thiocyanate, as shown by the equation

$$AgCl + CNS^- \rightarrow AgCNS + Cl^-$$

In addition to giving a poor endpoint, it causes too large an amount of thiocyanate to be consumed in the back titration and makes the calculated results of the chloride low. This is prevented by removing the precipitated silver chloride, or by adding nitrobenzene to the solution accompanied by very strong agitation. The surface of the silver chloride particles is coated with nitrobenzene so that the silver chloride does not react with the thiocyanate ion.

From the solubility product constant of silver thiocyanate (1.0×10^{-12}) the concentration of thiocyanate ion at the equivalence point is 1.0×10^{-6} *M*. By using a rather high concentration of iron(III) (approximately 0.2 *M*) it is possible to observe the endpoint at a concentration of thiocyanate that is the same as that at the equivalence point within the limits of experimental error.

The Volhard method can be used for the determination of bromide, iodide, and thiocyanate ions. The problem of the removal of the precipitate is of no consequence in these cases because of the insolubility of the silver precipitate. In the case of the iodide determination, the indicator, iron(III) alum, is not added until all of the iodide ion is precipitated as silver iodide, since the iodide ion will reduce the iron(III) ion and will itself be oxidized to iodine.

Formation of a Colored Adsorption Compound

Reactions using adsorption indicators are based on the fact that particles of a precipitate will, in the presence of an excess of one of its ions, adsorb this ion onto its surface. This will give a primary layer of charge on the particle. The primary layer will attract ions of opposite charge to form a secondary layer. It was suggested by Fajans and his coworkers that certain organic ions were strongly adsorbed on some precipitates to give a colored adsorption complex that could be used as a means of signaling the endpoint in a precipitation titration.

In the determination of the chloride ion by precipitation with silver nitrate, fluorescein or one of its derivatives (*e.g.* dichlorofluorescein) is used as an indicator. The action of the indicator can be explained in the following manner.

If the chloride solution is being titrated with standard silver nitrate solution, the silver chloride precipitate is formed in the presence of a large concentration of chloride ion. The colloidal precipitate strongly adsorbs the chloride ion present to form a charge complex

$$AgCl{\cdot}Cl^-$$

The charged complex attracts to it positively charged ions from the solution to form a secondary layer. If the chloride being titrated is a sodium salt, then the particle can be represented as

$$AgCl{\cdot}Cl^- \,\vdots\, Na^+$$

As the titration proceeds to the endpoint, this condition will remain, but, immediately after the endpoint, the silver chloride precipitate will be in the presence of excess silver ions and so the particles will adsorb silver ions and become positively charged. This complex is represented as

$$AgCl{\cdot}Ag^+$$

This charged complex will attract to it the negative ions in solution, and, if there are no other ions present except the nitrate ion from the silver nitrate, the complex is

$$AgCl{\cdot}Ag^+ \,\vdots\, NO_3^-$$

If an indicator such as dichlorofluorescein, a weak acid, is added to the solution prior to the addition of the silver nitrate, the color of the solution will be yellow because of the color of the dichlorofluorescein indicator. Upon the addition of silver nitrate the complex

$$AgCl{\cdot}Cl^- \,\vdots\, Na^+$$

will form, and the color of the solution will remain yellow until all of the chloride has been precipitated as silver chloride. Beyond this point, the endpoint, the silver chloride will be present in the solution with an excess of silver ion and the charged complex will be

$$AgCl{\cdot}Ag^+$$

To this charged particle the dichlorofluoresceinate anions of the weak acid are attracted as a secondary layer and give a complex represented as

$$AgCl{\cdot}Ag^+ \,\vdots\, \text{dichlorofluor}^-$$

When this happens the dichlorofluorescein undergoes an internal rearrangement that results in a change of color of the suspension from yellow to reddish pink (the color one usually associates with a strawberry milkshake). The appearance of the reddish-pink color indicates the endpoint has been reached.

In the reverse titration of silver ion with standard chloride solution, the color of the suspension with the indicator added will be reddish-pink after the first addition of the chloride ion and will change to a yellow color at the endpoint.

Since the fluorescein derivatives are weak organic acids, the hydrogen ion concentration of the solution must be controlled. Fluorescein can be used in a solution of pH 7–10, whereas dichlorofluorescein can be used in solutions that are slightly more acidic. The dependence of this method on colloidal adsorption requires that the precipitate not be allowed to coagulate. Stabilizing agents such as dextrin may be added to keep the particles in the colloidal state so that a maximum amount of surface is available for adsorption.

This method of using an adsorption indicator for the determination of chloride ion or silver ion has been named the **Fajans method** after its founder. Several other precipitation titrations using adsorption indicators are known. These methods are limited by the availability of known adsorption indicators.

Stoichiometry in Precipitimetric Methods

The equivalent weight of a substance taking part in the precipitimetric methods is defined as the weight required to furnish or react with one gram atom of a univalent cation. Using this definition in the precipitation of silver chloride, the equivalent weight of silver nitrate is its molecular weight, since one mole of silver nitrate will furnish one gram atom of silver ion, a univalent cation, in the precipitate. For the precipitation of silver chromate (Ag_2CrO_4), the equivalent weight of potassium chromate is the molecular weight divided by two $\left(\frac{K_2CrO_4}{2}\right)$. The potassium chromate furnishes the amount of chromate that reacts with two gram atoms of silver ion; thus the amount necessary to react with one gram atom of silver ion will be one-half a gram molecular weight. In each case the equivalency of the substance is determined by the amount of the substance in reaction with a univalent cation. It is also true of precipitation reactions that the equivalent weight can be determined by the relationship

$$\text{Eq. Wt.} = \frac{\text{M.W.}}{\text{Total } + \text{ or } - \text{ charge of the ions}} \tag{9.1}$$

Applying this to the previously stated examples, it can be seen that both values of the equivalent weights of each compound are identical.

The application of the stoichiometric calculations in precipitimetry can be illustrated by the following examples.

EXAMPLE I. What volume of 0.1500 N $AgNO_3$ solution is required to precipitate the chloride ion from 280.0 mg. $BaCl_2 \cdot 2H_2O$?

Solution:

The milliequivalent weight of $BaCl_2 \cdot 2H_2O$ is $\frac{BaCl_2 \cdot 2H_2O}{2}$; therefore the number of milliequivalents of $BaCl_2 \cdot 2H_2O$ can be calculated as follows:

$$\frac{280.0}{\frac{BaCl_2 \cdot 2H_2O}{2}} = \frac{280.0}{\frac{244.31}{2}} = 2.29 \text{ meq.}$$

Since the number of meq. $BaCl_2 \cdot 2H_2O$ equals the number of meq. $AgNO_3$, the volume of $AgNO_3$ required is

$$V \times 0.1500 = 2.29$$
$$V = 15.26 \text{ ml.}$$

EXAMPLE II. To a sample of impure soluble chloride weighing 500.0 mg., 50.00 ml. of 0.2100 N $AgNO_3$ is added. After filtering and washing the precipitated AgCl, it is found that the filtrate requires 25.50 ml. of 0.2800 N KCNS to titrate the silver ion, using iron(III) alum as an indicator. What is the percentage of Cl in the sample?

Solution:

$50.00 \times 0.2100 = 10.50$ meq. $AgNO_3$ added

$25.50 \times 0.2800 = 7.14$ meq. KCNS required, which is equivalent to the $AgNO_3$ in excess

$10.50 - 7.14 = 3.36$ meq. $AgNO_3$ that reacted with the chloride ion

The percentage of Cl in the sample is

$$\%Cl = 3.36 \times \frac{Cl}{1} \times \frac{100}{500} = 23.82\%$$

COMPLEX FORMATION METHODS

Volumetric methods involving the formation of complexes as a result of titration are limited in the same manner as precipitation reactions. The lack of suitable indicators and the fact that many of the reactions do not proceed sufficiently toward completion to give good endpoints limit the use of such titrations.

Dissociation Constants of Complex Ions

Each type of complex ion that is formed is dissociated to some extent. It exists in equilibrium with its constituents. The application of equilibrium principles to the complex ion and its component parts results in a numerical value for the equilibrium constant. These values are tabulated in many cases as instability (or stability) constants.

The silver amino ion dissociates slightly according to the equation

$$Ag(NH_3)_2^+ \rightleftharpoons Ag^+ + 2NH_3$$

Since all the species are in solution, at equilibrium the equilibrium constant can be written as

$$K_d = \frac{[Ag^+][NH_3]^2}{[Ag(NH_3)_2^+]}$$

where K_d is designated as the dissociation (ionization) constant for the complex ion, $Ag(NH_3)_2^+$, or the instability (or stability) constant. If the numerical value for K_d as it is formulated above is small, a more stable complex is indicated than if the numerical value is large.

Many complex ions can dissociate in a stepwise manner, making it possible for an instability constant to be expressed for each individual step. The instability constant for the overall reaction can be written in a manner analogous to the stepwise ionization of acids which have more than one ionizable hydrogen.

The complex ions most frequently encountered in analytical chemistry are the ammonia complexes (*e.g.* $Ag(NH_3)_2^+$, $Cu(NH_3)_4^{++}$, $Co(NH_3)_6^{+++}$), cyanide complexes (*e.g.* $Ag(CN)_2^-$, $Ni(CN)_4^=$, $Fe(CN)_6^{\equiv}$, $Fe(CN)_6^{\equiv}$, $Hg(CN)_4^=$), halide complexes (*e.g.* $FeCl_4^-$, $SnCl_6^=$, $Pt(Cl)_6^=$), and organo-metallic complexes (*e.g.* $FeSCN^{++}$, $Ca(EDTA)^{++}$, $Mg(C_2O_4)_2^=$, tartrates and citrates of iron and other metallic ions).

Reactions Involving Cyanide Complexes

Reactions involving cyanide complexes with certain metal ions (*e.g.* nickel, mercury, and silver) are commonly used for this type of volumetric titration. An example of the specific application of complex forming reactions is found in the **Liebig method** for the determination of cyanide ion using silver nitrate. Nickel can also be determined by using a complex formation titration with standard cyanide solution.

The quantitative determination of cyanide ion using standard silver nitrate can be explained in the following manner. As the solution of silver nitrate is added to the solution of cyanide ion, the following equation shows the reaction which occurs.

$$Ag^+ + 2CN^- \rightarrow Ag(CN)_2^- \quad \textbf{(9.2)}$$

As silver is added beyond the amount that is required to react in this manner with the cyanide ion that is present, a precipitate of silver argentocyanide is formed. The reaction proceeds in the following manner:

$$Ag(CN)_2^- + Ag^+ \rightarrow Ag[Ag(CN)_2] \quad \textbf{(9.3)}$$

The formation of a faint permanent turbidity is the indication of the endpoint in the titration.

The equivalent weight of the silver nitrate used in equation 9.2 is its molecular weight; therefore its molarity and normality are the same. Since there are two cyanide ions necessary to react with one univalent cation as shown by equation 9.2, then the equivalent weight of the cyanide ion will be twice its formula weight. Thus, if the cyanide ion is furnished by potassium cyanide, then the equivalent weight of potassium cyanide is $2 \times KCN = 130.2$.

There are certain combinations of cyanide ion and chloride ion that can be analyzed by using a combination of the Liebig method and the Volhard method. The cyanide is determined first, and then a measured excess of standard silver nitrate solution is added to precipitate the cyanide as $Ag[Ag(CN)_2]$ and the chloride ion as silver chloride. The excess silver nitrate is titrated according to the Volhard procedure, with standard potassium thiocyanate. From these data the amount of chloride ion and cyanide ion can be calculated.

Determination of Nickel by Cyanide

In ammoniacal solution nickel(II) can be determined quantitatively by titration with standard potassium cyanide solution. The equation for this reaction is

$$Ni(NH_3)_6^{++} + 4CN^- \rightarrow Ni(CN)_4^{=} + 6NH_3 \quad \textbf{(9.4)}$$

The endpoint of the titration is indicated by the use of silver iodide. To the solution to be titrated is added a measured amount of standard silver nitrate solution and a small amount of potassium iodide. A slight turbidity of silver iodide forms. The solution is titrated with potassium cyanide until the turbidity just disappears.

$$AgI + 2CN^- \rightarrow Ag(CN)_2^- + I^- \quad \textbf{(9.5)}$$

The amount of cyanide equivalent to the silver ion used is subtracted from the total amount of cyanide used, thereby giving the amount used for the nickel reaction. As in the Liebig method, the equivalent weight of potassium cyanide is twice its molecular weight (2 × KCN = 130.2). The following example will show the application of the stoichiometric calculations.

EXAMPLE I. How many milligrams of nickel are contained in an ammoniacal solution that is treated with 48.80 ml. of KCN solution (6.52 mg. KCN per ml.)? The excess KCN is treated with 5.00 ml. of 0.100 N $AgNO_3$, KI being the indicator.

Solution:

$$Ni(NH_3)_6^{++} + 4CN^- + 6H_2O \rightarrow Ni(CN)_4^{=} + 6NH_4OH$$

$$2CN^- + Ag^+ \rightarrow Ag(CN)_2^-$$

The excess Ag^+ is indicated by the formation of AgI.

$$\text{Normality KCN} = \frac{6.52}{65.1 \times 2} = 0.05\ N$$

$$5.00 \times 0.100 = V \times 0.05$$

$$V = 10.00 \text{ ml. KCN in excess}$$

$$48.80 - 10.00 = 39.80 \text{ ml. KCN used for nickel}$$

$$39.80 \times 0.05 \times \frac{Ni}{2} = 57.5 \text{ mg. nickel}$$

CHELOMETRIC METHODS

The classical work of Schwarzenbach (1) on the volumetric determination of calcium and magnesium has opened a new analytical approach to metal ion analysis. This procedure, which has been adopted for the estimation of permanent hardness in water, has been extended and applied to the determination of more than fifty elements. The volumetric methods based on this approach have been given the name **chelometric titrations.** This term arises from the fact that the titrant forms a stable 1 : 1 **chelate complex** with the metal ion. **Chelate** is derived from the Greek word χηλη (claw) meaning clawlike. Compounds known as chelates belong to a particular class of coordination compounds that result from the reaction between a metal ion and a donor species called a **ligand** (see Figure 9.1). The reagents that form these complexes are given the generic name **chelons** (2).

The constituent ion may be determined by a direct or a back titration using the chelon or, indirectly, by the determination of the quantity of another element which has been consumed in a known reaction with the constituent desired. This indirect method is illustrated in the determination of phosphorus. The phosphorus is precipitated as magnesium phosphate in the presence of a known excess of magnesium ion, and the unreacted magnesium ion is back titrated with standard ethylenediaminetetraacetic acid.

```
           O                              O
           ‖                              ‖
   H—O—C—CH2                     CH2—C—O—H
              \                     /
               N—CH2—CH2—N
              /    \      /    \
             /      \    /      \
          CH2        ++        CH2
                     Ca
           \        /  \        /
          O=C      /    \      C=O
             \    /      \    /
              O            O
```

Fig. 9.1. Representation of chelate complex of calcium ion and ethylenediaminetetraacetate (EDTA).

The endpoint in a chelometric titration can be detected visually by using a metal-sensitive indicator, or by any of the methods that can be used to detect the last trace of metal ion; for example, potentiometric, amperometric, or photometric techniques.

EDTA Titrations

EDTA (ethylenediaminetetraacetic acid) titrations can be used to illustrate chelometric methods. The formula for EDTA is

```
HOOCH2C                      CH2COOH
       \                    /
        N—CH2—CH2—N
       /                    \
HOOCH2C                      CH2COOH
```

The abbreviation for the acid is generally given as H_4Y.

Because of its solubility in water, the disodium dihydrate salt is commonly used to prepare the EDTA standard solution. When this salt is dissolved in water the major components of the solution are

```
           HOOCH2C                      CH2COO⁻
                  \                    /
2Na⁺ +             N—CH2—CH2—N
                  /                    \
          ⁻OOCH2C                      CH2COOH
```

The disodium dihydrate salt is represented by $Na_2H_2Y \cdot 2H_2O$. Then in water solution the ions present are Na^+ and $H_2Y^=$.

The incorporation of two nitrogen (ammonia type) ligands and four oxygen (acetate type) ligands gives a molecule that behaves as a droplet of concentrated ammonia and acetate ions. The requirement of the chelometric titration, namely, the formation of a 1 : 1 complex, is maintained. These two factors make the disodium dihydrate salt ($Na_2H_2Y \cdot 2H_2O$) an excellent reagent for the general complexing of metal ions.

Indicators for Chelometric Titrations

Metal sensitive indicators form complexes which differ in color from that of the free indicator. Thus a sudden color change indicates the endpoint. These visual indicators are usually dyes of the *o,o′*-dihydroxy azo type. Eriochrome T, a common metal-sensitive indicator, is an example of this type of dye. It is the sodium salt of 1(1-hydroxy-2-naphthylazo)-6-nitro-2-naphthol-4-sulfonic acid. The structure is indicated below.

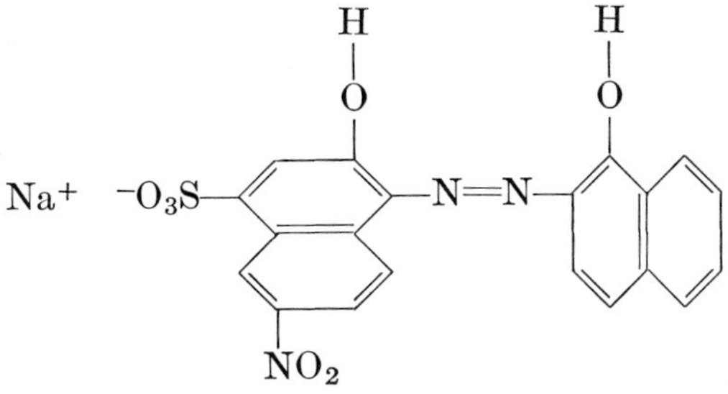

H H
O O
$Na^+ \; {}^-O_3S$— —N=N—
NO_2

The requirements for a visual metal-sensitive indicator, as far as color response to the eye is concerned, are the same as for acid-base visual indicators. The complex formed by the metal and the indicator must be less stable than the metallic ion-EDTA complex or else the EDTA will not be able to remove the metallic ion from the indicator complex. The indicator complex must be sufficiently less stable than the EDTA complex so that a sharp endpoint will result from the sudden shift in the equilibrium in favor of the metal-EDTA complex.

For example, in the titration of calcium ion with EDTA, a small amount of magnesium ion is added to the EDTA solution and the following equations show the course of the reaction.

$$Ca^{++} + HY^{\equiv} \rightarrow CaY^{=} + H^{+} \quad (9.6)$$

$$Mg^{++} + HIn^{=} \rightarrow MgIn^{-} + H^{+} \quad (9.7)$$

$$\underset{\text{(wine-red)}}{MgIn^{-}} + HY^{\equiv} \rightarrow MgY^{=} + \underset{\text{(blue)}}{HIn^{=}} \quad (9.8)$$

The complex $CaY^{=}$ formed in reaction 9.6 is required to be more stable than the metal-indicator complex $MgIn^{-}$ formed in reaction 9.7. At the point where all of the calcium ion has been removed from solution, the chelon ($HY^{\equiv}$) will remove the magnesium ion from the less stable indicator complex $MgIn^{-}$ to $MgY^{=}$ and $HIn^{=}$ as shown by equation 9.8. The appearance of the blue color that marks the formation of the $HIn^{=}$ indicates that the endpoint has been reached.

Factors That Affect Chelometric Titrations

To conduct a chelometric titration satisfactorily and successfully, certain factors must be considered. These factors are: conditions of titrations, *p*H and masking agents.

1. Conditions for Titration

The conditions must be determined for each specific metal ion, as well as in accordance with the particular chelon used. The specific conditions for the reaction of many common metal ions with EDTA can be found in the literature. Two excellent compilations are found in references 2 and 3 at the end of this chapter. Accordingly, it is unnecessary to give a complete list here, but an example is given to illustrate the type of information available.

Metal ion	*Means of Titration*	*Indicator*	*Buffer*	*Color*
Mg^{++}	Direct	Eriochrome T	NH_3 (*p*H 10)	blue to red

2. *p*H

The equation for the direct titration of a metal ion with standard EDTA can be illustrated as follows:

$$Ca^{++} + HY^{\equiv} \rightarrow CaY^{=} + H^{+} \qquad \textbf{(9.9)}$$

From equation 9.9, it can be seen that the hydrogen ion is competing with the metal ion for the chelon. As a result of this competition, those metal ions which form weak chelate complexes can be titrated effectively only in solutions of low hydrogen ion concentration (alkaline solution). Those metal ions that form strong chelate complexes can be titrated in solutions of high hydrogen ion content (acid solution). As a result the maintenance of the *p*H of the solution at a given value is rather critical.

3. Masking and Demasking Agents

The use of masking and demasking agents frequently eliminates the interference of certain metallic ions. For example, in the titration of alkaline earth metallic ions, the addition of cyanide ion in alkaline solution directly masks Cu(II), Zn(II), Cd(II), Co(II), Ni(II) and Hg(II) ions. These metallic ions are complexed more strongly by the cyanide ion than they are by the indicator and many times more strongly than by the chelon.

Masking agents may be used in an indirect manner. In this case the masking agent is added after the metal ion mixture has been titrated. The metallic ion is displaced from the complex by the masking agent. This causes an equivalent amount of free chelon to be liberated. The liberated chelon is titrated with the nonmasked metallic ion. This type of masking is particularly adaptable to the analysis of several metal ions consecutively in complex mixtures.

Masking with cyanide and then demasking with formaldehyde is an example which illustrates the use of demasking agents. The application of the principle of demasking provides a very convenient means of analysis of three component mixtures.

Titration Curves

A titration curve can be constructed as the result of following the change in concentration of the metallic ion (*e.g.*, Ca^{++}) during the course of the reaction with standard chelon solution (*e.g.*, $HY^{\equiv}$). The concentration of the calcium ion can be expressed as pCa where

$$\mathrm{pCa} = -\log [\mathrm{Ca}^{++}]$$

The pCa prior to the equivalence point can be calculated from the amount of the unreacted calcium ion. At the equivalence point the pCa can be calculated from the equilibrium constant of the reaction shown by equation 9.9 expressed in the following manner:

$$K_{eq} = \frac{[\mathrm{CaY}^{=}][\mathrm{H}^{+}]}{[\mathrm{Ca}^{++}][\mathrm{HY}^{\equiv}]}$$

Beyond the equivalence point only a small amount of calcium ion, resulting from the reverse reaction of equation 9.9, and an excess of EDTA reagent would be in the solution. The equilibrium constant is used to calculate the pCa beyond the equivalence point. From the calculated pCa values, a titration curve can be constructed.

Sources of Error in Chelometric Titrations

There are several factors that will cause unsatisfactory and inaccurate end-points. Among the most important are the following:

(1) Impurities in reagents, water, or from storage containers may react with the indicator and block its reactions. This can be eliminated or minimized by

using demineralized water, high purity reagents, and borosilicate glassware for solution preparation, followed by storage in polyethylene bottles.

(2) The indicator solution itself can decompose and deteriorate. This can be eliminated by using freshly prepared solutions (made up at least once a month), or by using a solid indicator ground and diluted 1:200 with reagent grade sodium chloride. Care must be taken to avoid the addition of too much indicator solution; this is a common error when determining metal ions whose concentration is low.

(3) The quantity of buffer added must be kept at a low value. Some buffers, if used in high concentration, tend to remove the metal ion from the indicator complex. This results in no real endpoint or, at best, one that is very indistinct.

In addition to those factors listed, there are such things as proper illumination, background contrast, and familiarity on the part of the analyst with color changes that are common to titrations whose endpoint is indicated by a change in color.

References

1. Bjerrum, Schwarzenbach, and Sillén, *Stability Constants*, Chemical Society, London, 1957.

2. Reilley, Schmid, and Sader, *J. Chem. Ed.* **36,** 555–564, 619–626 (1959).

3. Barnard, Broad, and Flaschka, *Chemist-Analyst*, **45,** 18, 46, 76 (1957).

4. Welcher, *The Analytical Uses of Ethylenediaminetetraacetic Acid*, D. Van Nostrand Company, Inc., Princeton, N.J., 1957.

Laboratory Experiment 15

Determination of Soluble Chloride
Volhard Method

Reagents

0.1 N $AgNO_3$

prepared by weighing accurately to the nearest tenth of a milligram 8.5000 grams of analytical reagent grade silver nitrate into a 500 ml. volumetric flask. Dissolve in distilled water and dilute to the mark with distilled water. Store in a dark bottle after thoroughly mixing the solution by inverting the stoppered flask several times.

0.1 N KCNS

prepared by weighing 4.9 grams of reagent grade potassium thiocyanate into a clean bottle, dissolving the salt in distilled water, and diluting the solution to about 500 ml. with distilled water.

Iron(III) alum indicator solution
prepared by dissolving 0.2 gram iron(III) alum in a boiling mixture of 4 ml. of 6 *N* HNO_3 and 16 ml. distilled water.

HNO_3
reagent grade, previously boiled to expel any oxides of nitrogen.

Procedure

A. STANDARDIZATION OF POTASSIUM THIOCYANATE

Into each of three 250 ml. beakers pipet 25 ml. of the standard $AgNO_3$ solution. To each solution add 5 ml. of 1:1 HNO_3 and 1 ml. of iron(III) alum indicator solution. Titrate each sample with potassium thiocyanate solution, stirring constantly until a reddish-brown color begins to spread throughout the solution. At this point, add the thiocyanate solution dropwise, stirring the solution thoroughly between the addition of each drop. The appearance of the reddish-brown color of the iron(III) thiocyanate complex that persists for 15 seconds marks the endpoint.

Using the data obtained from the titration of the triplicate samples, calculate the normality of the potassium thiocyanate.

B. DETERMINATION OF THE CHLORIDE BY THE VOLHARD METHOD

Into 250 ml. beakers, weigh from a weighing bottle to the nearest tenth of a milligram, three samples of the previously dried unknown chloride of about 0.2500 gram each. Dissolve the salt in 50 ml. of distilled water and add to each of the solutions 5 ml. of 1:1 HNO_3.

Calculate the volume of standard $AgNO_3$ solution theoretically required to precipitate the chloride ion from the solution, assuming the sample to consist of pure sodium chloride. To the amount calculated add 10% in excess. Add the total calculated volume of $AgNO_3$ to the solution in such a manner that the volume is accurately known to 0.05 ml. Keep the suspension hot and away from direct sunlight or strong fluorescent light until the silver chloride precipitate has coagulated sufficiently to yield a clear filtrate. Filter off the precipitate using filter paper, catching the filtrate in a 400 ml. beaker. The precipitate in the filter paper should be washed with four 20 ml. portions of hot water slightly acidified with HNO_3, that have been used to rinse the beaker which contained the original solution. The rinsings are allowed to run into the main filtrate. Drainage should be complete between each addition of rinse solution.

To each beaker is added 5 ml. of the iron(III) alum indicator solution. Each solution is titrated, using the same procedure that was used in the standardization of the potassium thiocyanate. The endpoint is taken when the reddish-brown color of the iron(III) cyanate complex presists after stirring for 15 seconds.

From the data obtained, calculate and report the percentage chloride in the sample.

Laboratory Experiment 16

Determination of Chloride by the Mohr Method

Reagents

0.1 *N* $AgNO_3$

prepared by weighing 8.5 grams of analytical reagent grade silver nitrate, dissolving it in distilled water and diluting the solution to 500 ml. with distilled water and storing it in a dark bottle.

5% K_2CrO_4

prepared by dissolving 5 grams of analytical reagent grade potassium chromate in 100 ml. of distilled water.

Procedure

A. STANDARDIZATION OF SILVER NITRATE SOLUTION

Into three 250 ml. beakers weigh to the nearest tenth of a milligram triplicate samples of about 0.200 gram each of sodium chloride previously dried at 100–105°C. Dissolve the sodium chloride in 50 ml. of distilled water. To each solution add 2 ml. of 5% potassium chromate solution and titrate each with 0.1 *N* silver nitrate solution until the first permanent appearance of the reddish-orange silver chromate precipitate.

By standardizing the silver nitrate in this manner and using it in the Mohr method for the determination of an unknown chloride, no blank is necessary provided the volumes used are approximately the same as in the standardization.

From the volume of silver nitrate used and the weight of sodium chloride, calculate the normality of the silver nitrate solution.

B. DETERMINATION OF THE UNKNOWN CHLORIDE

Into three 250 ml. beakers weigh triplicate samples of 0.250–0.350 gram each of the unknown chloride that has been previously dried at 100–105°C. Dissolve each sample in 50 ml. of distilled water. Add sodium bicarbonate to the solution a small amount at a time until no further effervescence is noted. To each solution add 2 ml. of 5% potassium chromate solution and titrate each solution with standard silver nitrate solution until the first permanent appearance of the reddish-orange silver chromate precipitate.

From the volume of the silver nitrate used and the weight of the sample calculate the percent chloride in the sample.

Laboratory Experiment 17

Determination of Chloride by Fajans Method

Reagents

0.1 *N* $AgNO_3$ solution

prepared by weighing accurately about 8.5 grams of analytical reagent grade silver nitrate into a 500 ml. volumetric flask, dissolving it in a small amount of distilled water and diluting the resulting solution to the line with distilled water.

0.1% dichlorofluorescein indicator solution

prepared by adding 0.100 gram of dichlorofluorescein to 100 ml. of 70% ethyl alcohol.

Procedure

Into three 250 ml. beakers weigh to the nearest tenth of a milligram triplicate samples of 0.200–0.300 gram of the unknown chloride that has been previously dried for one hour at 100–105°C. Dissolve the solid in each beaker in 100 ml. of distilled water. Add 1 ml. of the dichlorofluorescein indicator solution and titrate each solution with standard silver nitrate solution to the first permanent appearance of the pink color.

From the volume of the silver nitrate solution used and the weight of the sample calculate the percent chloride in the sample.

Laboratory Experiment 18

EDTA Analytical Determinations

Reagents

0.01 *M* EDTA solution

prepared by dissolving 4.0 grams of the disodium EDTA dihydrate and about 0.1 gram $MgCl_2 \cdot 6H_2O$ in one liter of demineralized water in a clean Pyrex or polystyrene bottle. Mix the solution thoroughly and label the bottle.

Standard solution of calcium chloride

prepared in the following manner: Weigh accurately to the nearest tenth of a milligram, 0.5000 gram of analytical reagent grade calcium carbonate that has been previously dried at 105–110°C. Transfer the solid to a 500 ml. volumetric flask and dissolve it in about 5 ml. of 1:1 HCl. Dilute to the mark with demineralized water and mix the solution thoroughly.

Ammonia-ammonium chloride buffer solution
prepared by dissolving 6.75 grams ammonium chloride in 57 ml. concentrated ammonium hydroxide and diluting the solution to 100 ml. with demineralized water. The *p*H of the buffer is a little above 10.

Eriochrome Black T indicator solution
prepared by dissolving 0.5 gram of reagent grade Eriochrome Black T in 100 ml. of methyl alcohol. If the solution is to be kept, date the bottle, since it is recommended that solutions older than 6–8 weeks not be used.

Procedure

A. STANDARDIZATION OF EDTA SOLUTION WITH CALCIUM CHLORIDE SOLUTION

Pipet a 50 ml. aliquot of the standard calcium chloride solution into a 250 ml. beaker, add 5 ml. of ammonia-ammonium chloride buffer solution. Then add 5 drops Eriochrome Black T indicator. Titrate the resulting solution with 0.01 *M* EDTA solution to a point of a color change from wine-red to pure blue with no tinge of red in the solution. The reaction is somewhat slow in the vicinity of the endpoint; therefore the solution must be stirred thoroughly between each drop that is added near the endpoint.

Repeat the titration with successive aliquots of the calcium chloride solution until the results are in substantial agreement. Calculate the molarity of the EDTA solution and the calcium carbonate titer (mg. $CaCO_3$ per ml. of EDTA solution).

B. DETERMINATION OF TOTAL HARDNESS OF WATER

Using the water obtained from the instructor, pipet an aliquot, large enough to require between 20 and 30 ml. of EDTA solution, into each of three 250 ml. beakers. Usually a sample of 100 to 150 ml. of the water will be satisfactory. Into the first beaker add 1 ml. of ammonia-ammonium chloride buffer solution and 5 drops of Eriochrome Black T indicator solution. Titrate with standard EDTA solution to the color change from wine-red to pure blue, observing the same procedure near the endpoint as in the standardization of the EDTA solution.

Repeat the procedure using the other two aliquot portions.

From the data obtained, calculate the total hardness of water as parts per million (ppm) of calcium carbonate as follows:

$$\frac{\text{Volume EDTA (ml.)} \times CaCO_3 \text{ titer (mg./ml.)} \times 1000 \text{ (ml./l.)}}{\text{Volume of Sample (ml.)}} = \text{mg. } CaCO_3\text{/liter (ppm)}$$

The average value of the results from the three portions is reported as the total hardness of water.

C. DETERMINATION OF ZINC BY DIRECT TITRATION

Obtain a sample in a 100 ml. volumetric flask from the instructor. Make the solution up to the mark, using demineralized water. Using three 250 ml. beakers, pipet a 25 ml. aliquot into each beaker. Add about 100 ml. of demineralized water, 4 ml. of ammonia-ammonium chloride buffer solution, and 5 drops of Eriochrome Black T indicator solution to one beaker. Titrate with standard EDTA solution until the indicator color changes from wine-red to pure blue. The same procedure should be used near the endpoint as in the previous titrations. Repeat this procedure with the solutions in the remaining two beakers.

From the data obtained, calculate the weight of zinc issued in the sample in the 100 ml. volumetric flask.

Problems

1. Calculate the normality of a solution which contains

(a) 6.1538 grams of pure $AgNO_3$ in 500 ml. of solution. *Ans.* *0.725 N*
(b) 3.7642 grams of pure $AgNO_3$ in 300 ml. of solution. *Ans.* *0.739 N*

2. A sample of pure sodium chloride weighing 0.350 gram is dissolved in water, and 50.00 ml. of silver nitrate solution is added. After filtering off the silver chloride, the excess silver in the filtrate requires 5.30 ml. of KCNS solution for titration. (1.00 ml. KCNS ≈ 1.150 ml. $AgNO_3$). Calculate the normality of the $AgNO_3$ and the KCNS solutions. *Ans.* *$AgNO_3$, 0.137 N; KCNS, 0.157 N*

3. What volume of 0.0950 *N* $BaCl_2$ solution is required to precipitate the sulfate from a solution containing 0.2500 gram of $FeSO_4{\cdot}7H_2O$? *Ans.* *18.9 ml.*

4. A mixture of pure LiCl and BaI_2 weighing 0.500 gram is treated with 43.25 ml. of 0.200 *N* $AgNO_3$ solution and the excess silver is then titrated with 22.00 ml. of 0.100 *N* KCNS solution with iron(III) alum as an indicator. What is the percentage of iodine present in the mixture? *Ans.* *40.5%*

5. In the analysis of silver coin metal containing 90.00% silver, a 250 mg. sample being used, what is the normality of a potassium thiocyanate solution of which 25.00 ml. will be required for the analysis? *Ans.* *0.0835 N*

6. A sample of pure calcium carbonate weighing 0.5026 gram is dissolved in dilute hydrochloric acid and the solution diluted to 500 ml. in a volumetric flask. A 50.00 ml. aliquot requires 40.32 ml. of sodium-EDTA solution for titration. Calculate the molarity of the EDTA solution. *Ans.* *0.011 M*

7. A 150 ml. sample of water was titrated with 0.01 *M* EDTA solution and 39.50 ml. were required. What is the hardness of water, in parts per million $CaCO_3$, if the calcium carbonate titer of the EDTA solution is 1.23 mg.? *Ans.* *326 ppm*

8. 4.00 grams of KCN are dissolved in water and made up to 500 ml. Calculate (a) the molarity of the solution and (b) the normality of the solution when determined by the Liebig method. *Ans.* (*a*) *0.123 M*; (*b*) *0.246 N*

9. A nickel ore contains 8.95% Ni. A 250.0 gram sample is decomposed and the ammoniacal solution treated with 50.00 ml. of a 0.0875 *M* solution of KCN. A little KI is added as an indicator, and the solution is titrated with 0.0750 *M* $AgNO_3$ to a faint permanent turbidity. What volume of the $AgNO_3$ is required? *Ans. 19.1 ml.*

10. What is the percentage of nickel in an ore if the ammoniacal solution of a 1.000 gram sample is treated with 3.445 grams of KCN and the excess KCN requires 52.00 ml. of 0.100 *M* $AgNO_3$ to obtain a turbidity with KI as an indicator? *Ans. 62.8%*

11. A solution contains KCN and KCl. The solution is titrated with 0.150 *N* $AgNO_3$ to a faint turbidity, requiring 10.00 ml. Then 31.50 ml. more of the $AgNO_3$ is added and the precipitates of $Ag[Ag(CN)_2]$ and AgCl are filtered off. The filtrate requires 6.80 ml. of 0.0875 *N* KCNS to give a red color with iron(III) alum as an indicator. How many grams of KCN and KCl were present in the original solution? *Ans. KCN, 0.195 gram; KCl, 0.196 gram*

12. A sample of 15% KCl and 35% NaCl is analyzed by the Volhard method. If 65.0 ml. of 0.15 *N* $AgNO_3$ is added, and 25.00 ml. of 0.10 *N* KCNS is used in the back titration, what size sample must be taken? *Ans. 0.905 gram*

PART III

GRAVIMETRIC METHODS OF ANALYSIS

CHAPTER 10

Introduction to Gravimetric Analysis

Methods of analysis that are based on the separation of the component that is being determined into a form of known composition that can be weighed, are called **gravimetric** methods. To arrive at the point in the analytical procedure where a separation is made and subsequently the desired constituent is obtained in a weighable form requires that the following steps must have been accomplished. A suitable representative sample must have been taken from the material for which the analysis was desired. The requirements for obtaining such a sample and the procedure to be used are generally the same regardless of the method of analysis. The next step is to bring the sample into solution using suitable reagents and/or solvents. Once the sample is in solution, then the appropriate separation procedure may be applied. The sampling requirements and the various methods used to put the sample into solution have been discussed in Chapter 3.

After the desired constituent is separated from the solution, either in the form of a pure phase of the constituent itself or a compound of known and definite composition containing the constituent, it is then weighed. From the weight of this separated substance, the weight of the desired constituent can be calculated.

The emphasis of gravimetric methods of analysis is placed on the performing of a measurement, in this case a weight determination, after the substance has been separated. It should be pointed out here that the weight obtained will be of little value to the analytical chemist unless the previous steps in the procedure have been accomplished with care. Many times, the taking of the sample and its dissolution become much more important than the separation and weighing steps. If the sample does not meet the requirements stated earlier, then the remainder of the analysis is relatively useless. The importance of correct sampling cannot be overemphasized.

In order to perform the weighing operation, the desired constituent must be separated completely from the remaining components of the solution. On the other hand, in the previous discussion of volumetric procedures, it was shown that in this case it is only necessary to perform a separation when there are substances present that will interfere with the chemical reaction of titration. Ultimately and continually associated with gravimetric methods are separation methods with all their problems.

The classification of gravimetric procedures is based on the methods of separation that are involved. One of the most common is that based on the precipitation of the constituent as a very slightly soluble compound which can either be weighed or converted into another precipitate form and weighed. Some of the other important methods of separation are volatilization, electrogravimetric, ion exchange, extraction, and chromatographic adsorption. Electrogravimetric methods are discussed in Chapter 16, while the remainder of the separation techniques will be discussed in Chapter 11.

Requirements for Gravimetric Analysis

For a gravimetric analysis to be successful the following requirements should be met.

(1) The separation of the desired constituent must be as complete as analytically possible. The amount that is left in solution will not be detectable after the separation has been performed.

(2) The separated substance must be pure and have a definite known composition. The amount of the desired constituent will be calculated from the weight of the separated substance. Therefore the substance must not have a variable composition and purity.

To fulfill these two requirements is, in many cases, very difficult if not impossible. The analyst must often make a compromise to accomplish his analysis. The separated substance may have a composition that varies with changes in the conditions of the analysis, so that under a given set of conditions, often not the best, a given composition must be used for calculation. This is common among separations accomplished by precipitation techniques. The problems of these techniques will be discussed in the section concerned with precipitation methods.

Once the separation is accomplished and the desired constituent is obtained in a weighable form, then the calculations of the weight of the constituent can be completed. Using the weight that is obtained, the percentage of the component can be calculated.

Calculations from Gravimetric Techniques

The basis of gravimetric techniques is the fact that the proportions by weight of the components in any pure compound are always the same, and the masses of the elements taking part in a chemical reaction show a definite and invariable ratio to one another. To determine the amount of a component in a mixture, it is necessary to obtain the component in a weighable compound of a definite known composition. Once this is done, the weight of the component can be calculated.

The calculation is very simple, and can be expressed mathematically in the general manner

$$\frac{W \times F_g \times 100}{W_s} = \% \text{ of desired constituent}$$

where W is the weight of the separated substance containing the desired constituent, F_g is the gravimetric factor (chemical factor) that converts the weight of the separated substance to the weight of the desired constituent, and W_s is the weight of the sample. It is apparent that the units of weight must be the same for W and W_s (*e.g.*, grams or milligrams). The value of the gravimetric factor is the numerical value of the ratio of the weight of one mole of the desired constituent to that of one mole of the substance weighed. It can also be defined as the weight of the desired substance equivalent to a unit weight of a given substance. Substances are said to be equivalent when they enter into direct or indirect reactions in the exact respective ratio of those weights. To illustrate the use of the gravimetric factor, the following examples are presented.

EXAMPLE I. What is the weight of chlorine in a sample of soluble chloride, if, on the solution of the sample and precipitation with silver nitrate, 2.000 grams of silver chloride is formed?

Solution:

$$NaCl + AgNO_3 \rightarrow AgCl + NaNO_3$$

For each mole of AgCl precipitated, one mole of $AgNO_3$ and one mole of NaCl must react. The ratio of chlorine to silver chloride is in the respective ratio of the atomic weight of chlorine to the molecular weight of AgCl. Therefore, in 2.000 grams of AgCl there is

$$2.000 \times \frac{Cl}{AgCl} = 2.000 \times \frac{35.46}{143.34} = 0.495 \text{ g. Cl}$$

The gravimetric factor is represented by $\frac{Cl}{AgCl}$.

EXAMPLE II. What weight of Fe_3O_4 will furnish 1.086 grams of Fe_2O_3?

Solution:

The stoichiometric relationship of the iron in the two compounds can be shown in the following manner to lead to the result that two moles of Fe_3O_4 are equivalent to three moles of Fe_2O_3.

$$2Fe_3O_4 \approx 3Fe_2O_3$$

The gravimetric factor in this case is

$$\frac{2Fe_3O_4}{3Fe_2O_3}$$

Thus,

$$1.086 \times \frac{2Fe_3O_4}{3Fe_2O_3} = 1.086 \times \frac{463.1}{479.1} = 1.050 \text{ g.}$$

By examining the gravimetric factor used in each of the above examples, it can be seen that the ratio is always written with the molecular weight of the substance desired in the numerator, and the molecular weight of the substance weighed in the denominator. Each molecular weight may be multiplied by a factor that will result in the same number of atoms of the substance concerned appearing in the numerator and denominator. For instance, in the solution to Example II, the gravimetric factor was shown to be $\frac{2Fe_3O_4}{3Fe_2O_3}$. The number of atoms of iron in the numerator is equal to the number in the denominator. It is customary to use the formula to represent the molecular weight when setting up a gravimetric factor. A few of the common gravimetric factors are given in Table 10.1.

In many applications the substance that is finally weighed does not contain the atoms of the constituent desired. The following example can be used as an illustration.

EXAMPLE III. A sample of $FeSO_4 \cdot (NH_4)_2 \cdot 6H_2O$ containing only inert impurities weighs 1.500 grams. After the sample has been dissolved, the iron is oxidized and precipitated as $Fe(OH)_3$. Then the $Fe(OH)_3$ is ignited, giving 0.3417 gram of Fe_2O_3. Calculate the percentage of S in the sample.

TABLE 10.1
Common Gravimetric Factors

SUBSTANCE WEIGHED	SUBSTANCE DESIRED	GRAVIMETRIC FACTOR
Al_2O_3	Al	$\frac{2Al}{Al_2O_3}$
$Mg_2P_2O_7$	$Mg(NH_4)PO_4$	$\frac{2Mg(NH_4)PO_4}{Mg_2P_2O_7}$
Fe_2O_3	FeO	$\frac{2FeO}{Fe_2O_3}$
KBF_4	$Na_2B_4O_7 \cdot 10H_2O$	$\frac{Na_2B_4O_7 \cdot 10H_2O}{4KBF_4}$
$BaSO_4$	SO_3	$\frac{SO_3}{BaSO_4}$

Solution:

In the final weighable substance there are no atoms of sulfur. From one mole of $FeSO_4 \cdot (NH_4)_2SO_4 \cdot 6H_2O$ there can be produced $\frac{1}{2}$ mole Fe_2O_3 according to the abbreviated reactions

$$2FeSO_4 \cdot (NH_4)_2SO_4 \cdot 6H_2O \rightarrow 2Fe(OH)_3 \rightarrow Fe_2O_3$$

Thus, one mole of Fe_2O_3 is equivalent to four moles of S, making the gravimetric factor $\frac{4S}{Fe_2O_3}$.

$$0.3417 \times \frac{4S}{Fe_2O_3} \times \frac{100}{1.500} = 0.3417 \times \frac{4 \times 32}{159.7} \times \frac{100}{1.500} = 27.35\%$$

An alternate solution to the problem can be expressed in the following manner:

$$\frac{0.3417}{} \left| \frac{2\,\not{Fe}}{Fe_2O_3} \right| \frac{2S}{\not{Fe}} \left| \frac{100}{1.500} \right. = 27.35\%$$

This relationship reduces to the same equation as before.

Indirect Analysis

Often two pure compounds can be isolated and weighed together. By using a second sample or performing a chemical separation on the sample containing two pure substances, the weight of one of the pair can be determined. The other weight can then be determined by difference. The determination of sodium and potassium can be ultimately accomplished by weighing as the combined chlorides. In the limestone analysis iron and aluminum are separated as the combined oxides. The iron can be determined volumetrically and the aluminum found by difference.

EXAMPLE IV. A mixture of CaO and BaO weighs 0.6411 gram and yields 1.1201 grams of mixed anhydrous sulfates. What are the percentages of Ca and Ba in the original mixture?

Solution:

$$\text{Let } x = \text{weight of CaO}$$
$$(0.6411 - x) = \text{weight of BaO}$$

The number of grams of $CaSO_4$ obtained from x grams of CaO is

$$x\left(\frac{CaSO_4}{CaO}\right) = x(2.43)$$

The number of grams of $BaSO_4$ obtained from $(0.6411 - x)$ grams of BaO is

$$(0.6411 - x)\left(\frac{BaSO_4}{BaO}\right) = (0.6411 - x)\,1.52$$

Thus

$$2.43x + 1.52(0.6411 - x) = 1.1201$$
$$x = 0.1601 \text{ g. weight CaO}$$
$$(0.6411 - x) = 0.4810 \text{ g. weight BaO}$$

$$\%\ Ca = \frac{0.1601}{} \left| \frac{Ca}{CaO} \right| \frac{100}{0.6411} = 17.85\%$$

$$\%\ Ba = \frac{0.4810}{} \left| \frac{Ba}{BaO} \right| \frac{100}{0.6411} = 67.21\%$$

Problems

1. Calculate the gravimetric factors for the following gravimetric conversions.

Substance weighed	*Substance desired*	
Fe_3O_4	Fe	*Ans. 0.725*
$Mg_2P_2O_7$	MgO	*Ans. 0.362*
$BaSO_4$	FeS_2	*Ans. 0.257*
Sb_2O_4	Sb	*Ans. 0.794*
Al_2O_3	$K_2SO_4Al_2(SO_4)_3 \cdot 24H_2O$	*Ans. 9.31*
$(NH_4)_3PO_4 \cdot 12MoO_3$	P_2O_5	*Ans. 0.0379*

2. A sample of limestone weighing 1.250 grams gives 0.0231 gram of Fe_2O_3, 1.3201 grams of $CaSO_4$, and 0.0621 gram of $Mg_2P_2O_7$. Calculate the percentage of (a) Fe, (b) MgO, and (c) $CaCO_3$ in the limestone. *Ans.* (*a*) *1.29%;* (*b*) *1.80%;* (*c*) *77.4%*

3. What weight of FeS_2 containing 37.20% sulfur must have been taken for analysis in order to give a precipitate of barium sulfate weighing 1.0310 grams? *Ans. 0.380 gram*

4. A sample of impure iron(II) ammonium sulfate weighs 0.5261 gram and furnishes 0.0943 gram of Fe_2O_3. What is the percentage of $Fe(NH_4)_2(SO_4)_2 \cdot 6H_2O$? *Ans. 88.2%*

5. A sample of Pb_3O_4 weighs 0.1835 gram and after dissolving, subsequently yields a precipitate of $PbSO_4$ weighing 0.2250 gram. What is the percentage purity of the sample in terms of Pb? *Ans. 83.9%*

6. What weight of hematite (impure Fe_2O_3) should be taken for analysis so that after decomposition of the sample, precipitation of the iron as $Fe(OH)_3$ and ignition to Fe_2O_3, the number of milligrams of Fe_2O_3 obtained is 3 times the percentage of Fe? *Ans. 0.209 gram*

7. A mixture of BaO and CaO weighing 2.350 grams is converted to mixed sulfates weighing 4.9863 grams. Calculate the percentage of calcium and barium in the mixture. *Ans. Ca, 46.9%; Ba, 30.6%*

8. How many grams of P_2O_5 can be obtained from a 1.000 gram sample of $(NH_4)_3PO_4 \cdot 12H_2O$? *Ans. 0.195 gram*

9. Calculate the grams of silver in 1.00 gram of silver bromide. *Ans. 0.574 gram*

10. What volume of $MgCl_2$ solution containing one formula weight per liter will be necessary to precipitate the phosphorus as $MgNH_4PO_4$ in a 1.00 gram sample of $Ca_3(PO_4)_2$? *Ans. 6.45 ml.*

11. A sample that weighs 0.5000 gram contains $CaCl_2$ and NaCl. The sample is treated with $AgNO_3$, giving a precipitate of AgCl which weighs 1.235 grams. Calculate the percentage of $CaCl_2$ in the sample. *Ans. 8.4%*

12. The aluminum in a rock sample weighing 0.500 gram is precipitated as $Al(OH)_3$ and ignited to give an amount of Al_2O_3 weighing 0.2950 gram. Calculate the percentage of aluminum in the rock. *Ans. 31.2%*

13. A 1.000 gram sample of a mineral yields a mixture of NaCl and KCl which weighs 0.2500 gram. This mixture of chlorides contains exactly 56% chlorine. What is the percentage of Na and K in the sample? *Ans. Na, 6.36%; K, 4.64%*

14. What weight of impure hydrated iron(II) ammonium sulfate should be taken for analysis so that the number of milligrams of $BaSO_4$ obtained will represent twice the percentage of sulfur in the sample? *Ans. 0.027 gram*

15. A sample of pure apatite with the formula $3Ca_3(PO_4)_2 \cdot CaFCl$ weighs 0.250 gram. What weight of $(NH_4)_3PO_4 \cdot 12MoO_3$ would be obtained from the sample of apatite? *Ans. 2.73 grams*

16. A sample of $KAlSi_3O_8$ weighing 1.00 gram is fused and the silica is determined. Calculate the weight of SiO_2 obtained. *Ans. 0.650 gram*

17. What is the percentage of iodine in a 1.000 gram sample of AgBr and AgI if the sample is found to contain 0.4945 gram silver? *Ans. 31.6%*

18. What is the percentage composition of a brass sample containing only copper, lead, and zinc if a 1.000 gram sample furnishes 0.0046 gram of $PbSO_4$ and 0.8216 gram of $ZnNH_4PO_4$? *Ans. Cu, 69.5%; Zn, 30.1%; Pb, 0.30%*

19. What weight of pyrolusite should be taken so that the weight of Mn_3O_4 obtained will represent 5 times the percentage of MnO_2 in the sample? *Ans. 0.570 gram*

20. A sample of dolomite weighing 1.500 grams yields a precipitate of hydrated oxides of aluminum and iron. These are filtered off and ignited to constant weight. The weight of the combined oxides, Al_2O_3 and Fe_2O_3, is 0.1210 gram. Iron, as determined by a volumetric method on a separate sample of the dolomite, is found to be 3.22%. Calculate the percentage of Al in the dolomite. *Ans. 1.86%*

CHAPTER 11

Analytical Separations

Since there is an increasing need to analyze more and more complicated materials, the role of analytical separations is becoming very important. In many determinations the isolation of the desired constituent necessitates more effort than the measurement procedure required after the separation. Sometimes the problem of separation becomes very complicated for the analyst because methods for the separation of all elements have not been devised. The increased emphasis placed on the determination of constituents present in very small amounts has necessitated a continual search for better means of separation.

Next to the sampling process, the separation procedure is the least reliable of all the steps in the analytical determination. The separation of the desired constituent must be quantitative. There must be no substance involved in the final physically separated form that will interfere with the measurement. Many times both of these criteria can not be met, and it is necessary for any departure from them to be capable of estimation so corrections can be applied.

The methods of separation can be divided into two broad categories, physical and chemical. Physical separations result from the application of mechanical methods, whereas chemical separations are a result of chemical reactions. Examples of physical separations are volatilization, extraction, and selective adsorption. Precipitation methods are examples of chemical methods.

PRECIPITATION

The most common and widely used method for separation is precipitation. This is the formation of an insoluble substance from soluble reactants. The precipitate generally contains the desired constituent or it may contain a substance chemically related to it. The latter case requires that the precipitate be subjected to further treatment before the final measurement can be accomplished. Even though the desired constituent is contained in the precipitate, it may not be suitable for weighing and it may be contaminated. Ignition to a weighable compound will be necessary and a means of minimizing contamination must be determined if precipitation is to be a useful means of separation. Precipitation may, in some cases, be unattractive because of other factors, such as difficulties in filtration, incomplete precipitation, and inability to minimize contamination.

The suitability of the process of precipitation as a method of separation depends on the following factors:

(1) The solubility of the precipitate.
(2) The physical character of the precipitate.
(3) The purity of the precipitate.

Solubility of Precipitates

In separation by precipitation, the desired constituent must be precipitated quantitatively. This requires that the small amount of the constituent that remains in solution cannot be detected by ordinary gravimetric means. Thus the precipitated substance must be virtually insoluble in the reaction mixture.

A solid in equilibrium with its saturated solution is in dynamic rather than static equilibrium. The rate at which the solid is going into the solution is equal to the rate at which the solid is coming out of the solution. To this system can be applied the Law of Mass Action. By assuming a state of dynamic equilibrium, the principle of the solubility product is explained. For example, if a solution of a slightly soluble salt, such as silver chloride, is in equilibrium with solid silver chloride, then this equation can be written

$$AgCl \rightleftharpoons Ag^+ + Cl^-$$

From the Law of Mass Action, the relationship

$$K_{eq} = \frac{[Ag^+][Cl^-]}{[AgCl]}$$

is obtained, where the $[Ag^+]$ and $[Cl^-]$ represent the concentration of the silver and chloride ions respectively, and the $[AgCl]$ represents the concentration of silver chloride. As long as the solid silver chloride is in equilibrium with the saturated solution, the concentration of the solid silver chloride will remain effectively constant. Thus, we can write

$$[Ag^+][Cl^-] = K_{eq} \times \text{constant} = K_{sp}$$

where K_{sp} is the solubility product constant of silver chloride. Since the mass action equilibrium constant is dependent on temperature, the solubility product constant will change with temperature. Thus the temperature must be specified when giving a value of the solubility product constant for a given reaction.

As a result of the solubility product relationship, it can readily be seen that the solubility product constant determines the product of the ion concentrations in any system where a solid is in equilibrium with its solution. When the value of the product of the silver ion concentration and the chloride ion concentration exceeds the solubility product constant of silver chloride, then precipitation can be expected to take place. If an excess of silver ions is added to a saturated solution of silver chloride, the concentration of the chloride ions in solution must be reduced accordingly. This reduction comes about by the increased precipitation of the silver chloride. Adding excess chloride ions to the solution will cause the silver ion concentration to be decreased and the amount of silver chloride precipitate to be increased.

To illustrate the application of the solubility product principle in precipitation reactions, the following examples are given.

EXAMPLE I. The solubility product of silver chloride is 1×10^{-10} at 25°C. What is the solubility of silver chloride at this temperature?

Solution:

$$AgCl \rightleftharpoons Ag^+ + Cl^-$$
$$K_{sp} = [Ag^+][Cl^-]$$

The $[Ag^+]$ is a measure of the solubility of silver chloride since each molecule of silver chloride going into solution produces one Ag^+ and one Cl^-. Therefore $[Ag^+] = [Cl^-]$.

$$1 \times 10^{-10} = [Ag^+]^2$$
$$1 \times 10^{-5} = [Ag^+]$$

The solubility of silver chloride at 25°C is 1×10^{-5} moles per liter or 1.43×10^{-3} grams per liter.

EXAMPLE II. The solubility of lead(II) chloride is 11 mg. per ml. What is the solubility product constant of lead(II) chloride?

Solution:

$$PbCl_2 \rightleftharpoons Pb^{++} + 2\ Cl^-$$
$$K_{sp} = [Pb^{++}][Cl^-]^2$$

The concentration of $PbCl_2$ is

$$\frac{11 \text{ mg./ml.}}{278 \text{ mg./mmole}} = 0.04 \text{ mmole/ml.} = 0.04\ M$$

Since each molecule of $PbCl_2$ will provide one Pb^{++} ion and two Cl^- ions, then

$$[Pb^{++}] = 0.04 \text{ mmole/ml.}$$
$$[Cl^-] = 2 \times 0.04 = 0.08 \text{ mmole/ml.}$$

From the solubility product relationship

$$K_{sp} = 0.04 \times (0.08)^2$$
$$K_{sp} = 2.6 \times 10^{-4}$$

EXAMPLE III. If the solubility product constant of barium fluoride is 1.7×10^{-6}, how many grams of barium would remain dissolved as a salt in 500 ml. of an aqueous solution containing 3.8 grams of fluoride ion?

Solution:

$$BaF_2 \rightleftharpoons Ba^{++} + 2\,F^-$$
$$K_{sp} = [Ba^{++}][F^-]^2$$

The concentration of the fluoride ion is

$$\frac{3.8}{19 \times 0.5} = 0.40 \text{ mole/l.} = 0.40\,M$$

From the solubility product relationship

$$1.7 \times 10^{-6} = [Ba^{++}][0.40]^2$$
$$[Ba^{++}] = \frac{1.7 \times 10^{-6}}{1.6 \times 10^{-1}} = 1.06 \times 10^{-5} \text{ moles/l.}$$
$$1.06 \times 10^{-5} \times 137.3 = 14.5 \times 10^{-4} \text{ g./l., barium}$$
$$\frac{14.5 \times 10^{-4}}{2} = 7.25 \times 10^{-4} \text{ g./500 ml., barium}$$

There are several factors that affect the solubility of the precipitate being formed during a chemical reaction.

(1) *Common Ion Effect.* An addition of a compound having an ion in common with a slightly soluble salt will decrease the solubility of this salt. This is called the "common ion effect." This principle has to be applied with caution, since it is entirely possible that the solubility of a precipitate may be greater than predicted by the calculations using the solubility product. For example, the solubility of zinc hydroxide increases with the addition of a large excess of hydroxyl ion. In general, the common ion concentration is kept to about a 10% excess over that theoretically required.

Under certain conditions, even though the solubility product has been exceeded, precipitation will not take place. The precipitate will not form due to the small particle size of the precipitate and the attendant adsorption phenomena. This can be demonstrated very dramatically with the precipitation of silver chloride from solutions of varying concentrations of silver and chloride ions.

(2) *Temperature.* The solubility of precipitates is affected by changes in temperature. Generally an increase in temperature will cause an increase in the solubility of the precipitate. There are some substances, such as sodium chloride, whose solubility changes very little with temperature. These substances are said to have "straight line" solubility. Other substances, such as calcium hydroxide, exhibit "retrograde solubility." This term defines the

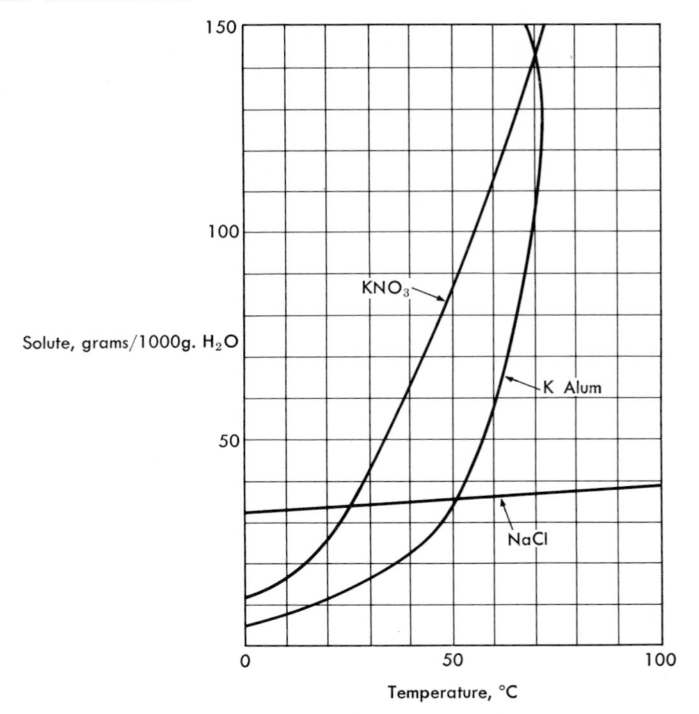

Fig. 11.1. Solubility of three salts in H_2O.

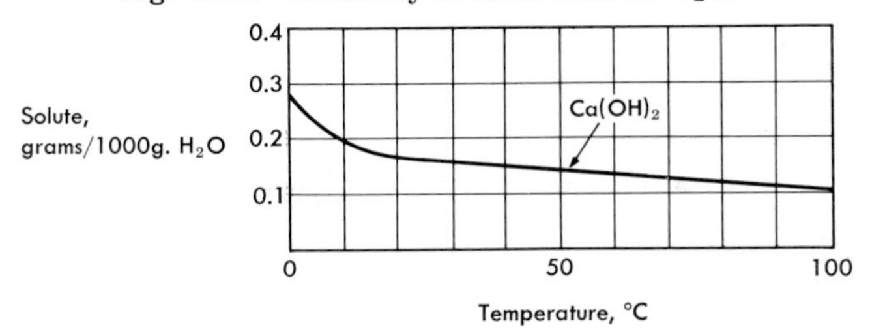

Fig. 11.2. Retrograde solubility of $Ca(OH)_2$ in H_2O.

situation where the solubility of a substance increases with a decrease in temperature. Figures 11.1 and 11.2 are a graphic representation of the effect of temperature on solubility.

The temperature effect is very pronounced in some cases, whereas in others it is much less. Generally the presence of an excess of the precipitating agent lowers the solubility to such an extent that the temperature effects are negligibly small. Nevertheless substances such as zinc ammonium phosphate, magnesium ammonium phosphate and lead sulfate are usually filtered at room temperature to reduce losses due to increased solubility at elevated temperatures.

(3) *p*H. The *p*H has a great influence on the solubility of a precipitate. The difference in solubility of slightly soluble metal sulfides due to changes in *p*H

is an outstanding example. Advantage of this fact is taken in the separation of the metal sulfides in the qualitative analytical scheme.

Acids have an effect on the solubility of the slightly soluble sulfates. The solubility of the sulfates tends to increase in acid solution. In the precipitation of lead sulfate during the analysis of brass, it is necessary to remove all of the nitric acid which was used to bring the sample into solution. The sulfate ions have a tendency to combine with the hydrogen ions present and this increases the solubility of the sulfate compound. On the other hand, even though barium sulfate has a higher solubility in acid solution, it is generally precipitated from a slightly acid medium because the precipitate obtained is easier to filter. Here is a case where the effect of an excess of precipitating reagent compensates for the increased solubility resulting from acidic conditions.

The effect of acids on solubility increases with an increase in the solubility product constant of the salt and a decrease in the ionization constant of the weak acid formed from the anion of the salt. The solvent effect of acids has to be taken into account in many quantitative precipitations.

(4) *Solvent.* The solvent used for the reactants has an influence on the solubility of the precipitate. In general, ionic compounds are soluble in polar solvents. The polar solvent molecules, acting as electric dipoles, are attracted to the positive or negative sites on the crystal, and the energy of interaction between the charged ions and the solvent dipole helps to overcome the attractive forces that hold the ions in the crystal framework known as the crystal lattice. As this happens, the crystal lattice breaks up and the solubility of the substance increases. Materials that are highly covalent are more soluble in nonpolar solvents such as benzene and carbon tetrachloride. Generally the solubility of inorganic compounds in water will decrease upon the addition of an organic solvent. It is necessary to be sure that the volume of organic solvent that is added is not so large that salts other than the desired one form. It is apparent that the decrease in solubility of a solute in a solvent by changing the nature of the solvent can be used as a means of separation. Another type of separation, called solvent extraction, is discussed on page 192.

Physical Character of the Precipitate

The physical character of the precipitate depends largely on whether the substance formed initially is crystalline or amorphous. If the precipitate is crystalline, the particle size and its form depend upon the conditions under which it has been precipitated, the individual characteristics of the particular substance, and the treatment before filtration.

Precipitates are classified according to particle size. An example of such a classification is given in Table 11.1. The problems involved in purity and

TABLE 11.1
Classification of Precipitates

PARTICLE SIZE	EXAMPLE
Fine Crystalline	$BaSO_4$
Coarse Crystalline	$PbSO_4$
Curdy	AgCl
Gelatinous	$Fe(OH)_3$
Colloidal Dispersion	As_2S_3

filtration of precipitates are directly related to the particle size of the precipitate. A colloidal precipitate will readily pass through a fine textured filter paper or other filtering media. It also carries an electric charge which causes contamination of the precipitate. The most important part of the pathway from ionic solution to crystalline precipitate is in the range of colloidal particle size. If the particle size of the precipitate remains in this region, then losses by filtration and errors resulting from contamination are very significant.

One of the predominant factors in the determination of the particle size of a precipitate formed is the relative degree of supersaturation of the solution with respect to the slightly soluble precipitate. Von Weimarn formulated a relationship which can be correlated with the particle size of the precipitate. This relationship can be expressed as

$$\frac{(Q - S)}{S}$$

where Q is the total concentration of the substance to be precipitated produced momentarily by mixing the reactants, and S is the solubility of the macro crystals of the precipitate. $(Q - S)$ is a measure of the degree of supersaturation at the instant that precipitation begins.

This expression is not absolutely exact because the solubility S, as a rule, is not exactly known under the specified experimental conditions. Nevertheless by changing the quantity $\frac{(Q - S)}{S}$ for a given precipitate, it is possible to change the particle size between rather wide limits. The larger the value of $(Q - S)$, the more rapid is the initial growth of the particles. The more rapid the growth of the particles, the greater the number of nuclei formed, thus the smaller the particle size of the resulting precipitate.

The S in the denominator represents the factor that is resisting precipitation. The larger the value of S, the smaller will be the value of the ratio $\frac{(Q - S)}{S}$, resulting in a smaller number of nuclei formed; thus there is a larger particle size crystalline precipitate. The value of $\frac{(Q - S)}{S}$ should be as small as possible in order to have a large particle size crystalline precipitate, for ease of filtering and less contamination. This can be accomplished in the following ways:

(1) *The value of Q can be decreased.* This can be done by using reasonably dilute solutions and adding the dilute solutions of the precipitating agent slowly.

(2) *The value of S can be increased.* Since S is concerned with solubility, those factors that affect the solubility will cause a change in its value. The factors and their effect on the solubility of precipitates have been discussed previously on page 182.

Most soluble substances have a wide metastable range (supersaturated state) indicating a high degree of supersaturation with slow addition of the precipitating agent. The precipitated material builds up slowly because relatively few nuclei are present. Substances that are highly insoluble have a short metastable range indicating a low degree of supersaturation. There is a tendency for the precipitated substance to crystallize in a finely divided crystalline state because of the large number of nuclei formed. The limiting condition would be when all of the material is precipitated initially in very fine primary particles which are unable to grow because the solution is not supersaturated. The size of the particles in such a primary precipitation can only be changed by the secondary process of aging.

The particle size of the precipitate can be controlled by methods other than controlling the actual precipitation process.

One method by which the size of the particle can be increased is called **digestion.**

In digestion the precipitate is kept in contact with the saturated solution of the precipitated material (mother liquor) at room temperature for a specified period of time. The smaller particles are more soluble and go into solution while the larger particles grow larger by material crystallizing from solution. In this manner a precipitate of larger particle size is formed at the expense of the smaller particles. This procedure when applied to crystalline precipitates brings good results with regard to filterability and purity of the precipitate. On the other hand, application of a digestion period to solutions containing a curdy or gelatinous precipitate has little advantage. Since the size of the particles formed in gelatinous or curdy precipitates does not differ greatly, the growth of larger particles at the expense of the smaller ones is not possible at room temperature. To bring about the formation of larger crystalline particles from these types of precipitates, it is necessary to digest at an elevated temperature.

Coarsely crystalline precipitates will be best obtained in most cases if the precipitation procedure is carried out in the following manner:

(1) Dilute solutions of the reactants are mixed slowly in a well agitated solution under conditions of increased solubility of the precipitate.
(2) A digestion period at an elevated temperature is employed.

Purity of Precipitate

Precipitates separated from solutions generally are not pure, but are usually contaminated to a greater or lesser degree by foreign substances including the mother liquor. The errors that result from this type of contamination as well as loss of material from the solubility of precipitates, are the most serious errors in gravimetric determinations.

The process by which a normally soluble foreign substance is precipitated along with the desired precipitate is called **coprecipitation.** The amount of coprecipitation depends on the following:

(1) The temperature at which the precipitation takes place.
(2) The concentration of the ions in the solution from which the precipitation is made.
(3) The kinds of ions present in solution.
(4) The particle size and nature of the precipitate.
(5) The time the precipitate is allowed to stand in contact with the mother liquor.

Types of coprecipitation can be classified according to the means used to explain the phenomenon.

1. Adsorption

The impurity in this case is held at the surface of the particle of the precipitate. This phenomenon of adsorption is most likely to occur with gelatinous and curdy precipitates which result from the flocculations of colloids. This is because of the large surface of the colloidal material. Contamination of this type becomes of practical importance when dealing with such precipitates as the hydrous oxides and silver halides. In the adsorption process the precipitate tends to adsorb ions that are common to itself. This property is one that is made good use of in titrations with adsorption indicators (page 152), but in the separation procedure it is not advantageous.

If the solution does not contain any ions in common with the precipitate, adsorption can be predicted by the Paneth-Fajans-Hahn rule. The ion that is most strongly adsorbed will be the one that forms the least soluble compound with an ion in the precipitate.

Precipitates that form with small particle size have a large surface area resulting in a favorable condition for contamination by adsorption.

2. Occlusion

This is the process by which foreign ions become incorporated into the precipitate during its formation. The impurity can be entrapped by the particle as it grows or, if the foreign material fits into the crystal lattice of the precipitate, it becomes occluded in the form of a mixed crystal or a solid solution. For example, lead ion can occupy positions in the lattice normally occupied by barium ion in barium sulfate. Ions of similar size are said to be isomorphous. Isomorphic relacement is common in the formation of natural minerals.

If the impurity is found as a mixed crystal, digestion will not lead to complete expulsion of the impurity. On the other hand if the impurity does not fit into the crystal lattice, digestion will cause these impurities to be expelled and a purer precipitate will result. To obtain a completely pure crystal in both cases, a recrystallization is necessary.

3. Formation of a Chemical Compound

The actual formation of chemical compounds in the precipitation process occurs very rarely and is hardly of any analytical interest. One example that has often been used to illustrate this type of coprecipitation is the compound resulting from the presence of barium chloride or potassium sulfate in barium sulfate. Many of the examples that can be given, using precipitates that separate with varying chemical composition, do not strictly represent the phenomenon of coprecipitation but instead one of postprecipitation (see the following section).

In general, curdy and gelatinous precipitates do not occlude particles. The contamination results from adsorption phenomena and, as a result, the foreign ions can usually be removed by washing, preferably with a solution of an electrolyte containing ammonium salts because their ignition products are volatile.

Postprecipitation

When the primary precipitate separates in a relatively pure form and a second foreign precipitate forms slowly afterward, the second crystalline material is not coprecipitated but **postprecipitated.** A very common example of postprecipitation occurs in the precipitation of calcium as calcium oxalate in the presence of magnesium. If the digestion period of the calcium oxalate extends over a long period, then magnesium oxalate will precipitate. Magnesium oxalate forms stable, supersaturated solutions that precipitate very slowly. Thus magnesium oxalate satisfies the requirement of a postprecipitate, namely, that the foreign ion forms a supersaturated solution that precipitates very slowly.

Of course a small amount of magnesium will also be coprecipitated with the calcium oxalate.

Postprecipitation is quite common with metal sulfides. This is apparent in the precipitation of copper sulfide in the presence of zinc. The conditions may be such that the zinc sulfide will precipitate but it will not separate, because of the formation of a supersaturated solution. The copper sulfide will precipitate immediately with little or no coprecipitation of zinc sulfide, but as time is increased before filtration, more and more zinc sulfide appears in the precipitate due to the postprecipitation process.

Optimum Conditions for Precipitation

A satisfactory separation by precipitation methods requires a precipitate of relatively large particle size and freedom from foreign ion contamination. This requirement can be attained by performing the separation under the following conditions:

(1) Use dilute solutions of the reactants which will cause the slow formation of the precipitate from the relatively small number of nuclei formed. There is a practical limit to the extent of dilution, dictated by the solubility of the precipitate and the difficulties of handling a large volume of solution.

(2) Add the precipitating reagent slowly to a well agitated solution. This minimizes the local areas of high supersaturation, which results in the formation of a small number of nuclei and a larger particle size precipitate.

(3) Precipitate from a hot solution. Most solids are more soluble at an elevated temperature. The relative supersaturation is small and the precipitation is slow giving larger, purer crystalline particles.

(4) Use a suitable digestion period. It has been pointed out previously (page 186) that a digestion period will result in the purification of crystalline precipitates. In the case of gelatinous precipitates the digestion period is short; just long enough to aid in the coagulation of the colloidal particles. Caution must be exercised in the selection of the length of the digestion period so that the length of time will not allow contamination resulting from the postprecipitation process.

(5) Use a second precipitation. This is a common procedure used with gelatinous and curdy precipitates and when contamination cannot be avoided. The second precipitate is formed from a solution that contains only the amount of contamination carried down by the first precipitate. Therefore the second precipitate will have less contamination than the first. It is very apparent that multiple precipitations could be used, each resulting in a purer precipitate. It is generally conceded that after the second precipitation the increase in the purity of the precipitate is not great enough to warrant the time required for

further precipitations. As a result a second precipitation is usually all that is attempted.

(6) Wash the precipitate thoroughly. A wash solution containing an ion in common with the precipitate decreases the solubility of the precipitate. The application of the common ion effect is unnecessary if the precipitate is very insoluble. Several successive small portions of wash liquid are more effective in washing a precipitate than a few large portions. A wash solution must not contain solutes that will leave a weighable residue after the precipitate is dried or ignited. The volatile acids, such as hydrochloric or nitric, and electrolytes containing ammonium salts are the most common wash solutions since their ignition products are volatile.

Precipitation from Homogeneous Solution

To minimize regions of high supersaturation that result on addition of the precipitant even under the most favorable conditions, precipitation from homogeneous solution can be used. In this process the precipitant is produced as a result of a chemical reaction taking place in solution. One of the best examples is the hydrolysis of urea, which is used to increase the *p*H of the solution. Urea hydrolyzes slowly at the boiling point of water according to the equation

$$CO(NH_2)_2 + H_2O \rightarrow CO_2 + 2NH_3$$

The ammonia generated homogeneously in the solution can be used to neutralize the hydrogen ion in the solution. Generation of a reactant in this manner can be used in the precipitation of hydrous oxides and has been applied to the precipitation of calcium oxalate. During the period of precipitation, usually about two hours, the particles attain a rather large size because of their slow growth. As a result, the particles contain a minimum of occluded contamination. Even with the precipitation of hydrous oxides, one precipitation is sufficient. The purity of the precipitate after the second precipitation is not enough better to make the second precipitation worthwhile.

Homogeneous precipitation of barium ion as barium sulfate can be accomplished by the hydrolysis of diethylsulfate.

$$(C_2H_5)_2SO_4 + 2H_2O \rightarrow 2C_2H_5OH + 2H^+ + SO_4^=$$

Other similar alkyl esters can be hydrolyzed to form the inorganic ion and can be used to precipitate oxalates and phosphates from homogeneous solution.

ORGANIC PRECIPITATING REAGENTS

Among the large number of organic compounds are some that possess reactive groups which enable them to form complex compounds with metal ions. The reaction products, known as chelate compounds, generally have a low solubility in water and are highly colored. One of the most familiar of this type of reagent is dimethylglyoxime, which reacts with nickel(II) ion to form an insoluble, red-colored precipitate that is used both qualitatively and quantitatively in the determination of nickel. There is an increasing amount of interest in the general field of organic precipitants, evidenced by the large amount of published material available.

Organic precipitating agents are classed as **specific,** those which react with one, perhaps two, metal ions; and **selective,** those which react with a number of metal ions. The number of selective reagents is relatively large; on the other hand, there are few specific reagents known. By careful regulation of the conditions of precipitation such as acidity, concentration range, temperature, and with the judicial use of masking agents, the action of many selective reagents can be narrowed to such an extent that they are practically specific.

The requirements of an organic precipitating reagent are the same as those for any precipitant used in the gravimetric precipitation process. In general, organic precipitants meet these requirements; the most important exception is their insolubility in water. For example, dimethylglyoxime, which is soluble in alcohol, will itself precipitate upon the addition of a slight excess to an aqueous solution. This is a source of contamination of the nickel dimethylglyoximate precipitate if the reagent is not removed by sufficient washing with alcohol. In many cases, the organic precipitates do not have suitable weighing forms. This results from uncertainties in the drying process. Thus many organic precipitants are used only as a means of separation, and an additional operation is required to complete the determination.

Organic precipitants have many important advantages in spite of the above disadvantages.

(1) Metallic ions can be precipitated by organic precipitants because of the insolubility of the reaction product in water.

(2) The molecular weight of the precipitant is usually rather high. A small quantity of the metal ion precipitated with the organic precipitant will result in a large weight of precipitate. As an example, nickel is 20.32% of the total weight of the nickel dimethylglyoximate.

(3) In general, the precipitates are coarse and bulky and as a result are easy to handle. One exception is that the bulkiness of organic precipitates limits the amount of metallic ion that can be precipitated from the solution conveniently.

(4) Organic precipitating agents, as pointed out earlier, can be made relatively specific by selecting the correct conditions.

(5) Organic precipitants can be used as a means of separation of metal ions from solution even though the precipitate is not in a good weighable form. A

specific procedure can be applied for the determination of the separated metal constituent.

Some of the more common organic precipitating reagents are listed in Table 11.2, pp. 194-195. For a more detailed and complete discussion of the application of organic precipitating agents, it is suggested that reference 2 listed at the end of this chapter be studied.

VOLATILIZATION

One of the most convenient separations can be achieved by evolving a component of the sample as a gas. Volatilization may be performed on a solid or a liquid. It may or may not be accompanied by a chemical reaction. This procedure is often used to remove a substance that is interfering with another determination.

The determination of carbon dioxide in a limestone where the carbon dioxide is evolved after treatment with an acid, adsorbed in ascarite, and then weighed, is an example of this type of separation. A similar example is the determination of silicon using the volatile silicon tetrafluoride, SiF_4, to remove the silicon from the inorganic materials such as iron and aluminum oxides.

A special type of volatilization method is called the **distillation method.** This method has common use in organic chemistry to separate substances by volatilization and then condensation. The Kjeldahl method for nitrogen determination, where ammonia is distilled from a sodium hydroxide solution, condensed and collected in a standard solution of hydrochloric acid, and the excess acid titrated, is an example of this type of separation. Arsenic, antimony, and tin can be separated from each other by a sequence of distillations of the chlorides of these metals.

The determination of water of crystallization or absorbed water can be accomplished by heating to a sufficiently high temperature to expel the water. The loss in weight is a measure of the water expelled.

EXTRACTION

Inorganic substances that are soluble in organic solvents such as carbon tetrachloride, ether, chloroform, and others can be removed from aqueous solution by extraction. Separations from substances that are insoluble in organic solvents can be attained. An example of this is the extraction of the metal dithizonates from water solution, using chloroform. The specificity of this extraction is dependent on the acidity of the solution.

A given material has some solubility in both the organic solvent and the water. After the mixture is well shaken, the substance distributes itself between the two solvents in a definite concentration ratio that is always the same for that substance in the two liquids. The numerical value of this constant ratio is called the **distribution coefficient.** It is expressed by the relationship

$$K = \frac{C_s}{C_w}$$

where K is the distribution coefficient, C_s is the concentration in the organic solvent and C_w is the concentration in the water. Since the concentration in the organic solvent is the numerator of this fraction, extractions are most nearly complete when the distribution coefficient has a large numerical value. Extractions from a concentrated aqueous solution are more efficient than from a dilute solution. The effectiveness of extraction increases with the volume of the immiscible solvent that is used, but is much greater if several successive extractions with small portions of solvent are done, than if the same total volume is used in a single extraction.

Most liquid-liquid extractions are carried out in a separatory funnel using repeated extractions. This procedure is one that is commonly used in organic preparations. The extraction of iron(III) chloride from hydrochloric acid solution by means of diethyl ether is an example of an extraction procedure. This separation becomes important in the determination of certain constituents, for example titanium, in iron alloys where a high concentration of iron(III) ion in solution is undesirable. Using a preliminary extraction by ether greatly increases the effectiveness of the determination of titanium.

Extraction of solid samples by an organic solvent can be accomplished. A Soxhlet extractor can be used for the continuous extraction by a given solvent (see Figure 11.3, p.196). The solid material is placed in a porous thimble made of paper or alundum. The solvent is boiled gently in the Soxhlet flask and the vapors are condensed in the water cooled condenser from which the solvent drips into the thimble where it comes in contact with the solid sample. When the solvent reaches a level slightly above the siphon tube, all the solvent in the chamber siphons off into the flask, carrying the dissolved material with it. This process repeats itself continually until all of the soluble substance is removed. The solvent flask is taken from the apparatus, the solvent is removed, and the separated material is recovered.

CHROMATOGRAPHY

The technique for the separation of closely related compounds by selective adsorption is at least a century old. It may have originated with the description by Pliny of the use of papyrus impregnated with an extract of gall nuts for the detection of iron(II) sulfate. A German scientist, F. F. Runge, recognized and demonstrated the possibilities of selective adsorptive techniques when he showed that inorganic cations could be separated by migration through porous

Table 11.2
Common Organic Precipitating Agents

NAME	FORMULA	APPLICATION
Aluminon	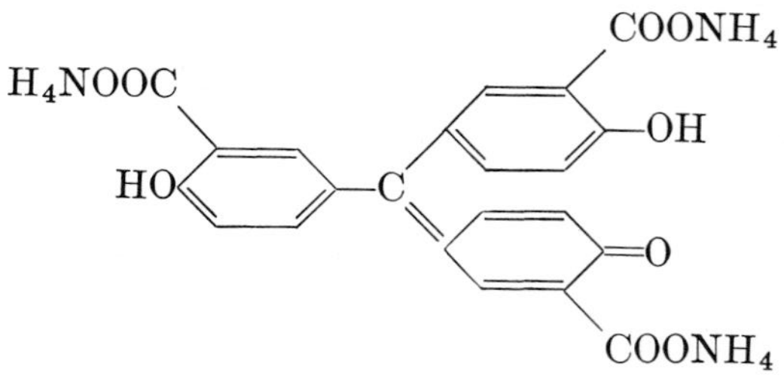 H_4NOOC, HO, C, $COONH_4$, OH, O, $COONH_4$	Reagent for Aluminum
α-Benzoin Oxime	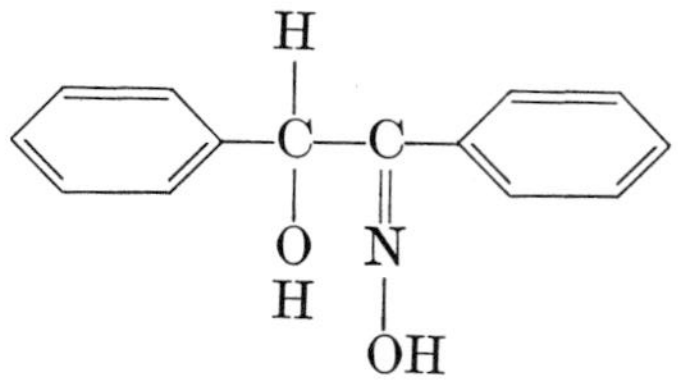 H, C, C, O, H, N, OH	Reagent for Copper, Molybdenum, and Tungsten
Chloranilic Acid	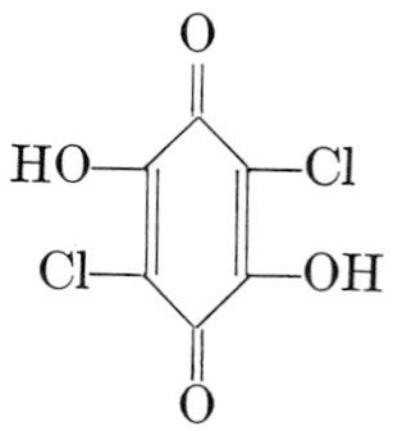 O, HO, Cl, Cl, OH, O	Reagent for Calcium, Strontium, and Zirconium

Reagent	Structure	Use
Cupferron	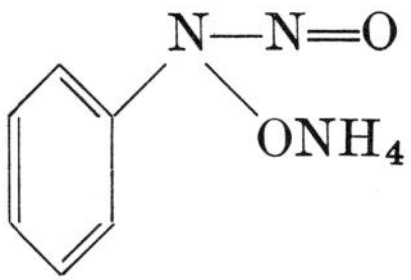 $N—N{=}O$, ONH_4	Reagent for Iron, Titanium, and Aluminum—Generally used for Aluminum after interferences have been removed
Dimethylglyoxime	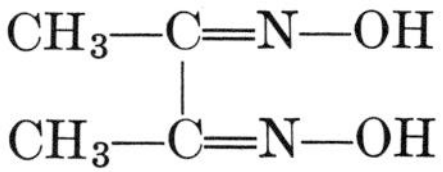 $CH_3—C{=}N—OH$ $CH_3—C{=}N—OH$	Reagent for Nickel primarily but can be used for Iron, Bismuth, and Palladium
Diphenylcarbazone	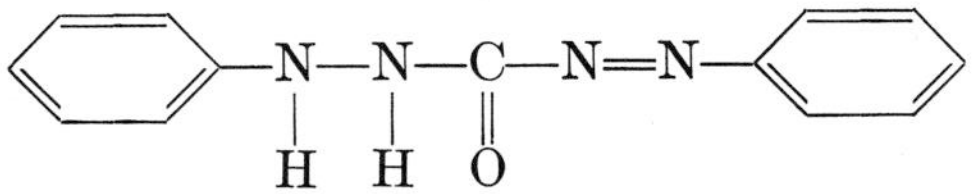 —N(H)—N(H)—C(=O)—N=N—	Reagent for Mercury—Can be used for many heavy metals by regulation of the conditions of precipitation
8-Hydroxyquinoline	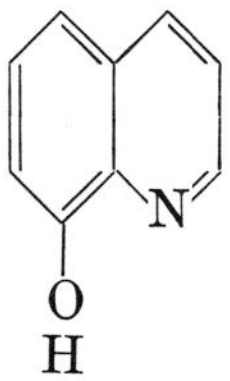 N, O—H	Reagent for many elements. Can be used for group separation by regulation of pH
1:10 Phenanthroline (*o*-phenanthroline)	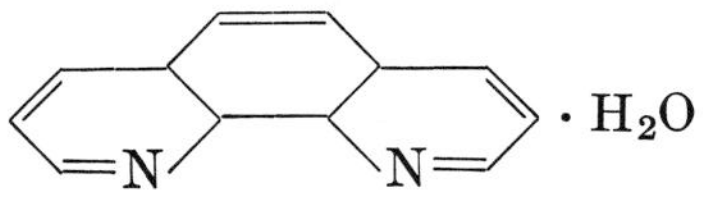 =N, N=, $\cdot H_2O$	Reagent for Iron, Palladium, Vanadium, and Copper

materials. A Polish botanist, N. Tswett, is generally given credit for the first successful application, in 1906, of a selective adsorption separation which he named *Chromatography*.

Chromatography is the name given to the technique used for the separation of similar chemical compounds. The word chromatography is a misnomer.

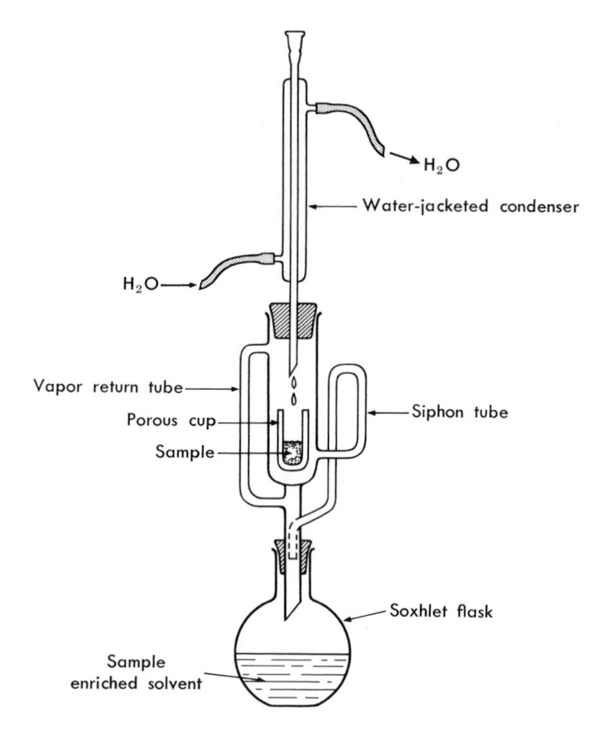

Fig. 11.3. Soxhlet extractor.

Tswett showed a visible separation of colored compounds but the process of separation is not a color separation; rather, it is a "partition" of a solute between two solvent systems. A term "fractometry" has been proposed as one that would describe the general process more adequately. The term chromatography is so well known, however, that it is hardly likely to be superseded.

Chromatography is divided into three general types: adsorption, partition, and ion exchange. The choice of method for a particular purpose is dependent on the nature and amount of the solutes whose separation is required. In many cases previous experimental work is a better guide than theory.

Basically, chromatography makes use of a two phase system, one of which is fixed and the other mobile. The fixed phase is termed the static or stationary phase. It may be either solid or liquid held by a solid. Adsorption chromatography makes use of the former while partition chromatography uses the latter.

The mobile phase is called the moving phase and it may be a liquid, gas, dissolved solid, or a colloidal solution. The sample is contained in or may itself be the mobile phase. An equilibrium is set up between the sample components and the moving and stationary phases. The sample is distributed or "partitioned" between the stationary phase and the mobile phase.

Partition Chromatography

The mixed solutes are applied to the top of a column of solid substance which holds one liquid phase statically while a second phase is allowed to flow down the column. One solute will separate from another in the mixture due to the difference in solubility in the immiscible liquid phase held by the solid substance. Paper can be used to substitute for the column material as the holding substance. This method has been developed by Consden, Gordon, and Martinand. It has had far reaching applications.

The method of paper partition chromatography consists of applying a small drop of the solution containing the constituents to be separated to a strip of filter paper a short distance from the end. The end of the paper nearer the spot is placed in the developing solution. This solution is usually water containing an organic solvent. The paper is placed in this solution so that the solvent flows past the "spot" by capillary action and on along the length of the paper. The individual components can be characterized by their R_f values (rate of flow) where

$$R_f = \frac{\text{distance moved by the component}}{\text{distance moved by the solvent front}}$$

An example of this type of separation is given in an experiment at the end of the chapter. Paper chromatography is an important means of separation of many organic and biochemical products. The separation of the amino acids is an outstanding example of the use of this technique.

Adsorption Chromatography

In general, a column of finely divided adsorbent wetted by one liquid moving phase is used in adsorption chromatography. A solution of the substances to be separated is applied to the top of the column. The amount of material loaded on the column is kept small in comparison to the total adsorptive capacity of the column. When loading is complete, pure solvent is allowed to percolate through the column. As the mixture is drawn down the column by the flowing solvent, the solutes gradually separate since they move with different rates down the column. Tswett applied this technique to the separation of the pigments from green leaves, using petroleum ether as a solvent and a column of finely divided chalk. The pigment mixture separated into several colored bands which were identified individually by breaking the chalk column and dissolving the bands separately.

Ion Exchange Chromatography

The use of ion exchange materials in columns and the subsequent separation has been termed **ion exchange** chromatography or **displacement** chromatography. The mixture to be resolved is applied to the top of the column after which a developing solution is applied. This solution contains a solute which is more strongly adsorbed on the column than any of the solutes in the original mixture. The original solutes are displaced as the solution flows down the column. The developing solution pushes the mixture of solutes farther and farther down the column. As the solutes move down the column those that are most strongly adsorbed are concentrated in a band formation as well as those that are less strongly adsorbed. The mixture passes down the column in a series of bands, having some overlap, with the least strongly adsorbed band appearing first at the outlet of the column and the most strongly adsorbed appearing last. The effluent from the column is collected in a series of fractions until the developing solution begins to come through. The column then is saturated with the developing solute. The column can be restored by running a solution with a suitable oppositely charged ion through the column and washing with distilled water. The limit on the number of times a column can be used is determined by the chemical stability of the resin.

Ion exchange resins were first introduced for water softening, but when their applications to chromatographic separations became known, many special resins were developed specifically for chromatographic separational use. Each resin is "monofunctional," meaning that each resin has only one type of chemical group which can take part in the ion exchange reaction.

Ion Exchange Resins

Synthetic ion exchange resins are high molecular weight, complex, organic polymers containing large numbers of ionic functional groups per molecule.

For anion exchange, the polymer contains substituted amines or quaternary ammonium compounds which are organic bases. An example of an anion exchange resin would be represented as $RNH_3^+ \cdot OH^-$ where R is the polymeric resin molecule and the $-NH_3^+ \cdot OH^-$ is the functional group, part of which can be interchanged with the anion in question. Such an interchange can be shown by the equation

$$RNH_3^+ \cdot OH^- + Cl^- \rightleftharpoons RNH_3^+ \cdot Cl^- + OH^-$$

In cation exchange resins the polymer molecule can contain strongly acidic functional groups such as ($-SO_3H$) or weakly acidic functional groups such as ($-COOH$). The resins containing the strongly acidic functional groups have a wide application. A cation exchange resin represented by RSO_3H can enter into an exchange reaction such as illustrated by the following equation:

$$R{-}SO_3^-{\cdot}H^+ + Na^+ \rightleftharpoons R{-}SO_3^-{\cdot}Na^+ + H^+$$

The cation exchanger of the sulfonic acid type exchanges its hydrogen ion for other cations much easier than the cation exchange resin of the carboxylic acid type. On the other hand the conversion back to the original resin is much easier with the carboxylic acid type than the sulfonic acid type. This can be taken advantage of in the exchange of calcium ion for sodium ion using a carboxylic acid type exchange resin. The following equations can be used as an illustration.

$$RCOO^-{\cdot}H^+ + Na^+ \rightleftharpoons RCOO^-{\cdot}Na^+ + H^+$$

$$2RCOO^-{\cdot}Na^+ + Ca^{++} \rightleftharpoons (RCOO)_2^={\cdot}Ca^{++} + 2Na^+$$

The sodium form of the exchange resin can be regenerated by treatment with concentrated sodium chloride solution.

The attraction (exchange affinity) by an ion exchange resin varies with ions of opposite charge and with the nature of the ions. In aqueous media at low concentrations and ordinary temperatures the exchange affinity increases with the charge on the cation. An example of this increase is shown by the following series $Na^+ < Ca^{++} < Al^{+++}$. The exchange affinity of hydrogen ions varies with the strength of the acid formed between the hydrogen ion and the functional group. For ions with the same charge the exchange affinity generally increases with an increase in atomic number (*e.g.* $Li^+ < Na^+ < K^+ < Rb^+ < Cs^+$).

For anion exchangers the exchange affinity generally increases with an increase of charge, although there are some exceptions with certain oxyanions, for example $PO_4^{\equiv} < NO_3^- < SO_4^=$. Within the halide group the exchange affinity of anion exchange resins increases with an increase in atomic number.

Methods of Removing Sample from the Column

The technique for removing the sample from the column is sometimes referred to as the development of the chromatogram. There are three general methods:

1. Displacement

This method consists of placing a small amount of the mixture to be separated at the top of the column. Then a liquid or vapor that has a greater affinity for the column packing than any of the components in the mixture is used to push the mixture through the column. As the displacer moves through the column, the components of the sample will be forced out of the column in the order of their increasing affinity for the column packing. Displacement analysis is usually applied to adsorption and ion exchange chromatography.

2. Frontal Analysis

In this method the mixture acts as its own displacer. As the mixture is forced down the column, the components tend to be separated, with the component having the least affinity appearing at the outlet first. In this method the only fraction that is recovered in the pure form is the component having the least affinity for the column packing. Since the sample is added continuously to the column, the remainder of the components that emerge from the column after the component having the least affinity will be mixed with the components that have a low affinity for the packing.

3. Elution

In this method the sample mixture is placed on top of the column and pure solvent is passed through the column; separation is attained as a result of the carrier solvent moving the individual components through the column at different speeds. This type of sample removal is usually preferred in vapor phase chromatography where a sample is injected into the continuous stream of carrier gas, and separation is achieved by the movement of the individual components through the column at different speeds.

Ion Exchange Resin Applications

With a resin column variance in exchange affinities can be used to separate ions. For example the separation of iron(III), cobalt, and nickel can be accomplished by using a cation exchange resin and changing the concentration of the hydrochloric acid used to wash the column.

Trace ions may be concentrated by the use of ion exchange resins. This process is illustrated using cation exchangers to remove trace amounts of metal ions from large volumes of natural water and concentrate them on the resin bed in the column. These metal ions can be released by acid treatment giving a concentrated sample for analytical treatment.

Ion exchange resins can be used as a means of removing interfering ions from a solution. A fractional separation of ions can be accomplished by using the differences in affinity of the exchange resin as described on page 199. The separation of the rare earth elements or separations of isotopes of certain elements can be accomplished by ion exchange methods, whereas such separations cannot be made by classical methods of separation.

Gas Chromatography

One of the most important modern developments of chromatographic separations has been in the field of gas chromatography. Gas chromatography is the collective name of gas-liquid and gas-solid chromatography. Vapor phase chromatography is the term that has been introduced to describe this type of chromatographic separation but as with the term chromatography itself, there is doubt that this term will supersede gas chromatography as a designation.

The impact of this technique on analytical chemistry in the field of separation is staggering. It is beyond the scope of this book to present a complete discussion of this valuable analytical tool. Reference 7 at the end of this chapter should be consulted for further reading concerning the theory, mechanics, and applications of this technique.

Thin Layer Chromatography

Thin layer chromatography (TLC) is best described as an "open micro column" which consists of a thin layer of adsorbent placed uniformly on a glass plate by a specially designed applicator. The plates are dried and stored until they are needed. The separation is achieved by applying the sample to the plate with a pipet and placing the plate vertically in the solvent chamber containing the solvent.

Thin layer chromatography supplements paper and column chromatography and many times offers more advantageous characteristics. Originally its greatest usefulness was in the separation of lipids and essential oils, but the scope of its usefulness has enlarged to include many of the same applications for which paper and column chromatography are used.

The advantages of this method lie in the simplicity of the method and the apparatus required, the speed of the separation, the size of the sample which may range from one microgram to ten milligrams, the fact that no limits are imposed on the use of corrosive spray agents, and that the layers may be acidic, neutral, or alkaline.

The most serious of the relatively few disadvantages is that R_f values are not as reproducible as in paper chromatography. This suggests the need for running standards along with the sample for comparison purposes.

Reference 10 at the end of the chapter contains an excellent review of the applications of this technique to the problems of separation.

References

Organic Precipitating Agents

1. *Organic Reagents for Metals,* edited by Johnson, Chemical Publishing Company Inc., New York, 1955.

2. Welcher, *Organic Analytical Reagents,* Vols. I–IV, D. Van Nostrand Company, Inc., New York, 1947.

Chromatography

3. Block, Durrum, and Zweig, *A Manual of Paper Chromatography and Paper Electrophoresis*, Academic Press, Inc., New York, 1955.
4. Brimley and Barrett, *Practical Chromatography*, Reinhold Publishing Corporation, New York, 1953.
5. Keulemans, *Gas Chromatography*, 2nd ed., Reinhold Publishing Corporation, New York, 1959.
6. Lederer and Lederer, *Chromatography, A Review of Principles and Applications*, 2nd ed., Elsevier Publishing Company, New York, 1957.
7. *Principles and Practices of Gas Chromatography*, edited by Pecsok, John Wiley and Sons, Inc., New York, 1959.
8. Smith, *Inorganic Chromatography*, D. Van Nostrand Company, Inc., New York, 1953.
9. Strain, *Chromatographic Adsorption Analysis*, Interscience Publishers, New York, 1945.
10. Wollish, Schmall, and Hawrylyshyn, *Anal. Chem.* **33**, 1139 (1961).

General

11. *Treatise on Analytical Chemistry*, Part I, Vol. 2, edited by Kolthoff and Elving, Interscience Publishers, Inc., New York, 1961.
12. Hillebrand, Lundell, Bright, and Hoffman, *Applied Inorganic Analysis*, 2nd ed., John Wiley and Sons, New York, 1953.
13. Lundell and Hoffman, *Outlines of Methods of Chemical Analysis*, John Wiley and Sons, New York, 1938.
14. Willard and Diehl, *Advanced Quantitative Analysis*, D. Van Nostrand Company, Inc., New York, 1943.

Laboratory Experiment 19

Separation of Ink Components Using Paper Chromatography

Apparatus

Chromatographic paper, Whatman #2, $\frac{1}{2}'' \times 12''$
6 12″ Test tubes or Nessler tubes

Reagents

H_2O
CH_3OH
NH_4OH
C_2H_5OH
1:1 C_2H_5OH—water
0.1 *M* HCl
Colored ink (*e.g.* black ink)

Procedure

Pour approximately 10 ml. of a different solvent into each of six 12-inch tubes. Place the tubes in a rack and label the tubes to indicate the solvent in each.

Cut six strips of ½″ chromatographic paper 12″ long. Trim a point on one end. Using a thumbtack, attach the other end to a cork stopper of a size that will fit the tube.

Place one drop of the colored ink on the paper one inch from the pointed tip. Add to the pointed end a weight such as a thumbtack or a small paper clip.

Place the strip of paper in the tube such that the pointed tip just dips into the solvent. Be careful that the paper does not touch the side of the tube. Do not handle the strip unnecessarily since finger marks and skin oil are undesirable.

Allow the chromatographic process to continue until the solvent has reached within one inch of the top of the paper, or until optimum separation has occurred. When this happens, remove the filter paper and allow it to dry.

Report the number of different colored substituents that were present in the colored ink. Indicate on each chromatogram the conditions and solvent used.

Laboratory Experiment 20

Column Chromatographic Separation

Apparatus

Pyrex tubing, 24 cm. × 1 cm.
Side arm suction flask, 500 ml.
Separation funnel, 250 ml.

Reagents

Finely-powdered sugar
Aluminum oxide (Chromatographic activated)
Calcium carbonate
Petroleum ether (b.p. 70°C)
Petroleum ether (b.p. 30–50°C)
Benzene
Diethyl ether
Methanol
Nitrogen gas
Spinach leaves

Procedure

Place about 4 to 6 spinach leaves in a 250 ml. beaker containing 30 ml. of petroleum ether (b.p. 70°C), 3.5 ml. of benzene, and 10 ml. of methanol. With the aid of a clean spatula, crush the spinach leaves. Allow to stand for 2 hours.

At the end of the 2 hours, remove the residue from the beaker containing the crushed spinach leaves by filtration, using suction. Wash the residue with 5 ml. of the solvent mixture.

Transfer the extract to a separatory funnel and wash out the methanol with water **without shaking vigorously.** Using a stoppered Erlenmeyer flask, dry the extract over anhydrous sodium sulfate until the next laboratory period.

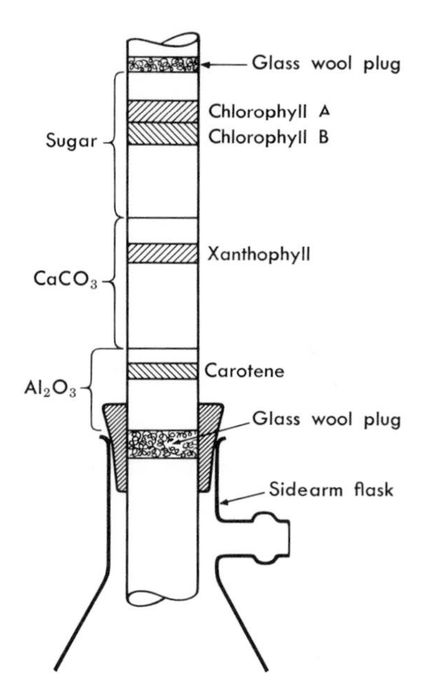

Fig. 11.4. Chromatographic column showing zones of separation of green extract from spinach leaves.

At the beginning of the second laboratory period, prepare an adsorption column, using a piece of 1 cm. diameter pyrex tubing 24 cm. long. Fit a glass wool plug into one end of the pyrex tubing and pass this end of the tubing through a one hole stopper that will fit the top of the side arm flask.

Pour aluminum oxide into the tube, a small portion at a time, tamping down gently with a glass rod that just fits the inner bore of the tube, until a layer 3 cm. in depth is formed. In the same manner, form a layer of calcium carbonate (dried at 105°C for 30 minutes) that is 6 cm. high. Cover with a layer of finely divided powdered sugar 9 cm. in length. Cover the sugar layer with a plug of glass wool. Figure 11.4 shows the completed column.

Pour into the column petroleum ether (b.p. 70°C) until there is a layer of about 5 cm. on the top of the upper glass wool plug. Apply gentle suction so that the eluate comes through at the rate of 1 to 2 drops per second. A layer of solvent about 1 cm. deep must be maintained at all times above the glass wool plug.

Follow the petroleum ether with the green extract obtained from the spinach leaves. When all of the extract has been added, the colored zones are developed by adding to the column 20 ml. of petroleum ether (b.p. 70°C). Finally wash with petroleum ether (b.p. 30–50°C) to check any extension of the zones. Approximately 15 ml. is used.

The column is dried by passing a stream of nitrogen gas through the column while maintaining the suction.

Cut the column between the colored zones, and dissolve the pigments of each zone with ethyl ether containing a little methanol. The absorption spectrum of each colored extract is taken, using the Spectronic 20 or similar spectrophotometer. The absorption spectra obtained are compared with the spectra of chlorophyll B, chlorophyll A, xanthophyll, and carotene, which are available from the literature.

References

1. Tswett, Ber. **24,** 234, 361, 384 (1906).
2. Harrow, *Laboratory Manual of Biochemistry,* W. B. Saunders Company, Philadelphia, Pa., 1944, p. 115.

Problems

1. If the solubility products of $BaCrO_4$ and BaF_2 are 3.0×10^{-10} and 1.7×10^{-6}, respectively, what is the solubility of each in milligrams per 250 ml.? *Ans. $BaCrO_4$, 1.02 mg.; BaF_2, 324 mg.*

2. The concentration of a saturated solution of Ag_2SO_4 is 0.104 *M*. What is the solubility product constant of Ag_2SO_4? *Ans. 4.5×10^{-3}*

3. Calculate the weight of iron(III) ion which must be present in one liter of solution in order to cause precipitation of the hydroxide when the hydroxyl ion concentration is 7.0×10^{-6} mole per liter? *Ans. 1.78×10^{-19} gr.*

4. Calculate the solubility product of Bi_2S_3 if 9×10^{-11} mg. are soluble in 100 ml. of solution. *Ans. 1.8×10^{-72}*

5. Using the solubility product constants of $Mg(OH)_2$ and $Fe(OH)_3$, calculate the number of grams of Mg^{++} and Fe^{+++} that remain in a solution whose pH = 4.75. *Ans. Mg^{++}, 2.62×10^9 grams/liter; Fe^{+++}, 3.48×10^{-7} grams/liter*

6. What is the solubility product constant of AgCl if 0.1434 gram of AgCl dissolves in one liter? How many grams of silver will remain in 250 ml. of solution containing 3.55 grams of chloride ions? How many grams of chloride ion could be dissolved in a liter of solution that is maintained 0.01 molar in $AgNO_3$? *Ans. 1.0×10^{-6}; 2.7×10^{-4} grams; 3.55×10^{-3} grams*

7. Calculate the concentration in milligrams per liter of manganese(II) ions that remain in solution if the concentration of hydroxyl ion is 3.0×10^{-9} *M*. *Ans.* 2.48×10^{8} *mg.*

8. Calculate the molar concentration of sulfide ion required to start precipitation of a metal sulfide from a saturated solution of silver chloride. *Ans.* 1.6×10^{-39} *M*

9. Solid sodium sulfate is added slowly to a solution that is 0.001 *M* in Pb^{++} ion and 0.001 *M* in Ba^{++} ion. At what concentration of sulfate ion does a precipitate appear? Which compound will precipitate first, $PbSO_4$ or $BaSO_4$? *Ans.* $[SO_4^{=}]$, 1×10^{-7} *M*; $BaSO_4$

10. Calculate the solubility of $Al(OH)_3$ in mg. per 100 ml. What *p*H is required to just start the precipitation in a solution that contains 0.0269 gram $Al(OH)_3$ per 100 ml.? *Ans.* 2.9×10^{-5} *mg./100 ml.; pH* = *4*

CHAPTER **12**

Selected Gravimetric Determinations

In the previous chapter various methods of separation have been discussed, with special emphasis on precipitation methods. The determinations in this chapter have been selected to include a variety of types of precipitates, procedures, and principles. Each of the procedures that are presented is a practical laboratory method of analysis for the constituent listed. The choice of examples ranges from the determination of a single constituent with no interferences present to the analysis of more complex samples where interferences are present and where separation problems are encountered.

There are many other determinations that could have been selected, but it is felt that this group will illustrate the desired gravimetric principles and will give the student analyst an insight into the scope of some of the problems associated with gravimetric determinations.

SOLUBLE SULFATE

One of the most common gravimetric analyses is the determination of sulfur or barium by precipitation as barium sulfate, according to the reaction

$$Ba^{++} + SO_4^{=} \rightleftharpoons BaSO_4$$

Although the solubility of barium sulfate is very low, the purity of the precipitate is very low, which results in an accuracy that is not very great.

Properties of the Precipitate

The particle size of barium sulfate is usually very small, so fine that the precipitate will pass through all filter papers unless the conditions of precipitation are controlled. If cold concentrated solutions are used, a finely divided precipitate is obtained, but if the barium sulfate is precipitated from hot dilute solutions and a digestion period is used, a precipitate of larger particle size is obtained which may be easily filtered.

The slight solubility of barium sulfate in pure water is made even less by the common ion effect of an excess of barium ion or sulfate ion. The presence of hydrogen ion increases the solubility by decreasing the concentration of the sulfate ion by the formation of the bisulfate ion.

$$H^+ + SO_4^= \rightleftharpoons HSO_4^-$$

It is customary, regardless of the increased solubility in acid solution, to precipitate barium sulfate from a solution that contains a small amount of hydrochloric acid. The precipitate formed under these conditions is coarser and contains fewer impurities than the one formed in neutral solution. The presence of acid prevents the precipitation of barium salts that are insoluble in neutral solution (*e.g.*, barium carbonate, barium phosphate).

The contamination of the barium sulfate precipitate resulting from coprecipitation has been studied very extensively. Even though the precipitate is formed under the most favorable conditions, coprecipitation of nearly all of the constituents in the solution is possible. The presence of ions that have slightly soluble sulfates must be avoided. Of the salts of univalent cations present, the chlorides and sulfates are coprecipitated the least. The trivalent ions that are most likely to be present in solution are iron, aluminum, and chromium. Iron is coprecipitated to a large extent, usually as the basic sulfate, whereas aluminum and chromium are coprecipitated to a lesser degree. Chromium will, however, form a complex with the sulfate ion; thus it should be avoided wherever possible.

Since there is no solvent in which barium sulfate is soluble, a reprecipitation to lower the contamination is not possible. As it is impossible to remove all interfering substances prior to precipitation, proper conditions for precipitation and digestion must be used in order to minimize the contamination.

Errors

The errors in the determination resulting from coprecipitation may be positive or negative. The adsorption of barium chloride by barium sulfate precipitate will cause the results to be high. Adsorption of iron(III) ion as iron(III) sulfate will cause the results to be low. The loss of sulfur trioxide by volatilization during the ignition of the precipitate is the reason for the low results.

During the ignition of barium sulfate, difficulties can arise resulting from the reduction of the precipitate by carbon.

$$BaSO_4 + 4C \rightarrow BaS + 4CO$$

These errors can be minimized by careful ashing off of the filter paper and by having a ready access of air during the ashing off process. One means to eliminate this source of error is to use a porous base filtering crucible.

Pure barium sulfate can be ignited to temperatures up to 1400°C, but the presence of small amounts of impurities may cause appreciable amounts of decomposition at temperatures of 800°–900°C. Temperatures of 700°C–800°C are necessary to remove the water present in the precipitate.

Applications

This method can be used for the determination of barium and for all compounds containing sulfur that can be quantitatively oxidized to sulfate. To use a similar procedure for the quantitative determination of lead and strontium as sulfates, alcohol must be added to the solution to decrease their solubility. The use of this method for the standardization of sulfuric acid solutions is not recommended because of the errors due to coprecipitation.

Laboratory Experiment 21

Determination of Soluble Sulfate

Reagents

HCl

5% $BaCl_2$ solution

prepared by dissolving 5 grams of $BaCl_2 \cdot 2H_2O$ in 100 ml. of distilled water.

0.1 M $AgNO_3$ solution

Procedure

Dry the sample in an oven at 105°C for one hour. Into each of three 600 ml. beakers weigh accurately to the nearest tenth of a milligram three samples of approximately 0.5000 gram of the dried material. Dissolve each sample in about 400 ml. of distilled water to which has been added 1 ml. of concentrated hydrochloric acid. Heat the solution to boiling.

Calculate the volume of 5% $BaCl_2 \cdot 2H_2O$ solution to be added to each beaker, assuming the sample to be pure sodium sulfate. Add 10% in addition to the theoretical value.

Add the calculated volume of $BaCl_2 \cdot 2H_2O$ solution to the hot solution in successive 5 ml. portions with constant stirring. After the last addition, allow the precipitate to settle and test the supernatant liquid for completeness of precipitation.

After the precipitation is complete, cover the beaker with a watch glass and allow the precipitate to digest for a minimum of one hour or preferably overnight.

Filter the hot solution through Whatman No. 42 filter paper or its equivalent. Decant the clear supernatant solution through the filter. Rinse the precipitate in the beaker, using hot water, and wash the rinsings and precipitate into the funnel with hot water. Remove any precipitate from the walls of the beaker with a rubber policeman, and wash such particles into the filter with hot water. Rinse the precipitate with successive small portions of hot water until a portion of the filtrate does not give a chloride test using a drop of 0.1 M $AgNO_3$.

After the washing is complete, carefully fold the paper holding the precipitate and transfer it to a crucible previously brought to constant weight. Dry the precipitate carefully over a low flame. Ash off the paper carefully. Ignite the precipitate at the highest temperature of a Tirrill burner. The uncovered crucible should be slanted to allow free access of air so that reduction of the barium sulfate to barium sulfide is prevented. Cool and weigh the crucible and its contents, then reignite until constant weight is attained.

From the difference in weight of the empty crucible and the crucible and its contents, obtain the weight of the barium sulfate. The common practice is to report sulfur as percentage sulfur trioxide. From the weight of barium sulfate calculate and report the percentage of sulfur trioxide in the unknown sample.

IRON

The gravimetric methods for the determination of iron are seldom used in iron and steel analysis because of the accuracy and convenience of instrumental methods, but they are important in the analysis of minerals since iron and its related elements are separated by precipitation. Gravimetric methods offer valuable training to the student analyst in the handling of gelatinous precipitates. The procedure given for the determination of iron can be applied to those other trivalent ions that precipitate as hydrous oxides upon the addition of ammonia.

Iron as iron(III) ion, when treated with ammonia forms a gelatinous precipitate of hydrous iron(III) oxide according to the reaction

$$2Fe^{+++} + 6NH_3 + xH_2O \rightarrow Fe_2O_3{\cdot}yH_2O + 6NH_4^+$$

The composition of the precipitate is indefinite because of the water that is bound to it. On ignition the precipitate of hydrous oxide yields iron(III) oxide, Fe_2O_3, which can be weighed.

The determination of iron can be made by a single homogeneous precipitation, using basic iron formate solution and boiling with urea to raise the pH and precipitate the hydrous oxide.

Properties of Hydrous Iron(III) Oxide

Hydrous iron(III) oxide is very insoluble; thus precipitation is quantitative even from somewhat acid solution. As it is first formed, the precipitate is in a dispersed colloidal phase which can be coagulated in the presence of an electrolyte by heating. Prolonged heating causes the aggregates of the precipitate to break up and the resulting precipitate becomes slimy. A well coagulated precipitate can be filtered easily on porous paper. Washing of the precipitate is done by decantation. The filtration and washing can be accomplished with hot solutions without the loss of precipitate, as a consequence of the insolubility of the precipitate. Generally ammonium salts are added to the wash water to prevent dispersion of the coagulated precipitate.

Because of the gelatinous character of the precipitate, it is to be expected that the precipitate will be contaminated to a large extent by the adsorption of the ions present. The addition of a large excess of ammonium ions in the precipitating and wash solutions will minimize the adsorption of other positive ions. The ammonium ions are volatilized on ignition, so contamination by adsorption of foreign positive ions will be of little consequence. Since the precipitate is easily dissolved by acid, reprecipitation can be used to further minimize the contamination.

When the hydrous iron(III) oxide is formed by a homogeneous precipitation using the hydrolysis of urea, the particles are coarser and the contamination at a minimum so that a reprecipitation is usually unnecessary.

In order to drive off water from the hydrous iron(III) oxide, a temperature of about 1000°C is necessary. The iron(III) oxide is reduced rather easily to the magnetic oxide of iron, Fe_3O_4, by carbon or the reducing gases from the burning filter paper. To minimize this reduction and to allow the oxidation of any Fe_3O_4 formed, it is necessary to permit free access of air to the crucible while ashing off the paper.

Laboratory Experiment 22

Determination of Iron in a Limonite Ore

Discussion

Two procedures for the analysis of iron in a limonite ore, one requiring a double precipitation and the other employing homogeneous precipitation, are given in this experiment. It is interesting to apply both of these procedures to the determination of iron in the same ore sample, and to compare the final results of the analysis.

Reagents

6 *N* HCl

prepared by mixing equal volumes of concentrated hydrochloric acid and distilled water.

1:1 NH_4OH

prepared by mixing equal volumes of ammonium hydroxide and distilled water.

$1\%\ NH_4NO_3$

prepared by dissolving 1 gram ammonium nitrate in 100 ml. of distilled water.

HNO_3

concentrated nitric acid, analytical reagent grade.

HCl

concentrated hydrochloric acid, analytical reagent grade.

Procedure

From a weighing bottle containing the previously dried unknown ore, weigh to the nearest tenth of a milligram, three samples of about 0.5000 gram each into 400 ml. beakers. Add 10 ml. of water and 15–20 ml. concentrated hydrochloric acid to the ore in the beakers. Heat to just below boiling until all the dark particles are dissolved. A slight white residue of silica is usually present. Add 1 ml. of concentrated nitric acid to the solution dropwise and boil to oxidize any iron(II). Dilute the solution to 100 ml. with distilled water. Filter the solution into 600 ml. beakers. Wash the filter thoroughly with dilute hydrochloric acid (1 ml. of concentrated acid to 100 ml. of distilled water). Dilute the filtrate to 300 ml.

Heat the solution to boiling and add filtered 1:1 ammonium hydroxide solution slowly with constant stirring until the precipitate of hydrous iron(III) oxide coagulates. Boil the solution gently for one minute; then let the precipitate coagulate and settle from the hot solution. The supernatant liquid should be clear. As soon as most of the precipitate has settled, decant the hot supernatant liquid through a filter but leave as much of the precipitate in the original beaker as possible. Wash the precipitate twice by decantation, using 50 ml. of hot water for each wash. During the last wash transfer the bulk of the precipitate to the filter.

Replace the beaker containing the filtrate and washings from under the filter with the beaker from which the original precipitation was made. Dissolve the precipitate from the filter with hot 6 *N* hydrochloric acid. Use as little acid as possible. Examine the paper to be sure that all of the precipitate has been removed. Dilute the solution in the beaker to 200 ml., heat nearly to boiling, and precipitate the iron with filtered 1:1 ammonium hydroxide as before. Heat the solution for 1 minute and allow the coagulated precipitate to settle. As soon as most of the precipitate has settled, decant the hot supernatant liquid through the original filter paper after neutralizing the acid on the filter paper with a little ammonium hydroxide. Wash the precipitate twice by decantation using 50 ml. of hot water for each wash. During the second wash transfer the precipitate to the filter, using a rubber policeman to aid in the transferring of the last portions of the precipitate to the filter paper. Be sure that the precipitate has been quantitatively transferred to the filter. Wash the precipitate 5 or 6 times with hot 1% ammonium nitrate solution or until a 3 ml. portion of the wash solution shows only a faint turbidity with a drop of nitric acid and silver nitrate solution.

Remove the paper from the filter, fold the top of the filter paper over the precipitate, and transfer it cautiously to a crucible previously brought to constant weight. Dry the precipitate carefully over a low flame. Cautiously ash off the paper at the lowest possible temperature. Do not allow the flame to enter the crucible thus subjecting the contents to the reducing effects of the unburned gases. When the paper is fully ashed off, ignite the uncovered crucible to the full heat of a Meker burner for thirty minutes. Cool in a desiccator and weigh the crucible and its contents. Reignite the crucible until constant weight is attained.

From the weight of the iron(III) oxide, Fe_2O_3, obtained, calculate and report the percentage iron, Fe, in the sample.

Laboratory Experiment 23

Homogeneous Precipitation of Iron in Limonite Ore

Reagents

6 *N* HCl
: prepared by mixing equal volumes of concentrated hydrochloric acid and distilled water.

1:1 NH_4OH
: prepared by mixing equal volumes of ammonium hydroxide and distilled water.

1% NH_4NO_3
: prepared by dissolving 1 gram ammonium nitrate in 100 ml. of distilled water.

HCOOH
: formic acid (88–90%).

3% H_2O_2
: analytical reagent grade.

$CO(NH_2)_2$
: urea analytical reagent grade.

0.02% gelatin
: prepared by dissolving 0.020 gram gelatin in 100 ml. of boiling distilled water.

HCl
: concentrated hydrochloric acid, analytical reagent grade.

HNO_3
: concentrated nitric acid, analytical reagent grade.

Procedure

From a weighing bottle containing the previously dried unknown ore, weigh to the nearest tenth of a milligram, three samples of about 0.5000 gram each into 400 ml. beakers. Add 10 ml. of distilled water and 15–20 ml. concentrated hydrochloric acid to the ore in the beakers. Heat to just below boiling until all of the dark particles are dissolved. A slight white residue of silica is usually present. Add 1 ml. of concentrated nitric acid to the solution dropwise and boil to oxidize any iron(II). Dilute the solution to 100 ml. with distilled water. Filter the solution into a 600 ml. beaker. Wash the filter thoroughly with dilute hydrochloric acid (1 ml. of concentrated acid to 100 ml. of water). Dilute the filtrate to 300 ml.

Adjust the *p*H of the solution until the first precipitate of hydrous iron(III) oxide just begins to form by adding dropwise, from a medicine dropper, freshly filtered 1:1 ammonium hydroxide. A reddish brown cloudiness is not evidence of the precipitate. When a definite precipitate is observed, add concentrated hydrochloric acid dropwise, stirring and letting stand a minute or so after each 2 or 3 drops, until a clear solution is obtained again. Add 1.5 ml. of hydrochloric acid in excess.

Add 2 ml. of formic acid, HCOOH, (88–90%) and 10 grams of urea, $CO(NH_2)_2$, and mix well. Heat the solution to boiling. To prevent bumping during this stage, use a stirring rod with a 1 mm. indentation made with a carpet tack. Maintain the volume during boiling.

The precipitate should begin to appear 5–20 minutes after the boiling point is reached. If the precipitate does not appear within 30 minutes, a very few drops of 1:1 ammonium hydroxide may be added. Keep the solution at gentle boiling (a stream of bubbles should just issue from the stirring rod indentation) for $1\frac{1}{2}$ to 2 hours, until test paper indicates a *p*H of 4.0 or slightly greater has been reached.

Carefully add 5 ml. of 3% H_2O_2 and heat for an additional 2 or 3 minutes, then add 10 ml. of 0.02% gelatin solution.

Filter the precipitate on Whatman No. 40 filter paper. Remove the adherent precipitate from the beaker with a rubber policeman and transfer it to the filter. Wash 15 times with hot 1% ammonium nitrate solution.

Remove the paper from the filter and fold the top of the filter paper over the precipitate. Transfer the filter paper cautiously to a crucible previously brought to constant weight. Dry the precipitate over a low flame. Carefully ash off the filter paper at the lowest possible temperature. Do not allow the flame to enter the crucible thus subjecting the contents to the reducing effects of the unburned gases. Ignite the uncovered crucible to the full heat of a Meker burner for 30 minutes after the paper is fully ashed off. Cool in a desiccator and weigh the crucible and its contents. Reignite the crucible until constant weight is attained.

From the weight of the iron(III) oxide, Fe_2O_3, obtained, calculate and report the percentage of iron, Fe, in the sample.

NICKEL

In the discussion of the use of organic precipitating reagents in Chapter 11, the specificity of dimethylglyoxime for the determination of nickel both qualitatively and quantitatively was described.

The red colored precipitate of nickel dimethylglyoximate, $NiC_8H_{14}N_4O_4$, is a familiar confirmatory test for the presence of nickel. Where the amount of nickel in the sample is very small the absorption of the red colored solution can be used as a basis for the spectrophotometric determination of nickel. The determination of samples containing larger amounts of nickel can be accomplished by use of gravimetric procedures, such as precipitation using dimethylglyoxime. The precipitate obtained is very bulky and if the solution contains more than 0.1 gram of nickel, the bulkiness of the precipitate makes it inconvenient to handle.

Properties of the Precipitate

The precipitate is formed according to the reaction

$$Ni^{++} + 2\left[\begin{array}{c} CH_3—C{=}NOH \\ | \\ CH_3—C{=}NOH \end{array}\right] \rightarrow \begin{array}{ccccc} & & H & & \\ & O\nearrow & & \searrow O & \\ CH_3—C{=}N & & & & N{=}C—CH_3 \\ | & \searrow & & \swarrow & | \\ & & Ni & & \\ | & \nearrow & & \searrow & | \\ CH_3—C{=}N & & & & N{=}C—CH_3 \\ & \searrow O & & O\nearrow & \\ & & H & & \end{array} + 2H^+$$

Nickel dimethylglyoximate is quite insoluble in ammoniacal solution containing ammonium salts and an excess of dimethylglyoxime. Iron(II), palladium, and gold interfere. The iron(II) is oxidized to iron(III) and held in solution by the addition of tartaric acid to form soluble complexes of iron(III). Other trivalent ions that would form hydrous oxides in the presence of ammonia also are held in solution by complexing with tartaric acid. Ammonia must be present in large amounts to prevent the precipitation of the hydroxides of zinc, magnesium, and other bivalent ions.

Since dimethylglyoxime is insoluble in water and will precipitate out in aqueous solution (see page 191), the sodium salt of dimethylglyoxime, which is water soluble, can be used as the precipitating agent.

The coprecipitation of other ions with nickel dimethylglyoximate is surprisingly small. The determination is relatively simple and very accurate.

Laboratory Experiment 24

Determination of Nickel in Steel

Reagents

6 *N* HCl
: prepared by mixing equal volumes of concentrated hydrochloric acid and distilled water.

6 *N* HNO_3
: prepared by diluting 38.0 ml. of concentrated nitric acid to 100 ml. with distilled water.

1% Sodium dimethylglyoxim ate
: prepared by dissolving 1 gram of sodium dimethylglyoximate in 100 ml. of distilled water.

$C_4H_6O_6$
: tartaric acid reagent grade.

NH_4OH
: reagent grade.

Procedure

Prepare three Gooch crucibles and heat to constant weight in an oven set at 140°–150°C. Weigh to the nearest one tenth milligram a one gram sample of the unknown steel sample into a 400 ml. beaker. Cover with a watch glass and treat with 60 ml. of 6 *N* hydrochloric acid. Warm until the solvent action is complete. Add 10 ml. of 6 *N* nitric acid and boil until the iron and carbides are oxidized. Continue boiling to expel the oxides of nitrogen. Carefully transfer the contents of the beaker to a 250 ml. volumetric flask. Wash the beaker with several portions of distilled water. Combine the washings with original sample in the 250 ml. volumetric flask, and dilute to the mark with distilled water. Mix the contents well before taking aliquot parts.

Using a clean 50 ml. transfer pipet, transfer three 50 ml. aliquot portions to three 400 ml. beakers. Add 5 grams tartaric acid, neutralize with ammonium hydroxide, then add a slight excess of ammonium hydroxide. No precipitate should form at this point. Add hydrochloric acid until slightly acid, warm to about 70°C, and add 20 ml. of a 1% solution of sodium dimethylglyoximate. Then add ammonium hydroxide until slightly alkaline and allow to stand about 30 minutes.

Filter the mixture through a weighed Gooch crucible under gentle suction. Wash the precipitate thoroughly with hot water. The final wash is made with 95% ethyl alcohol.

Dry the precipitate at 140°–150°C in an oven to constant weight. Calculate the percentage nickel in the sample. The precipitate contains 20.32% nickel.

MAGNESIUM

The sample containing magnesium is dissolved in dilute hydrochloric acid and ammonium phosphate is added to the acid solution. As long as the solution is strongly acid, no precipitate will form. The precipitate of magnesium ammonium phosphate is obtained by making the solution basic with the slow addition of concentrated ammonium hydroxide. The precipitation of magnesium can be illustrated by the following equation:

$$Mg^{++} + HPO_4^{=} + NH_4OH \rightarrow MgNH_4PO_4 + H_2O$$

The coarsely crystalline precipitate forms slowly, requiring that the solution stand for several hours before being filtered.

Because of the solubility of magnesium ammonium phosphate, the precipitate is washed with dilute ammonium hydroxide (1:20) since this is the optimum concentration for minimum losses due to washing. The volume of wash liquid must be kept as small as possible to prevent excessive losses due to the aforementioned solubility of the precipitate.

The precipitate is ignited to constant weight and weighed as magnesium pyrophosphate, $Mg_2P_2O_7$.

Properties of the Precipitate

The solubility product of $MgNH_4PO_4$ can be expressed as

$$K_{sp} = [Mg^{++}][NH_4^+][PO_4^{\equiv}]$$

Both ammonium ions and phosphate ions hydrolyze according to the equations

$$NH_4^+ + H_2O \rightarrow NH_4OH + H^+$$
$$PO_4^{\equiv} + H_2O \rightarrow HPO_4^{=} + OH^-$$

As a result of this hydrolysis, it is more accurate to express the solubility product of $MgNH_4PO_4$ as

$$K_{sp} = [Mg^{++}][NH_4OH][HPO_4^{=}]$$

From the solubility product relationships expressed in this manner, it is evident that the concentration of NH_4OH rather than the NH_4^+ ion affects the solubility of the precipitate. In excess NH_4OH the solubility of the $MgNH_4PO_4$ precipitate is decreased.

Using small volumes and low temperatures as conditions for the precipitation causes errors resulting from coprecipitation effects. Therefore reprecipitation is necessary for the most accurate results.

If the solution containing the Mg^{++} is the filtrate from the calcium determination, large accumulations of ammonium ion and oxalate ion will be present. The large concentration of ammonium ion favors coprecipitation effects and a high concentration of oxalate ion retards the formation of the magnesium ammonium phosphate precipitate. Both of these interferences can be removed by oxidation using concentrated nitric acid. The ammonium ion will be oxidized to nitrogen and oxides of nitrogen and the oxalate ion will go to carbon dioxide.

Laboratory Experiment 25

Determination of Magnesium

Reagents

$(NH_4)_2HPO_4$
diammonium hydrogen phosphate, analytical reagent grade.

NH_4OH
ammonium hydroxide, analytical reagent grade.

NH_4OH (1:20)
prepared by adding one part concentrated ammonium hydroxide to nineteen parts distilled water.

HCl
hydrochloric acid, analytical reagent grade.

2 *N* HCl
prepared by adding 16 ml. of concentrated hydrochloric acid to 84 ml. distilled water.

Methyl red indicator solution
prepared by dissolving 0.1 gram methyl red in 60 ml. of ethyl alcohol and diluting to 100 ml. with distilled water.

Procedure

Into three 250 ml. beakers weigh to the nearest tenth of a milligram triplicate samples of the unknown that has been previously dried at 100–105°C. Cover each beaker with a watch glass. Slide the watch glass aside and add 20 ml. of distilled water and 5 ml. of concentrated hydrochloric acid to each beaker. If all of the solid has not dissolved when the evolution of gas ceases, warm the covered beaker gently until all of the solid goes into solution. Rinse off the watch glass with distilled water. Rinse down the sides of the beaker using a jet of distilled water. Dilute the solution in each beaker to 150 ml. and cool to room temperature or below. Continue the determination by omitting the next paragraph.

If the determination of magnesium is to be made on the combined filtrates from the precipitation of calcium, then the following procedure is to be used.

To the combined filtrates from the precipitation of calcium, add 50 ml. of concentrated nitric acid and evaporate the solution to dryness. If on evaporation a large residue of ammonium salts remains, add 20 ml. of water, 30 ml. of concentrated nitric acid and 15 ml. of concentrated hydrochloric acid. Evaporate this solution to dryness. To the residue that remains after evaporation add 10 ml. of concentrated hydrochloric acid. Add 40 ml. of distilled water and warm the solution. Examine the solution for silica residue. If it is present, filter through a small filter and wash well with hot distilled water. Add the washings to the main filtrate. Dilute the filtrate to 150 ml. with distilled water and cool to room temperature or below.

To each beaker add 3 grams of diammonium hydrogen phosphate dissolved in a small quantity of distilled water. At this point no precipitate should appear. To each solution add 4–6 drops of methyl red indicator solution. To each clear solution cooled in a bath of ice water, add dropwise with vigorous agitation concentrated ammonium hydroxide until the color of the solution becomes yellow. Add to each beaker a volume of concentrated ammonium hydroxide approximately one-twentieth that of the solution. Allow the solutions to stand for four hours or preferably overnight.

Decant the supernatant liquid through a porous base filtering crucible previously brought to constant weight. Transfer the phosphate precipitate quantitatively to the filtering crucible. Wash the precipitate with 1:20 ammonium hydroxide.

Dry the crucible and its contents in an oven set at 100–105°C. Place the porous base crucible inside a porcelain crucible and ignite both crucibles carefully to the full heat of a Meker burner to constant weight.

From the weight of the magnesium pyrophosphate, $Mg_2P_2O_7$, calculate and report the percentage of MgO in the sample.

Brass

Brass is one of the most important of the nonferrous metals. It is an alloy of copper and zinc usually containing varied amounts of tin, lead, and iron. Small amounts of other elements may be present as impurities. The procedure to be described can also be used for the analysis of bronze. Bronze is an alloy of copper and tin with smaller amounts of other elements present either as impurities or added to give specific properties to the alloy.

General Outline of Analysis

A single portion of the sample is used for the determination of copper, zinc, tin, and iron. The sample of the alloy is treated with nitric acid to bring copper, zinc, lead, and iron into solution. The tin is precipitated as the hydrous oxide and weighed as such. The filtrate is treated with sulfuric acid and evaporated to fumes to expel all the nitric acid. Distilled water is added to the residual liquid and lead sulfate remains undissolved. The precipitate is filtered, washed, and ignited at a low temperature and weighed as lead sulfate. The filtrate from the lead determination is electrolyzed to deposit the copper on a platinum gauze cathode. The iron and the zinc remain in solution. The solution remaining after the electrolysis is treated with bromine to oxidize the iron to iron(III). Iron then can be separated by precipitation with ammonium hydroxide. The hydrous iron(III) oxide is ignited to iron(III) oxide and weighed as such. The solution from the iron determination is treated with diammonium hydrogen phosphate. The precipitate is carefully ignited to zinc pyrophosphate and weighed.

Tin

When the sample of the alloy is dissolved in nitric acid, a precipitate of hydrous tin(IV) oxide is formed as the other constituents go into solution. The reaction can be written

$$3Sn + 4HNO_3 + H_2O \rightarrow 3SnO_2{\cdot}H_2O + 4NO$$

The precipitate is filtered off and ignited to tin(IV) oxide. The solution of the sample is an illustration of a means of separating one component, the tin, from the remainder of the solution by utilizing differences in solubility in the solvent.

Tin(IV) oxide is easily reduced to metallic tin; therefore, care must be taken during the ashing off of the filter paper to prevent this reduction. The ashing off procedure should be conducted at as low a temperature as possible. The reducing gases of the flame should not have access to the precipitate in the crucible. The precipitate will be white if it is pure. Any color of the precipitate indicates the presence of reduction products and/or ignition products of the coprecipitated ions that were not completely removed by the washing procedure.

Lead

The sample solution, after the tin has been removed, is acidified with sulfuric acid and evaporated until the fumes of sulfur trioxide appear. Since the solubility of lead sulfate is increased considerably if nitrate ions are present, it is necessary to remove all of the nitric acid. The appearance of sulfur trioxide fumes indicates that this has been accomplished. The solution is then diluted and the insoluble lead sulfate precipitates. The precipitate is filtered using a Gooch crucible or a porous base filtering crucible, since filter paper is not recommended for use.

The ignition of the precipitate is conducted at 500°C. Above this temperature lead sulfate will decompose with the loss of sulfur trioxide.

Lead, in samples containing small amounts, can be determined simultaneously with copper electrogravimetrically. With large percentages of lead it is preferable to remove the lead as the sulfate prior to the electrolytic deposition of copper.

Copper

Generally in the analytical procedure for brass, the copper is removed electrolytically after the removal of lead. If properly carried out this is one of the most accurate determinations in analytical chemistry. The copper(II) ions, in the presence of moderately low hydrogen ion concentration, will be reduced at the cathode. If the conditions are correct, a smooth, closely adhering plate will result. The necessary conditions are described in the discussion of electrogravimetric separations in Chapter 16.

Addition of a small amount of nitric acid to the sulfuric acid solution from the lead determination is necessary to obtain a good plate. The nitrate ions present in solution act as a depolarizer and are reduced in part at the cathode to nitrite ions, according to the equation

$$NO_3^- + 2H^+ + 2e \rightarrow NO_2^- + H_2O$$

The resulting nitrous acid that is formed tends to hold back the deposition of copper at the cathode as well as to dissolve the copper before the electrode can be removed and washed. Urea, added in small amounts, can be used to remove any nitrous acid formed as shown by the equation

$$2HNO_2 + CO(NH_2)_2 \rightarrow 2N_2 + CO_2 + 3H_2O$$

If the equipment for electrogravimetric separation is not available, the copper may be determined by a gravimetric method based on the precipitation of copper as copper(I) thiocyanate.

Iron

After the copper has been removed, the solution is treated with bromine water to oxidize any iron(II) ions to iron(III) ions. The solution is boiled to destroy the excess bromine and the hydrous iron(III) oxide is precipitated with ammonium hydroxide. An indication as to the complete removal of copper is available at this point since the blue color of the copper(II)-ammonia complex ion will appear if copper still remains in solution.

The precipitate of hydrous iron(III) oxide is then filtered, ignited to the oxide, and weighed in the manner described earlier in the gravimetric procedure for iron (see page 211).

Zinc

In many analyses zinc is determined "by difference." The sum of the percentages of the tin, lead, copper, and iron is subtracted from 100, giving the percentage of zinc. It is preferable to determine the zinc directly in case there might be an error in one of the previous determinations.

Zinc is precipitated as zinc ammonium phosphate, $ZnNH_4PO_4 \cdot 6H_2O$, from a nearly neutral solution. Use is made of the buffer system made up of the two phosphates formed to keep the solution at a *p*H near 7 during the precipitation. The following equations illustrate the action of this system.

$$Zn^{++} + NH_4^+ + HPO_4^{=} + 6H_2O \rightarrow ZnNH_4PO_4 \cdot 6H_2O + H^+$$
$$H^+ + HPO_4^{=} \rightarrow H_2PO_4^-$$

A flocculent precipitate of zinc phosphate is obtained initially and, as the digestion period progresses, the crystalline double salt is formed. The precipitate is ignited to zinc pyrophosphate, $Zn_2P_2O_7$, and weighed as such.

This procedure is analogous to the precipitation of magnesium, except that zinc ammonium phosphate is soluble in excess ammonium hydroxide as well as in acids. During the ignition a reducing atmosphere must be avoided to prevent the reduction of the pyrophosphate. Care should be taken during the initial part of the ignition to prevent mechanical loss of the precipitate due to the expulsion of ammonia gas.

Laboratory Experiment 26

Procedure for Analysis of a Brass Alloy

Apparatus

Electrolysis apparatus
Platinum gauze cathode
Platinum paddle anode

Reagents

6 N HNO_3
prepared by diluting 38.0 ml. of concentrated nitric acid with distilled water to 100 ml.

0.3 N HNO_3
prepared by diluting 2.0 ml. of concentrated nitric acid with distilled water to 100 ml.

0.3 N H_2SO_4
prepared by diluting 1.0 ml. of concentrated sulfuric acid with distilled water to 100 ml.

6 *N* NH_4OH

prepared by diluting 40 ml. of concentrated ammonium hydroxide with distilled water to 100 ml.

Methyl red

prepared by dissolving 0.1 gram of methyl red indicator powder in 60 ml. of ethyl alcohol and diluting with distilled water to 100 ml.

$(NH_4)_2HPO_4$

20% solution, prepared by adding 20 grams of $(NH_4)_2HPO_4$ to 100 ml. of distilled water. 1% solution prepared by adding 1 gram of $(NH_4)_2HPO_4$ to 100 ml. of distilled water.

C_2H_5OH

50% solution, prepared by diluting 50 ml. of C_2H_5OH to 100 ml. with distilled water.

$CO(NH_2)_2$

analytical reagent grade.

Procedure

Weigh accurately to the nearest one tenth of a milligram three samples, each of one gram of the alloy turnings, into three 250 ml. beakers. If necessary, wash the turnings with diethyl ether to remove any oily matter and dry to remove any residual ether. (The brass samples usually provided for student analysis do not require this washing.) Add 35 ml. of 6 *N* HNO_3, cover the beaker with a watch glass, and warm gently. As soon as the reaction has ceased, wash down the sides of the beaker and the bottom of the watch glass with distilled water. Slowly evaporate the solution on a low temperature hot plate or steam bath to about 5 ml. Do not allow the mixture to go to dryness. When the volume of the solution has reached about 5 ml. (usually about an hour is required), dilute to 40 ml. with distilled water and heat to boiling. Hold the solution to just below boiling for about 15 minutes. Add a small quantity of ashless filter pulp to aid in the filtration procedure. Filter the hot solution through a "slow" ashless filter paper (Whatman No. 42, for example). Wash the precipitate repeatedly, 10 to 12 times, with hot 0.3 *N* HNO_3. Add the washings to the main filtrate and save for the lead determination. Transfer the filter paper and precipitate to a porcelain crucible previously brought to constant weight. Dry the paper and precipitate over a small flame and then ash off the paper carefully at as low a temperature as possible. During the time of the removal of the paper free circulation of air is maintained. Insert the crucible through a hole in an asbestos board and ignite the precipitate in an open crucible to the highest temperature of the Meker burner for about 30 minutes. Reignite the precipitate to constant weight.

Weigh the precipitate as SnO_2, calculate and report the percentage of tin, Sn, in the alloy.

Determination of Lead

To the filtrate from the tin determination, add 3 ml. of concentrated H_2SO_4. Evaporate the solution until dense white fumes of SO_3 appear. Do not carry the evaporation beyond the appearance of white fumes. Caution in heating is necessary just prior to the appearance of the fumes to eliminate the danger of loss by spattering. Cool, add 50 ml. of distilled water, and heat just below the boiling point for 10 minutes. Cool to room temperature and filter through a Gooch crucible previously brought to constant weight. Wash the precipitate with 0.3 N H_2SO_4. Add the washings to the main filtrate and save for the copper determination.

Place the Gooch crucible in a larger procelain crucible and ignite the outer crucible to the faintest visible redness and complete the ignition at this temperature for about 30 minutes. Care must be taken that oxidizing conditions prevail since the precipitate is reducible. Repeat the ignition until constant weight is attained. Weigh the precipitate as $PbSO_4$. Calculate and report the percentage of lead, Pb, in the alloy.

Determination of Copper

Adjust the volume of the filtrate from the lead determination to 150 ml. Add 1 ml. of concentrated HNO_3. Connect the electrodes to the electrolysis apparatus so that the platinum gauze electrode is the cathode and the paddle electrode is the anode. Place the cathode and the anode into the solution such that the cathode is about three-quarters immersed in the solution. Start the rotating mechanism and electrolyze at 1.5 amp. until the solution becomes colorless. Add a pinch of urea and continue electrolysis for 10 minutes. Raise the beaker or add distilled water so that the level of the solution in the beaker is raised about one-quarter of an inch. Continue the electrolysis for 10 minutes. At the end of this time, examine the cathode to determine whether a deposit of copper is obtained on the newly submerged platinum surface. If a copper deposit is obtained, raise the level of the solution again and electrolyze for 10 minutes. After this period of time, observe whether a deposit has formed.

After all of the copper has been removed from the solution, turn off the rotating mechanism. Slowly remove the electrodes from the solution, washing the cathode with a stream of distilled water during the removal operation. When the electrodes are completely out of the solution, turn off the current. Wash both electrodes well and add the washings to the main solution, which is to be used for the determination of the iron and zinc.

Dip the cathode bearing the copper deposit in alcohol and place it in a drying oven set at 100°–105°C until dry (about 3–4 minutes). The drying time should not be longer than 5 minutes since the copper plate will become coated with a thin layer of oxide if left in the oven for a longer period of time. Cool the cathode in a desiccator and weigh. Calculate the percentage of copper, Cu, in the alloy.

Determination of Iron

Add 1 ml. of bromine water to the solution from the electrolysis of copper and heat until the excess bromine is volatilized. The bromine oxidizes the iron(II) to iron(III). The excess must be destroyed so that it will not oxidize the indicator used in the subsequent determination of zinc. After removing the excess bromine, add concentrated ammonium hydroxide dropwise until the precipitate of $Zn(OH)_2$ that first forms redissolves, leaving only a slightly reddish precipitate of hydrous iron(III) oxide. If the solution becomes blue upon the addition of the ammonium hydroxide, the copper was not completely removed from the solution. Filter off the precipitate using filter paper. Wash the precipitate several times with hot water, returning the washings to the original solution. Test a small portion of the last washing with a dilute solution of $(NH_4)_2S$ to be sure that the zinc ions have been completely removed. Ignite the precipitate in a porcelain crucible previously brought to constant weight for 30 minutes. Reignite the precipitate to constant weight and weigh as iron(III) oxide, Fe_2O_3. Calculate and report the percentage of iron, Fe, in the alloy.

Determination of Zinc

Add a drop or two of methyl red indicator solution to the filtrate from the iron determination. Acidify the solution with 6 N HNO_3. Concentrate the solution to 150 ml. Adjust the acidity of the solution until the color of the indicator just changes to yellow, by dropwise addition of either 6 N HNO_3 or 6 N NH_4OH, whichever is needed. It is very important that this point be not overstepped in either direction. Heat the solution to just below boiling and pour in slowly about 30 ml. of a freshly prepared 20% solution of diammonium hydrogen phosphate. Keep the solution just below boiling for about 15 minutes, stirring frequently. Allow the solution to cool for about four hours, although standing a longer time does no harm. Filter the zinc ammonium phosphate using a porous base filtering crucible that has been previously brought to constant weight. Test the main filtrate by adding NH_4OH and $(NH_4)_2S$.

Wash the precipitate several times with a 1% solution of diammonium hydrogen phosphate. Wash five times with 50% alcohol.

Dry the crucible in a drying oven. Place the crucible inside an ordinary crucible and heat the outer crucible gradually to the full heat of the Meker burner. Continue heating at the full heat of the Meker burner for 30 minutes. Weigh and reignite the crucible until the crucible attains constant weight. Weigh the precipitate as $Zn_2P_2O_7$ and calculate the percentage of zinc, Zn, in the alloy.

The analysis of the brass sample is finally reported in terms of the percentages of tin, lead, copper, iron, and zinc.

Problems

1. What volume of barium chloride solution containing 5% $BaCl_2 \cdot 2H_2O$ is required to precipitate the sulfate as $BaSO_4$ from a solution containing 0.5000 gram of pure $Na_2SO_4 \cdot 10H_2O$? *Ans. 7.57 ml.*

2. A sample of hematite containing 63.5% Fe_2O_3 is dissolved in acid, the iron oxidized to Fe(III) and precipitated with ammonia. The $Fe(OH)_3$ formed is filtered, washed, and ignited to Fe_2O_3 which weighs 0.4950 gram. What was the weight of the original sample? *Ans. 0.780 gram*

3. How many milliliters of ammonia water of specific gravity 0.930 containing 18.64% NH_3 by weight are required to precipitate the iron from a 0.500 gram sample of limonite ore containing 37.5% Fe_2O_3 after the iron has been oxidized from Fe(II) to Fe(III)? *Ans. 1.40 ml.*

4. A sample of ore weighing 1.000 gram yields a precipitate with dimethylglyoxime weighing 1.1150 grams. What is the percentage of nickel in the ore? *Ans. 22.7%*

5. A sample of steel containing nickel was dissolved in acid, tartaric acid added, and the nickel precipitated from the ammoniacal solution using dimethylglyoxime. What weight of dried glyoxime precipitate would be obtained from a 5 gram sample of steel containing 1.19% nickel? *Ans. 0.293 gram*

6. What is the percentage of nickel in a nickel steel if the weight of the dimethylglyoxime precipitate is 1.2 times the weight of the sample taken for analysis? *Ans. 24.4%*

7. A brass sample weighing 0.750 gram contains 74.63% copper, 22.40% zinc, and 2.97% lead. What weight of zinc pyrophosphate would be obtained? What would be the gain in weight of the cathode in the electrolysis of the acid solution after the removal of the lead? What weight of $PbSO_4$ would be obtained? *Ans. 0.391 gram; 0.560 gram; 0.0334 gram*

8. In the analysis of a brass containing 27.0% zinc, what volume of a 20% solution of diammonium hydrogen phosphate would be required to precipitate the zinc from a 1.500 gram sample? What weight of zinc pyrophosphate would be obtained upon heating the $ZnNH_4PO_4$ precipitate? *Ans. 2.04 ml.; 0.947 gram*

PART IV

INTRODUCTION TO INSTRUMENTAL METHODS OF ANALYSIS

CHAPTER 13

Absorption Spectroscopy

Although methods that depend on the absorption of electromagnetic radiation have been known for years, it is only since about 1940 that these techniques have been numbered among the routine methods used by the analytical chemist. They have been classed as absorptiometric methods. Measurements have been made in the visible, ultraviolet, infrared, microwave, and x-ray regions of the spectrum. Major advances in instrumentation and the availability of a variety of commercial instruments have been primarily responsible for this important expansion in absorption spectroscopy.

Absorptiometric methods are used in the identification, determination of the concentrations of components in mixtures, and for the calculation of molecular constants. Thus, absorptiometric methods are among the most important tools of the chemist.

NATURE OF SPECTRA

Regions of the Spectrum

The electromagnetic spectrum is commonly divided into regions as shown in Figure 13.1.

The visible portion of the spectrum is contained within a region of wavelengths from about 7000 A. (Angstrom) in the red portion to about 4000 A. in the violet.* The ultraviolet portion is generally considered to be the region between 4000 A. and 2000 A. The far ultraviolet region, also called the vacuum ultraviolet, is that region below 2000 A. The vacuum ultraviolet merges into the soft x-ray region at about 100 A. The infrared region of the spectrum is subdivided into the near infrared and the far infrared. The near infrared extends from about 7000 A. (0.7μ) to 15μ. From 15μ to about 250μ is generally considered the far infrared.

Absorption that occurs in the ultraviolet region of the spectrum and in the visible region of the spectrum will be referred to as **absorption in the ultraviolet** and **absorption in the visible** in the remainder of this discussion of absorption spectroscopy.

* See page 234 for a discussion of the Angstrom, A.

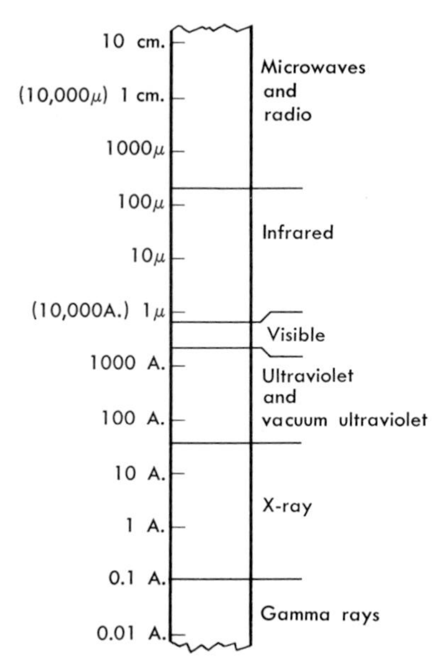

Fig. 13.1. The electromagnetic spectrum.

Origin of Absorption Spectra

All electromagnetic energy appears to be composed of discrete bundles of energy called **photons** or **quanta.** The energy of the photon is proportional to the frequency. Photons of equal energy content constitute radiation of one wavelength or frequency, and this property is dependent upon the energy of the photon. The energy of a photon can be expressed as

$$E = h\nu$$

where E represents the energy of a photon in ergs, h is Planck's constant with a value of 6.62×10^{-27} erg-seconds, and ν is the frequency of the radiation in cycles per second.

The frequency is related to the wavelength as follows:

$$\lambda\nu = c$$

where c is the velocity of light through a vacuum in cm./sec. and λ is the wavelength measured in cm.

When radiation is absorbed by matter, the absorption takes place in discrete units. Thus,

$$h\nu = E' - E'' = \Delta E$$

where E' is the energy of the higher energy state after absorption of a photon of radiant energy, and E'' is the energy of the lower state, often the ground state, of the matter.

Radiation is absorbed by matter only when the energy content of the photon corresponds to some energy requirement of the substance with which it interacts. These requirements depend on the electronic structure of the molecules.

The absorbed energy can be used to increase the vibrational and rotational energy of the molecules. The photon of energy can also excite electrons to a higher energy level. The latter may include increases in vibrational and rotational energy. The total energy of a molecule can be considered to be composed of the sum of the translational, electronic, rotational, and vibrational energies of the molecule. In absorptiometric theory the contribution of translational energy to the overall energy of the molecule is of little interest. Absorption of energy from the electromagnetic spectrum can only accompany a change in the molecule which involves a change in the electrical moment such as: changes in electron distribution–electronic energy; separation between two nuclei–vibrational energy; rotation of dipole–rotational energy. There is no interest at this point in the final fate of the energy; rather the interest is in the process responsible for absorption.

When a difference in energy between the ground state and some higher excited state is the same as the energy of the photons used to irradiate the molecule, absorption will take place. The molecule is capable of absorbing energy only in discrete amounts. If there is an appreciable difference between the energy of the photon and the energy separation between the ground state and higher excited state of the molecule, no absorption occurs.

Figure 13.2 gives a pictorial representation of electronic, vibrational, and rotational energy changes.

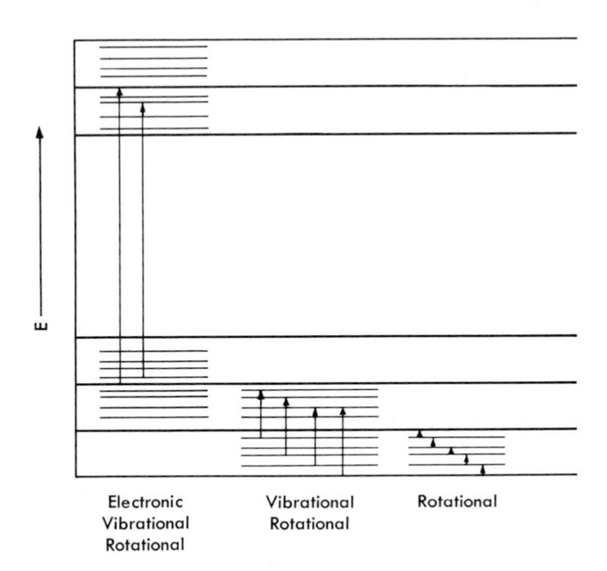

Fig. 13.2. Schematic diagram of energy changes.

Relationship to Molecular Structure

Neglecting translational motion, the total energy, E, of the molecule can be expressed as

$$E = E_{el} + E_{vib} + E_{rot}$$

where E_{el} is defined as electronic energy, E_{vib} is the vibrational energy and E_{rot} is the rotational energy of the molecule.

Electronic energy transitions require photons of high energy. These photons are available in the ultraviolet. Substances that have rather loosely bound electrons show absorption in the far ultraviolet. Valence electrons and bonding electrons that can be raised to a higher energy state absorb radiation that is in the ultraviolet and visible portion of the spectrum. As can be seen from Figure 13.2, the energy levels corresponding to electronic transitions within the molecule are much farther apart than are the vibrational or rotational levels, therefore requiring photons of higher energy to accomplish the transition. The absorption is also dependent on the electronic structure of the molecule in the ground state. Groups within the molecule that absorb visible and/or ultraviolet radiation are called **chromophoric groups.** Unsaturated carbon-carbon linkages, azo linkages, the nitro group, the permanganate ion, and the dichromate ion are examples of chromophoric groups.

Vibrational energy transitions result when the absorption of radiation causes changes in the energy of molecular vibration. The energy is absorbed in discrete amounts and in the amounts that are permitted within the molecule. The energy differences are much less than electronic transitions but approximately 100 times greater than those in rotational spectra. Generally a change in vibrational energy is accompanied by changes in rotational energies. The energy differences between rotational levels are of the magnitude of the photons in the infrared portion of the spectrum. Vibrational spectra appear as discrete lines rather than a continuous band.

Rotational transitions are quantized; only certain discrete values of rotational energy are possessed by the molecules. The energy differences are so small that absorption of photons from the far infrared and microwave regions is all that can take place.

The position of the absorption bands in the scale of wavelengths depends on the energies involved in the transitions within the molecule. The complexity of the spectrum increases as the analyst goes from the ultraviolet to the visible to the infrared portion of the spectrum. The correlation between the structure of molecules and their absorption spectra is an important and interesting topic but is beyond the scope of this text. More complete discussion of these two subjects can be found in references listed at the end of this chapter.

SPECTROMETRY NOMENCLATURE

At the present time there can be found in the literature many symbols and terms used to present absorptiometric data. Several systems have been proposed but, as yet, no one system has been universally adopted by textbook writers and all current journals. Since it is necessary to choose a system, the nomenclature suggested by the advisory board of *Analytical Chemistry*, set forth in *Anal. Chem.* **33,** 1968 (1961), has been selected.

Absorbance

Absorbance, A, is the negative logarithm to the base 10 of the transmittance. Thus,

$$A = -\log T \qquad \text{or} \qquad A = \log 1/T \tag{13.1}$$

When a standard is used for comparison, the absorbance, A, of the standard is defined as zero. The standard must be specified whenever absorbance data are given. To convert $\%T$ (percent transmittance) values to absorbance values, the following relationship can be used.

$$A = 2 - \log \%T$$

This expression can be derived as follows:

$$\begin{aligned} \%T &= 100\, I/I_0 \\ I/I_0 &= T \\ \frac{\%T}{100} &= T \\ A &= -\log T \\ A &= -\log \frac{\%T}{100} \\ A &= -\log \%T - (-\log 100) \\ A &= 2 - \log \%T \end{aligned} \tag{13.2}$$

Absorptivity

Absorptivity, a, is defined as the absorbance, A, divided by the product of the length of the sample (b) in centimeters and the concentration, c, in grams per liter.

$$a = \frac{A}{bc} \tag{13.3}$$

The product of the absorptivity, a, and the molecular weight of the substance is the Molar Absorptivity, ϵ.

Angstrom

The Angstrom, A., is a unit of length equal to 1/6438.4696 of the wavelength of the red line of cadmium. It is considered to be approximately equal to 10^{-8} cm.

Band Width

Band width is described as the span of the group of wavelengths of radiant energy emerging from the monochromator. For any practical monochromator, the light that emerges is a group of wavelengths rather than a single wavelength.

Frequency

Frequency, ν, is the number of cycles per unit time.

Transmittance

Transmittance, T, is the ratio of the radiant energy transmitted by the sample, I, to the radiant energy incident upon the sample, I_0. Both I and I_0 must be obtained at the same wavelength with the same spectral slit width. This ratio can be expressed as follows:

$$T = \frac{I}{I_0} \tag{13.4}$$

Transmittance is usually given in percent which is

$$\%T = 100 \frac{I}{I_0} \tag{13.5}$$

In general practice, the transmittance of the sample is compared to the transmittance of a standard solution. The comparison can be made using the same cell or two cells that are matched. The percent transmittance of the standard is defined as 100%. Using this method, the standard to which the sample is compared must be specified whenever the transmittance of the sample is given.

Micron

The micron, μ, is a unit of wavelength equal to 10^{-4} cm.

Millimicron

The millimicron, mμ, is equal to one-thousandth of a micron and approximately equal to 10 A.

Wavelength

Wavelength, λ, is the distance measured along the line of propagation between two points that are in phase on adjacent waves.

Wave Number

Wave number, $\tilde{\nu}$, is defined as the number of waves per unit length expressed in reciprocal centimeters, cm^{-1}.

It is important when reading the literature concerned with absorption spectroscopy that the reader be absolutely certain of the definition of terms and symbols used by the author.

Since analytical chemists generally present absorption data by plotting absorbance, A, as the ordinate and wavelength in millimicrons, mμ, as the abscissa, the figures in this text will be presented in this manner.

LAWS OF ABSORPTION

Bouguer's Law

Bouguer formulated one of the fundamental laws upon which are based the quantitative principles of absorptiometry. This law gives the relationship between the absorbance and the thickness of the absorbing medium. As a beam of parallel monochromatic radiation passes through an absorbing medium, each layer of equal thickness absorbs an equal fraction of the light which traverses it. Bouguer's Law can be expressed mathematically as follows:

$$\log \frac{I_0}{I} = Kb \qquad \textbf{(13.6)}$$

where K is a constant depending on the nature of the medium, the wavelength, and the concentration of the solution; b is the thickness of the absorbing medium, which is the sample path length measured in centimeters; I_0 is the intensity of incident radiation, and I is the intensity of the radiation emerging from the absorbing medium. The absorbance $\left(\log \frac{I_0}{I}\right)$ varies directly with the thickness.

Beer's Law

The second fundamental law of absorptiometry, as stated by Beer, gives the relationship between absorbance and the concentration of the absorbing substance in a solution. Beer's Law can be stated as

$$\log \frac{I_0}{I} = Kc \qquad \textbf{(13.7)}$$

where K is a constant depending on wavelength, the nature of the absorbing solution, and the sample thickness. The light must be reasonably monochromatic and the nature of the absorbing material must be the same in solutions of different concentrations if the absorbance is to be directly proportional to the concentration. Any factors that affect the nature of the absorbing substances will cause a change in absorbance. Examples of these factors are association of the absorbing substance with the solvent, ionization or dissociation. The change in absorbance due to the dilution of a solution of dichromate ion with water involving the following equilibrium is a very familiar example.

$$Cr_2O_7^{=} + H_2O \rightleftarrows 2HCrO_4^{-} \rightleftarrows 2H^{+} + 2CrO_4^{=}$$

Beer-Bouguer Law or Beer-Lambert Law

A combination of Beer's Law and Bouguer's (Lambert's) Law, sometimes called the Beer-Lambert Law or simply Beer's Law can be stated as

$$\log \frac{I_0}{I} = abc \qquad \textbf{(13.8)}$$

where a, the absorptivity, is a constant depending only on the wavelength of the radiation and the nature of the solution. Figure 13.3 gives a schematic representation of the transmission of radiation through the sample solution.

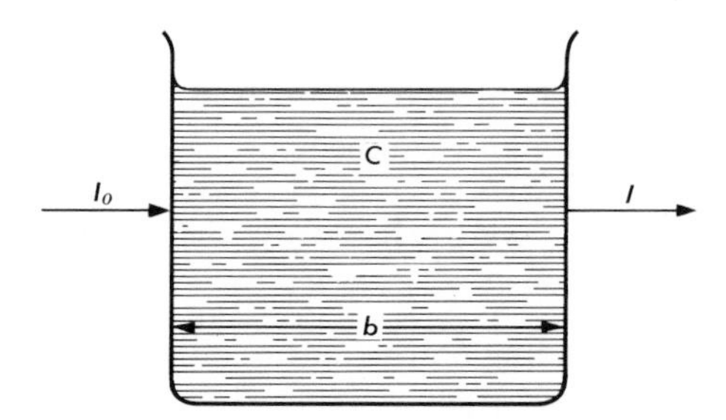

Fig. 13.3. Transmission of radiation through a solution.

The use of the Beer-Lambert Law to determine the concentration of an unknown absorbing substance requires that the incident radiation be monochromatic or nearly so and that the nature of the absorbing substance be the same in the unknown and in the standards that were prepared for comparison. It is not practical in the design of commercial spectrophotometers to produce purely monochromatic radiation. Therefore, when using the Beer-Lambert Law for quantitative application of data obtained from commercial instruments, it is necessary that a wavelength be selected where the absorptivity is nearly constant. The wavelength at which an absorption maximum or transmittance minimum occurs will fulfill this requirement. It is also best when the concentrations of the standards used are near the concentration of the substance desired. Generally, if the absorbance, A, or the log $\%T$ is plotted versus concentration and a straight line can be drawn passing through these points and the origin (in the case of absorbance) or 100% (in the case of log $\%T$), the requirements of the Beer-Lambert Law have been satisfied.

Beer's Law Applied to Color Comparators

Applying Beer's Law to color comparators, it can be shown that the following relationship is true.

$$b_1c_1 = b_2c_2 \tag{13.9}$$

where c_1 = concentration of the standard solution
c_2 = concentration of the unknown solution
b_1 = length of the light path of the standard
b_2 = length of the light path of the unknown

The concentration of the standard solution, c_1, is known. The length of the sample of the standard, b_1, and the unknown, b_2, can be obtained from the color comparator. Having these data, the concentration of the unknown solution, c_2, can be calculated from the relationship

$$c_2 = \frac{c_1b_1}{b_2}$$

Deviations from Beer's Law

Since there are no known exceptions to Bouguer's Law, any failure of the combination of Bouguer's Law and Beer's Law indicates that the system is not being adequately explained by Beer's Law. The explanation of the deviations due to Beer's Law can be divided into two parts: (1) chemical deviations, and (2) instrumental deviations.

Chemical deviations of a system from Beer's Law generally result from the fact that the analyst is not measuring the concentration of the absorbing species of the ion or molecule that is in the solution. In the previous discussion of Beer's Law (see page 236), it was shown that any factor that affects the nature of the absorbing species will cause a change in absorbance. Systems in which any solvent interaction with the absorbing ion or molecule occurs, systems containing weak bases or weak acids, or those systems which are involved in any equilibrium changes that result in absorbance changes will all be expected to show deviation from Beer's Law.

Instrumental deviations are usually concerned with the degree of purity of the monochromatic light. The width of the band pass has an effect on this apparent deviation. As the band pass becomes wider the deviation becomes greater. When the absorption curve is essentially flat over the range of wavelengths applied, then this deviation becomes negligible. For this reason, when choosing a wavelength at which to prepare a standardization curve, the analyst selects a wavelength where the absorption is at a maximum. From Figure 13.4

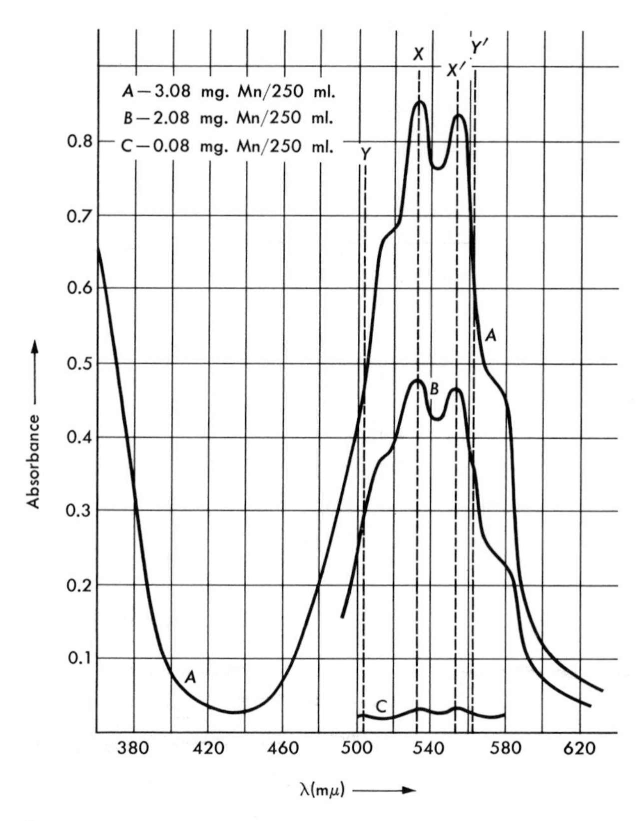

Fig. 13.4. The absorption spectra for aqueous solutions of potassium permanganate at different concentrations. Curves are plotted as absorbance *vs.* wavelength.

the wavelength that would give the least apparent deviation is indicated by X and X'. On the other hand, the wavelength shown by Y and Y' would not fulfill the requirements of Beer's Law. In the latter case the absorptivity is changing and the absorbance would not be entirely a function of the absorbing species in the solution.

There are no apparent deviations from Beer's Law if all of the requirements are maintained.

Range of Minimum Error

It is desirable experimentally to have as large a variation in absorbance as possible for a given change in concentration. Even in a system that shows no deviation from Beer's Law, the useful concentration range of the method is limited. At very high concentrations of the absorbing species, the intensity of the radiant energy emerging from the sample is so weak that the spectrophotometer is not sensitive enough to detect the change in intensity due to changes in concentration. When the concentrations are low, the error in the measuring device becomes very large in proportion to the quantity being measured. Between these extremes, there is an optimum range of concentration where the error is at a minimum.

If the values of percent transmittance are plotted versus concentration of manganese, a curve such as the one shown in Figure 13.5 is obtained.

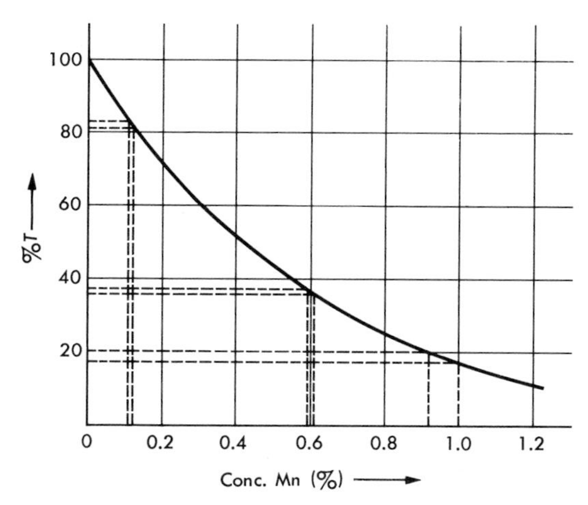

Fig. 13.5. Graph showing percent transmittance versus concentration of manganese in percent.

An arbitrary value of 2% change is taken at 18%, 36%, and 82% T. The uncertainty of the concentration is shown for each point. The greatest uncertainty is at 18% T. At 82% T the uncertainty is smaller but it represents a greater portion of the total concentration. In fact, in both regions of concentration the precision of the values will be poor. The point 36% T represents the point between the extremes where the error tends to be a minimum. Even though the minimum is 37% T, the error is not much greater over a range of 15% T to 65% T (absorbance 0.8 to 0.2).

The straight line obtained when Beer's Law is plotted in the form of $A = abc$ or $\log T = -abc$ indicates the region of concentrations that satisfy the requirements of Beer's Law. This type of curve does not give any information as to the shape of the curve over all concentrations. By plotting $(1 - T)$ against $\log c$, an S-shaped curve known as a Ringbom curve (reference 1) is obtained (Figure 13.6). If the system satisfies Beer's Law requirements, an inflection point will come at $T = 0.368$ or about 37%. If Beer's Law is not satisfied, the inflection point will be at some other value but the shape of the curve will be the same. The straight portion of the curve gives the optimum range of concentrations for experimental measurements. Solutions of high concentration outside the range can be brought into the more favorable range by suitable dilution.

The steeper the curve, the greater will be the variation of absorbance in relation to concentration changes. This increases the sensitivity of the method.

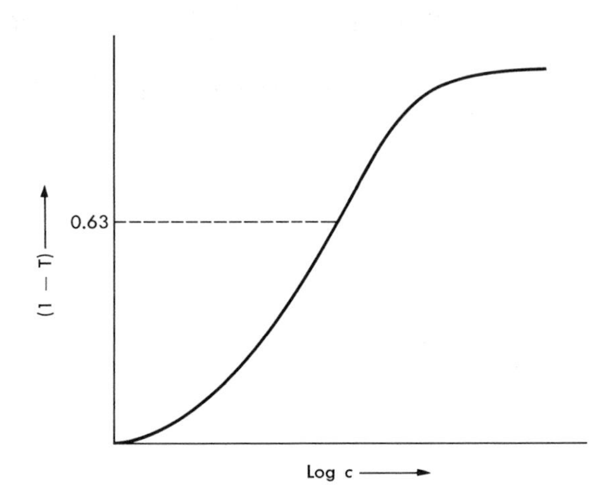

Fig. 13.6. Ringbom curve, $(1 - T)$ *vs.* Log c.

Another method for decreasing the analysis error in more concentrated solutions is the differential method. This uses as a reference a standard solution of known concentration rather than a blank. This method was introduced by Kortüm (Kortüm, *Angew. Chem.* **50,** 193 (1937)), and has been studied further by Hiskey (reference 2). For a more detailed discussion, it is recommended that the papers by Hiskey and Young (3) and others (4, 5) be consulted.

References

1. Ringbom, *Z. Analytical Chemistry* **115,** 332 (1939).
2. Hiskey, *Analytical Chemistry* **21,** 1440 (1949).
3. Hiskey and Young, *Analytical Chemistry* **23,** 1196 (1951).
4. Bastian, *Analytical Chemistry* **21,** 972 (1949).
5. Reilley and Crawford, *Analytical Chemistry* **27,** 716 (1955).
6. Delahay, *Instrumental Analysis,* The Macmillan Company, New York, 1957.
7. Ewing, *Instrumental Methods of Chemical Analysis,* 2nd ed., McGraw-Hill Book Company, Inc., New York, 1960.
8. Harley and Wiberley, *Instrumental Analysis,* John Wiley and Sons, Inc., New York, 1954.
9. Meites and Thomas, *Advanced Analytical Chemistry,* McGraw-Hill Book Company, New York, 1958.

10. *Analytical Absorption Spectroscopy*, edited by Mellon, John Wiley and Sons, Inc., New York, 1950.

11. Reilley and Sawyer, *Experiments for Instrumental Methods*, McGraw-Hill Book Company, Inc., New York, 1961.

12. *Technique of Organic Chemistry*, 2nd ed., edited by Weissberger, Vol. IX, "Chemical Applications of Spectroscopy." Interscience Publishers, Inc., New York, 1956.

13. Willard, Merritt, and Dean, *Instrumental Methods of Analysis*, 3rd ed., D. Van Nostrand Company, Inc., Princeton, N.J., 1958.

CHAPTER **14**

Absorption Instrumentation

An instrument used to measure the intensity of radiant energy falling upon a detector is called a photometer. The intensity can be measured absolutely or by comparison to a standard. Generally when a photometer is used in chemical analysis, it is combined with a dispersing element which is used to spread the spectrum. Such combinations used in the visible region of the spectrum are classed as visual photometers (color comparators), filter photometers, and spectrophotometers. In the ultraviolet and infrared portions of the spectrum, the spectrophotometric type is most commonly used.

The basic principle of each of the various types of instruments is the measurement of the extent to which radiation composed of a narrow band of wavelengths is absorbed as it passes through the sample. The means of providing the narrow band of wavelengths (monochromatic radiation), the detection and measuring devices, and the materials used for the necessary optical parts are the important factors that determine the design of the various types of instruments used in absorptiometric methods.

There are two properties of radiant energy which are important and of interest in absorptiometric techniques. The first is the quality of the radiant energy. This is usually expressed in terms of wavelength or frequency. The second is the quantity or amount of radiant energy, usually described as intensity. The frequency of the radiant energy determines its ability to interact with matter. A comparison of the original intensity of the beam with its intensity as it emerges from the sample gives a measure of the extent of interaction between the radiant energy and matter.

PHOTOMETERS

Photometers that are used to measure the absorbance in the visible region of the spectrum are called colorimeters, filter photometers, and visual photometers or color comparators. Colorimeters and filter photometers are members of a larger group of instruments called absorptiometers. Using this term to describe instruments that measure absorbance does not limit the range of wavelengths only to those in the visible. The construction of all photometers is similar and differs only in specific parts of the individual instruments.

The principal parts of a photometer are the light source, filter, detector (reference and/or working), and sample holder. This is illustrated schematically in Figure 14.1. Read out systems vary with the type of photometers.

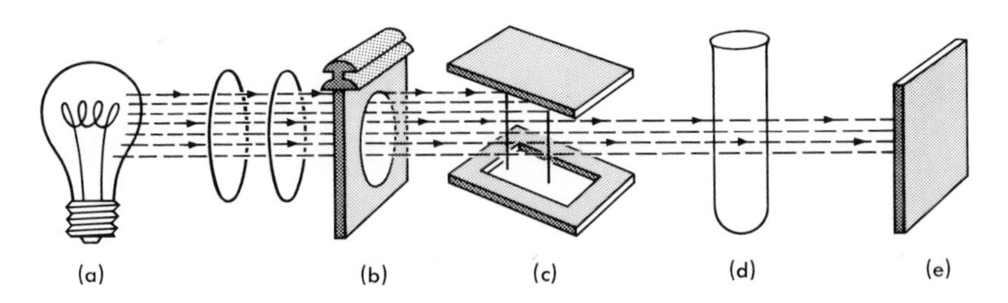

Fig. 14.1. Schematic diagram of the basic components of a filter photometer as represented by the Fisher Electrophotometer. (**a**) Light source, (**b**) Filter, (**c**) Reference detector (photocell), (**d**) Sample holder, (**e**) Working detector (photocell). *Courtesy Fisher Scientific Company*

Light Source

The tungsten lamp is used as a source for absorption measurements made in the visible region of the spectrum. A high intensity is very desirable since the output signal from the detector will in consequence be stronger. However, an optimum efficiency is used rather than the maximum efficiency. This optimum efficiency is dependent on two factors: the lamp life and the heat dissipation to the temperature sensitive part of the instrument.

Filter

The filter restricts the band of wavelengths that is passed through the sample. The band width of wavelengths passing through the filter has an effect on the sensitivity of the measurements to changes in concentration. The smaller the band width, the closer the approach to monochromatic light and the more sensitive are the instrumental measurements to changes in concentration of the sample.

The important characteristics of the filter are the wavelength of the center of the band pass, its transmission at the peak of the band width and its band pass width. These will determine the intensity and kind of wavelengths of radiant energy passing through the filter. Figure 14.2 illustrates the application of these terms.

Filters are of the following types: (1) gelatin, (2) tinted glass, (3) liquid, and (4) interference. A description of each of these filter types can be found in references 2, 3, and 4. The most common type used in filter photometers found in analytical laboratories is the glass filter. These filters have a fairly broad band pass. The band pass can be made narrower by using a combination of

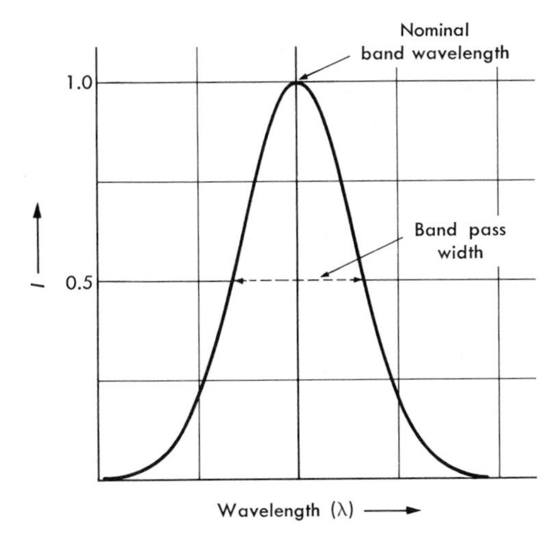

Fig. 14.2. Band pass width of filter.

two or more glass filters. The one disadvantage of using several filters of this type is that the intensity of the beam emerging from the filter is considerably lower. This decrease in energy necessitates the use of a sensitive detector.

The selection of a filter for a particular analysis is made on the basis of the color of the solution, or from data obtained from the absorption spectrum of the solution. If a spectrophotometer is available, it can be used to obtain the data for an absorption spectrum. A filter is chosen that absorbs in the area of maximum absorbance of the solution. If a spectrophotometer is not available, a good approximation is to choose a filter having the complementary color of the solution (see Table 14.1).

Sample Holder

The sample holder, called a cuvette, is made of material that is transparent in the visible region of the spectrum. Glass is a suitable material for use in the visible. Quartz can be used in both the visible and ultraviolet portions of the spectrum.

A means of slipping the cuvette in and out of the light path is necessary. Exact reproduction of the position of the cuvette is not required in most filter photometers since it is only necessary to have the entire bundle of wavelengths pass through the sample when it is in position. The sample must be far enough away from the source so that the sample is not heated appreciably by the lamp. In some cases, infrared filters are used to decrease the amount of heat energy transferred.

Curved cuvettes and plane cuvettes whose sides are not absolutely parallel produce effects that may be large enough to throw a portion of the beam off the sensitive detector surface. Each cuvette should be tested for these effects by rotating the cell in the sample holder to observe whether a change in the value of the measurement occurs.

TABLE 14.1
Colors of the Visible Spectrum

COLOR	COMPLEMENTARY COLOR
Purple	Green-yellow
Blue	Yellow-red
Blue-green	Red
Green	Red-purple
Green-yellow	Purple
Yellow	Blue-purple
Yellow-red	Blue
Red	Blue-green

Detectors and Read Out

The detector used in a photometer can be the eye, a photovoltaic cell, or a phototube. Since photometers are nondispersive instruments in contrast to spectrophotometers, the intensity of the radiant energy emerging from the sample is large enough to produce a good signal-to-noise ratio with a simple detector.

The eye is employed as a detector in visual photometers (color comparators). It is used to match the intensities of two spots or the two halves of a field in an eyepiece. Instruments designed on this principle are recommended if the precision required is not high, and requirements of ruggedness and low cost predominate.

Photovoltaic cells do not need a power supply or electronic amplifier. A low resistance, high sensitivity galvanometer is necessary for read out. The circuit is simple, so that the instrument is readily portable. On the other hand, the sensitive read out meter makes it expensive. The sensitivity of the meter could also be a disadvantage if it were necessary to use the instrument in an area of high vibration. Photovoltaic cells show fatigue effects, particularly at high light intensities.

Phototubes require an external power supply and an amplifier that are rather expensive. A rather rugged, inexpensive meter can be employed as a read out. Where there is rapidly changing absorbance in solutions that show very little absorbance, a phototube will give better results than the photocell since the fatigue factor of the photocell would be important. A phototube does not show fatigue effects.

Visual Photometers (Color Comparators)

Visual photometers, more commonly called color comparators, use the eye as the detector. The common types of visual photometers are Nessler tubes, Heyner cylinders, fixed standard type (illustrated by the Hellige comparator), color titration type, and the Duboscq color comparator.

The schematic diagram of the Duboscq color comparator is given in Figure 14.3. The intensity of the incident light striking both solutions is equal.

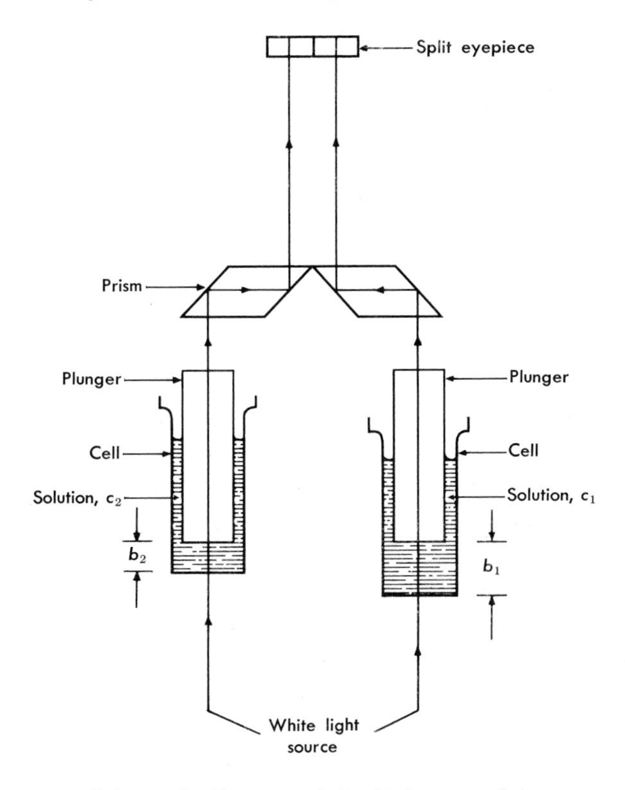

Fig. 14.3. Schematic diagram of the Duboscq color comparator.

Assuming that the sample holders are identical in refraction and reflection errors and that the preparation of the standard and the unknown has been the same, then, by adjusting the depth of the glass plungers in the two solutions, the intensity of the light emerging from the two solutions can be made to be equal. The result is that the absorbance, A, and the absorptivity, a, is the same for the two solutions. Thus, equation 13.9, $b_1c_1 = b_2c_2$, becomes the fundamental relationship for use with color comparators.

The limitations of the visual comparator are the limitations of the eye. Fatigue and insensitivity to low levels of illumination are typical examples of these limitations.

Color comparators are often used in the colorimetric determination of pH. A series of solutions of known pH containing a given indicator is compared with the solution of unknown pH containing the same indicator. The LaMotte color comparator is an example of this type of comparator. The Hellige color comparator uses colored glass standards as a comparison. This eliminates the difficulty of maintaining a series of standard solutions. Whichever system is used, the absolute reproducibility of chemical procedure is required for good results. In addition to pH determinations, color comparison methods can be used for soil and water testing.

Filter Photometers

Photometers using a filter and a photovoltaic cell are commonly called filter photometers. The use of a photovoltaic cell as a detector makes it possible to convert radiant energy into electrical energy to be used as a means of measuring the amount of light absorbed by a solution.

In order for the intensity of the radiant energy emerging from the solution to be measured as a function of concentration, the remaining terms of Beer's Law must be kept constant. Therefore, in the relationship

$$\log \frac{I_0}{I} = abc$$

the quantities I_0, a, and b must not vary. Constancy in the intensity of the incident radiation (I_0), is a function of the reproducibility of the source. Constancy in path length, b, is a matter of uniform construction of sample cuvettes, and a is concerned with the reproduction of chemical treatment and with the monochromatic character of the radiation.

Since the absorbance characteristics of different filters vary, and absorption and reflection within the optics of the instrument contribute to the absorbance of the solution, it is customary to refer the absorbance of a solution to that of an equivalent cell containing the solvent, measured under the same conditions. The measurements made in this way will reflect only the absorbance of the absorbing species in the solution.

According to Beer's Law, the concentration of the absorbing material in the solution is a linear function of the absorbance. By plotting absorbance, A, versus concentration, c, of a series of solutions of varying concentrations, a standard curve is obtained. As long as I_0, a, and b remain constant, this curve can be used.

To eliminate photocell fatigue, a dual photocell instrument is used. The incident light beam is split after going through the filter, with part passing through the sample solution to a measuring photocell and the other part going to a balancing cell. The photocells are connected in opposition and show an

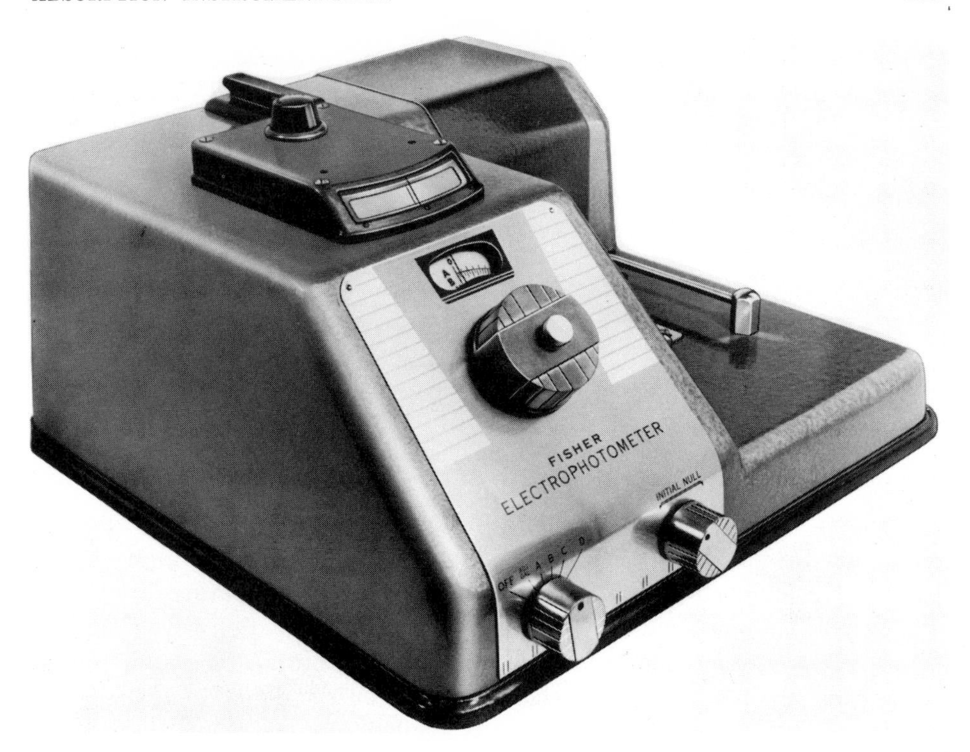

Fig. 14.4. Fisher Electrophotometer. *Courtesy Fisher Scientific Company*

unbalance as a result of the absorption of the light by the sample solution. Connecting the photocells through a galvanometer, the amount of unbalance can be measured and the value indicated on the read out meter. Even so, this only partially eliminates the fatigue effects. Using two photocells requires that they be matched both in frequency response and output level. An example of this type of filter photometer is the Fisher Electrophotometer (see Figure 14.4), the schematic diagram of which is given in Figure 14.5.

There are many filter photometers available commercially. Among these are the single beam Evelyn photoelectric colorimeter and the double beam instruments such as the Klett Summerson, the Lumetron photoelectric colorimeter, the Fisher Electrophotometer, and Fisher Nefluorophotometer.

Filter photometers have an advantage where routine analysis of the same substance is being carried out. The analysis of manganese in steel is an example of this type of analysis.

SPECTROPHOTOMETERS

To provide information on the measurement of the intensity of radiation, either continuously or point-by-point over a range of wavelengths, an instru-

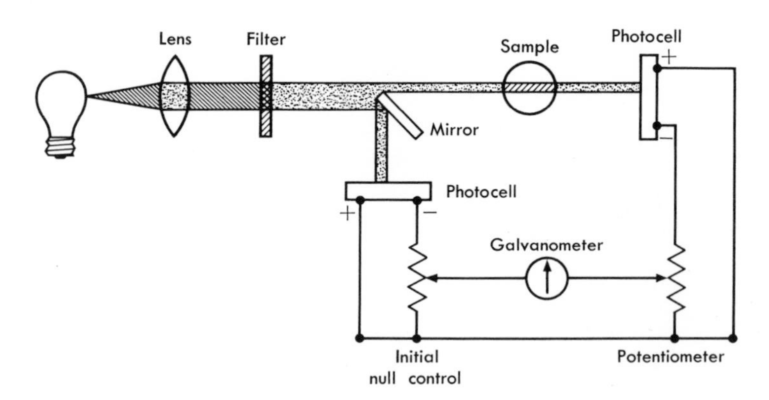

Fig. 14.5. Schematic optical and wiring diagram for the Fisher Electrophotometer. *Courtesy Fisher Scientific Company*

ment called a spectrophotometer has been designed. This instrument is a photometer equipped with a dispersive element such as a grating or a prism. The spectrophotometer allows the choice of a narrow band of wavelengths to be made from a wide range of the electromagnetic spectrum. The extent of the range from which to make this choice depends on the design of the spectrophotometer. Much more information is available from measurements made with a spectrophotometer than from those made using the broad band pass of the filter photometer.

The main difference in the design of the spectrophotometer in comparison with that of the filter photometer is in the type of monochromator and detector. Compare Figure 14.6, the schematic block diagram of a spectrophotometer, with Figure 14.1, which is a similar diagram for a filter photometer. Since spectrophotometers are used to measure absorption in regions of the spectrum other than the visible, the materials from which the optics are made, as well as source and detector differences, constitute major changes in the instrument design.

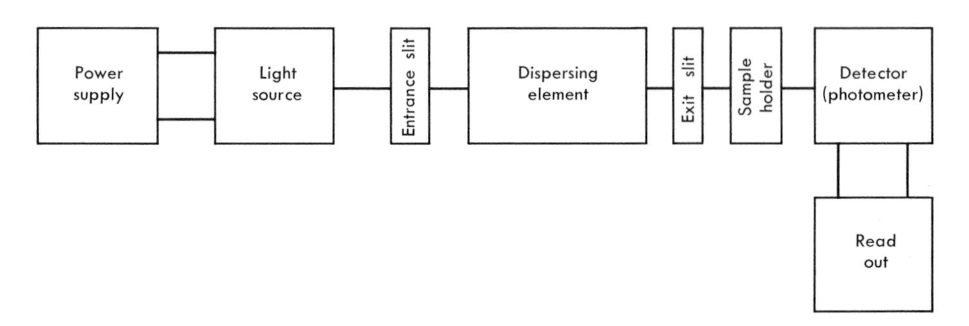

Fig. 14.6. Schematic diagram of basic components of a spectrophotometer.

Source

The source that is used depends on the region of the electromagnetic spectrum being used. A tungsten filament incandescent lamp may be used in the visible region; a hydrogen gas discharge tube is commonly used in the ultraviolet, while a Nernst glower or Globar is used in the infrared.

In many cases it is necessary to prevent undesirable extraneous radiation from reaching the monochromator. This must be accomplished without seriously diminishing the intensity of the desired wavelengths. Usually a suitable filter is used for this. Scattered light that reaches the photometer will also impair the validity of the measurements.

If a constant output of the source is to be maintained, the applied voltage must be very rigorously controlled at a constant value. The fact that the output varies with the fourth power of the applied voltage makes this control necessary. A battery, a constant voltage transformer, or an electronic constant voltage power supply will fulfill this requirement of voltage control.

Monochromator

The monochromator consists of a dispersing element and a slit system to regulate the dimensions of the beam of radiation. The presence of a slit system is a significant characteristic of this type of instrument. The dispersion element is used to spread out the radiation in space from which the slit system makes it possible to select the desired band of wavelengths.

The **entrance slit** governs the intensity of the radiant energy entering the monochromator and the purity of light at all places in the dispersed spectrum. The narrower the entrance slit, the greater is the spectral purity of the light; the lower the intensity of the radiation entering the monochromator, the lower the intensity at any point in the dispersed spectrum. Since the spectral properties of the source vary with wavelength, it is generally necessary to be able to adjust the entrance slit continuously.

The **exit slit** selects a portion of the dispersed spectrum for viewing by the detector. If the spectrum being viewed by the detector is continuous, the spread in the wavelengths is proportional to the width of the exit slit. The width of the exit slit also controls the intensity of the total radiation falling on the detector.

The spectral purity and intensity of the radiant energy have a critical dependence on the entrance and exit slit system. The theoretical distribution of the radiant energy emerging from the exit slit at any numerical wavelength is given by Figure 14.7. The means of varying the widths of the entrance and exit slits vary with different instruments. In some instruments the entrance and exit slits are varied individually; in others both slits are varied simultaneously.

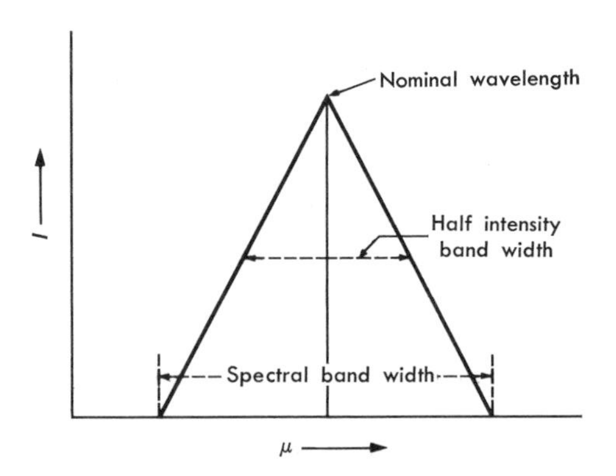

Fig. 14.7. Theoretical distribution of radiant energy with wavelength leaving exit slit.

Prism

The dispersive element, the other component of the monochromator, can be either of two types. One of these types is the prism. The prism disperses a polychromatic beam of radiant energy into a spectrum. This occurs because the refractive index of a prism is different for different wavelengths. The variation in refractive index with wavelength is called the dispersive power of the prism and is a fundamental characteristic of the material from which the prism is made.

The dispersion of a prism is nonlinear with wavelength. With a quartz prism the dispersion is lowest in the visible region of the spectrum and highest in the ultraviolet region. Figure 14.8 illustrates this fact. It is fortunate that the

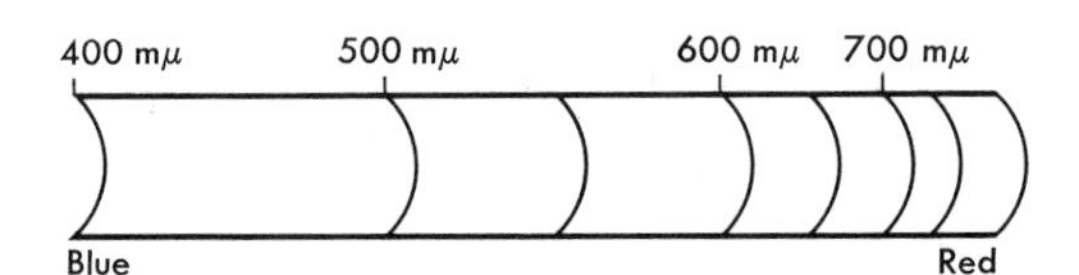

Fig. 14.8. Dispersion of visible spectrum from a prism.

intensity of the spectrum is greatest in the red portion of the spectrum where the spectral slit width must be the smallest. In the ultraviolet region of the spectrum, a larger spectral slit width is necessary because of the weaker intensity of this portion of the spectrum. Since the dispersion is greater in the ultraviolet, the overall resolution is very good.

Spectrophotometers using a prism as a dispersion element must have a variable slit system. This allows adjustment for the difference in intensity and dispersion as the spectrum is traversed from 200 mμ to 800 mμ as is the case of instruments operating in the ultraviolet-visible region of the spectrum.

Table 14.2
Limits of Transmission of Prism Materials

MATERIAL	RANGE OF TRANSMISSION	MOST SUITABLE REGION
Crystalline Quartz	0.180μ to 3.5μ	Ultraviolet
Glass	0.450μ to 0.7μ	Visible
Lithium Fluoride	0.12μ to 6.0μ	Infrared
Calcium Fluoride	0.12μ to 8.5μ	Infrared
Sodium Chloride	0.2μ to 15.0μ	Infrared
Potassium Bromide	0.2μ to 28.0μ	Infrared

The prism material dictates the range of the spectrum within which the instrument may be used. Spectrophotometers that have a glass prism and glass optics are usable only in the visible region. Quartz can be used in both the ultraviolet and visible ranges. Table 14.2 lists the various materials used for optical parts of spectrophotometers and the region of the spectrum for which they are most useful.

Diffraction Grating

The second type of dispersion element used in spectrophotometers is the diffraction grating. A diffraction grating consists of a transparent or reflecting surface that has been ruled with a large number of closely spaced parallel lines. Each line functions as a scattering center for the radiation impinging upon it. When the grating is illuminated by a beam containing radiant energy of several wavelengths, each wavelength will produce its own set of diffraction maxima. These maxima will be separated in space from those of the other wavelengths. If the original radiant energy consists of a continuous spectrum of wavelengths, then the diffracted radiant energy will show a dispersed spectrum for each order with the exception of the zero order. The dispersion will be proportional to the order number.

The dispersion of a diffraction grating is linear with wavelength (see Figure 14.9). Because of this, a fixed slit width can be used over the entire spectrum.

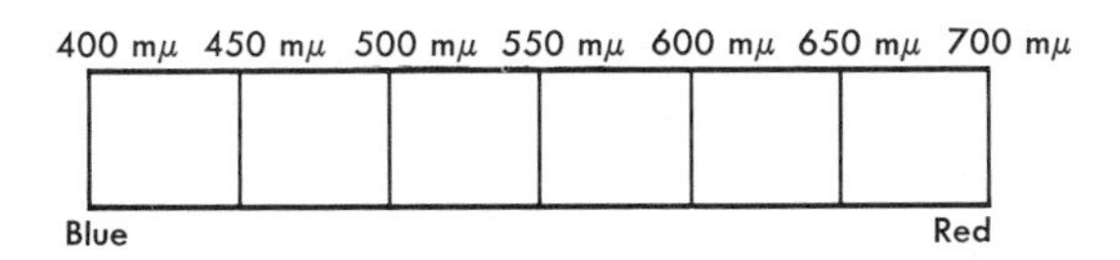

Fig. 14.9. Dispersion of visible spectrum from a grating.

In order to allow adjustment for intensity differences in the visible and ultraviolet regions, an occluder must be introduced into the optical path before the light emerges from the exit slit. This can be accomplished by using an adjustable optical wedge.

The constant band pass of a spectrophotometer using a diffraction grating insures a reproducibility of readings and a reproducibility between instruments that is very difficult to achieve where band pass cannot be duplicated.

One of the problems encountered in the use of diffraction gratings arises from the fact that the various orders of diffraction tend to overlap each other. However, a filter or low resolution prism can be used to separate out the unwanted wavelengths. By use of special ruling tools the shape of the groove in the diffraction grating can be changed. As a result, it is possible to concentrate most of the diffracted intensity in one order of the spectrum.

The advantages of diffraction grating spectrophotometers are as follows:

(1) The dispersion is linear over the entire spectral range

(2) Diffraction gratings can be used in all spectral ranges

(3) The high resolving power is very practical

(4) The introduction of replica gratings has caused the cost differential between grating and prism instruments to be nearly eliminated. Hence, the formerly existing disadvantage of high cost in comparison to prism instruments is no longer apparent.

Prism instruments do have advantages, however, in that prisms tend to be more rugged than gratings. Gratings require extremely careful handling and must be kept scrupulously free of dust. Less scattered light is generated by prisms than by gratings. In the regions of highest transparency, prisms produce a more intense spectrum.

Some commercially available instruments have two or three prisms or gratings as monochromators in order to increase the dispersion and resolution of the spectrophotometer.

Receptor

After emerging from the sample and passing through the exit slit, the radiant energy falls upon a receptor which may be one of several types. It may be a photovoltaic cell, a phototube, or a photomultiplier tube. The main characteristic of each type is its wavelength response. Radiant energy in the ultraviolet falling on a red-sensitive phototube would give a weak response, if any at all. A blue-sensitive phototube will respond to wavelengths in the ultraviolet, whereas a red-sensitive tube responds to wavelengths in the visible and near infrared. A receptor must be used that responds to energy in the region of the spectrum in which it is being used. Phototubes and photomultiplier tubes produce small measuring currents. However, since the internal resistance of these tubes is high, these small currents can be electronically amplified and used to activate the read out system. Phototubes do not suffer from fatigue as do photovoltaic cells.

The current output of a photovoltaic cell falls off with time of exposure to radiation. The current signal from a photovoltaic cell is difficult to amplify without destroying the characteristics of the signal. Like the photocell, the human eye suffers from fatigue, but to a much greater extent. It responds to gradations in shade but only slightly to gradations in wavelength. The eye is useful for a comparison indicator but not as a measuring device.

The use of phototubes as detectors requires a means of eliminating the current that flows when the tubes are in operation but are not being illuminated by radiation. This current, called the **dark current,** results from the stray electrons flowing within the tube due to the potential difference between the cathode and anode. The elimination of the dark current is taken care of in the design of the instrument.

Detectors that are sensitive to wavelengths found in the infrared region of the spectrum are thermocouples, bolometers, and Golay detectors. A complete discussion of the operation, advantages and disadvantages of detectors of these types is beyond the scope of this text, but can be found in references on instrumental methods of analysis listed at the end of the chapter.

Read Out Systems

The output from the detector can be used to activate read out systems of various types. A direct deflection meter is relatively inexpensive, rapid, and convenient (see Figure 14.10). However, it tends to be less accurate and less stable than a compensation method. An electrical compensation circuit using a potentiometer or bridge circuit is time-consuming in its operation but very accurate as a read out system. This system can be used for point-by-point plotting at several wavelengths. On the other hand, it cannot be used for rapid measurements and survey work.

Fig. 14.10. Direct deflection read out meter showing scale for $\%T$ and optical density or absorbance. *Courtesy Bausch and Lomb, Incorporated*

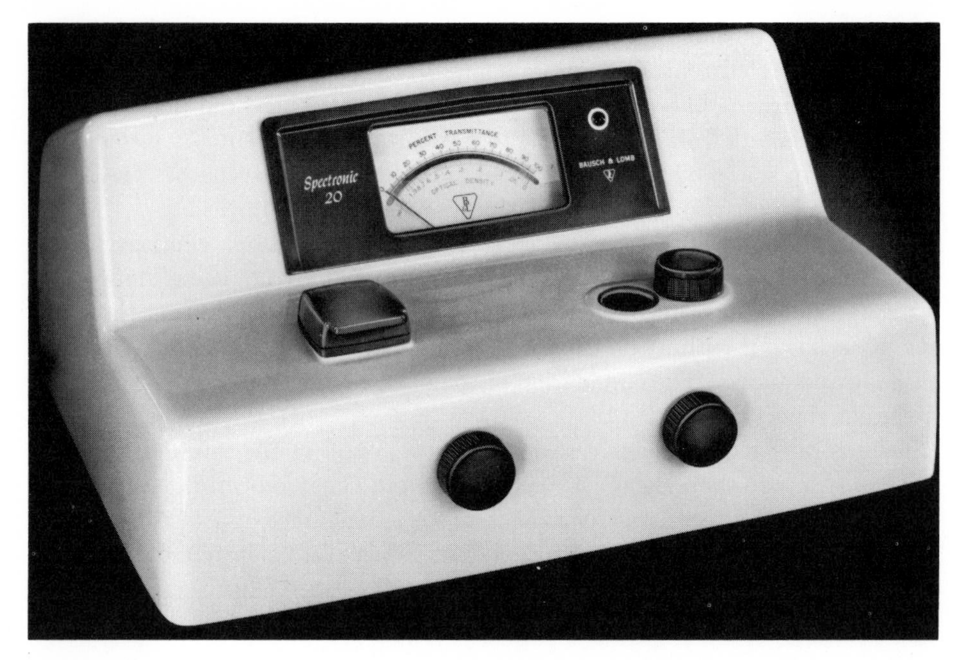

Fig. 14.11. Bausch and Lomb Spectronic 20 spectrophotometer. The Spectronic 20 is a single beam instrument. *Courtesy Bausch and Lomb, Incorporated*

For rapid measurements and survey work a recorder is most efficient. Although the recorder is less accurate than the compensation method, and more expensive instrumentation is necessary, the amount of detailed information available in a short time defies comparison.

Types of Spectrophotometers

The design of the spectrophotometer places it in one of two general types of instruments. These are the single beam and double beam instruments.

In a single beam spectrophotometer (Figure 14.11) there is only one beam of incident radiation traversing the optical path from source to detector. The sample is placed in this beam either before or after the monochromator. The sample is usually inserted after a reference material has been used to standardize the instrument. The reliability of the measurements made depends on the stability and constancy of the instrumental characteristics during the time needed to make reference adjustments and sample measurements.

The double beam spectrophotometer splits the energy from the source and passes part through the sample solution and part through a reference material, usually the solvent which was used in the sample solution. The two paths through the spectrophotometer may be separate in space and simultaneous in time, or they may be the same in space but alternate in time. The resulting read out will show only the absorption of the species that is in the sample and not in the sample and reference combined.

Commercial instruments having multiple monochromators (usually composed of dual gratings or a grating and a prism) are also available. These are most common in the infrared spectrophotometers.

References

1. Delahay, *Instrumental Analysis,* The Macmillan Company, New York, 1957.

2. Ewing, *Instrumental Methods of Chemical Analysis,* 2nd ed., McGraw-Hill Book Company, Inc., New York, 1960.

3. Harley and Wiberley, *Instrumental Analysis,* John Wiley and Sons, Inc., New York, 1954.

4. Lewin, *Journal of Chemical Education,* **37,** A341, A401, A455, A507, A637, (1960).

5. Willard, Merritt, and Dean, *Instrumental Methods of Analysis,* 3rd ed., D. Van Nostrand Company, Inc., Princeton, N.J., 1958.

CHAPTER 15

Spectrophotometric Methodology

Since the principles underlying absorption measurements, as well as a discussion of the instruments used to make these measurements, have already been presented, it now seems appropriate to consider the methods of presentation and use of these measurements.

Presentation of Spectrophotometric Data

Just as the nomenclature and symbols of absorption spectroscopy are not standardized, there is no standard manner in which the data obtained from absorption measurements are presented. In order to make the discussion of absorption measurements complete, it is worthwhile to give the common means of presentation here. As was previously pointed out (page 235), analytical chemists usually plot spectrophotometric data as absorbance *vs.* wavelength. Oftentimes the data are presented as percent transmittance, [%T], *vs.* wavelength. Figure 15.1 illustrates the absorption spectra of potassium permanganate solutions at different concentrations plotted as %T *vs.* wavelength(mμ). Figure 15.2 shows absorption data of the same solutions plotted as absorbance *vs.* wavelength, mμ. These two curves are not mirror images, since absorbance and transmittance have a logarithmic relationship ($A = -\log T$). It should be noted, nevertheless, that a minimum in the transmittance curve corresponds to a maximum in the absorbance curve.

If the logarithm of the absorbance, $\log A$, is plotted versus wavelength, the shape of the curve is independent of concentration. The curves of various concentrations are displaced above or below each other by a constant increment (see Figure 15.3, p. 262). This can be seen by consideration of the following.

$$A = abc$$
$$\log A = \log (abc) = \log a + \log b + \log c$$

The concentration term is added rather than multiplied. Therefore, raising or lowering the concentration adds the increment, $\log c$, to $\log A$ at each wavelength of the spectrum. Plotting the data in this manner allows the direct comparison of a known spectrum with that of an unknown spectrum. This is advantageous where the concentrations are not the same or are unknown.

The absorptivity, a, or molar absorptivity, ϵ, versus wavelength is used by many investigators. This type of presentation has the same advantage of comparison as do the curves resulting from plotting log A *vs.* wavelength, mμ.

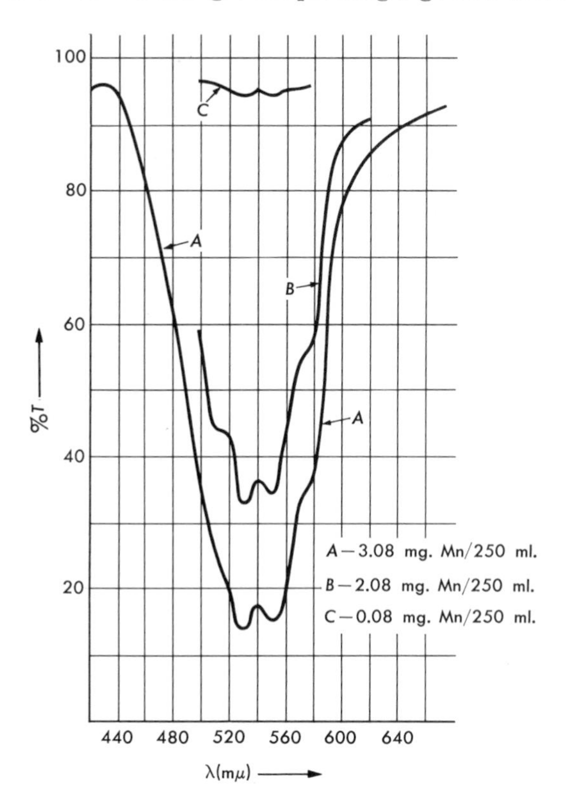

Fig. 15.1. The absorption spectra for aqueous solutions of potassium permanganate at different concentrations. Curves are plotted as percent transmittance *vs.* wavelength.

The shape of the absorption curve of a substance, taken in the visible or ultraviolet (and more so in the infrared) region of the spectrum, can be used as one more piece of evidence to aid in the characterization of the substance. The absorption spectrum is not an infallible proof, but intelligent application of the information that is gained from the spectrum provides a forceful tool to help understand many structural problems involving both simple and complex molecules.

Quantitative Use of Data

The fundamental basis for the quantitative use of spectrophotometric data is Beer's Law. This basis has been developed in Chapter 13 where the Beer-Bouguer Law was discussed. The common means of presenting quantitative data is to prepare a calibration curve using a series of standard solutions of known concentrations and plotting either absorbance or $\% T$ versus concentration. Figures 15.4 and 15.5, p. 263, show such calibration curves for manganese

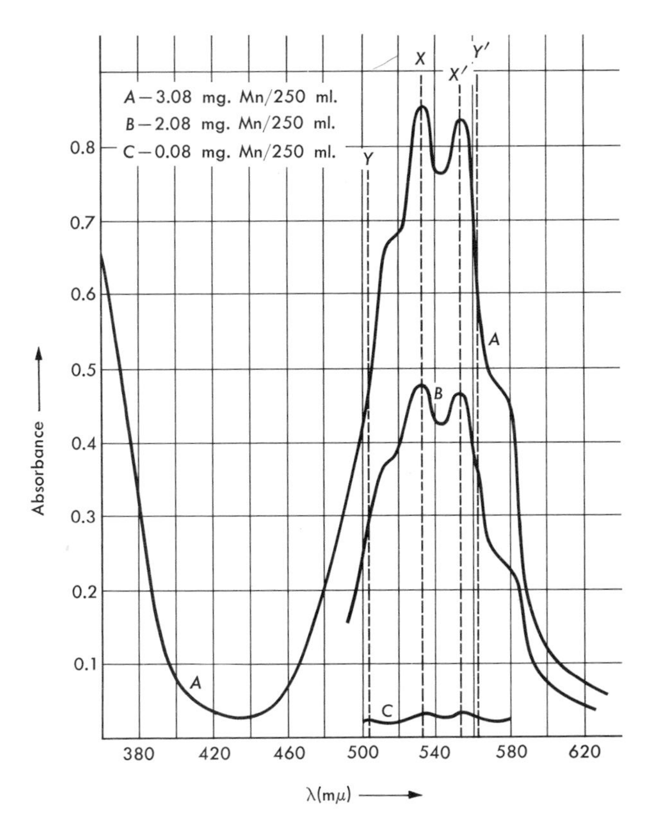

Fig. 15.2. The absorption spectra for aqueous solutions of potassium permanganate at different concentrations. Curves are plotted as absorbance *vs.* wavelength.

determinations. As long as the requirements of Beer's Law are satisfied and there are no changes made in the instrumentation, such a standard curve need be prepared only once. It is good practice to check the calibration curve occasionally to be sure that the instrument is operating correctly and that all the requirements of Beer's Law are being fulfilled.

It is no longer necessary to limit the discussion of quantitative methods to those that depend on colored solutions. Commercial instruments designed to give data in the ultraviolet and infrared regions of the spectrum are common pieces of equipment to be found in nearly all laboratories. The basic principles used in the development of photometric methods for colored systems can be used in ultraviolet and infrared absorptiometric methods. Many substances that are transparent in the visible region of the spectrum show useful absorption bands in the ultraviolet and infrared. An example of such a substance is benzene, which is transparent in the visible region but can be used for wavelength calibration in the ultraviolet since the absorption bands are so sharp and characteristic.

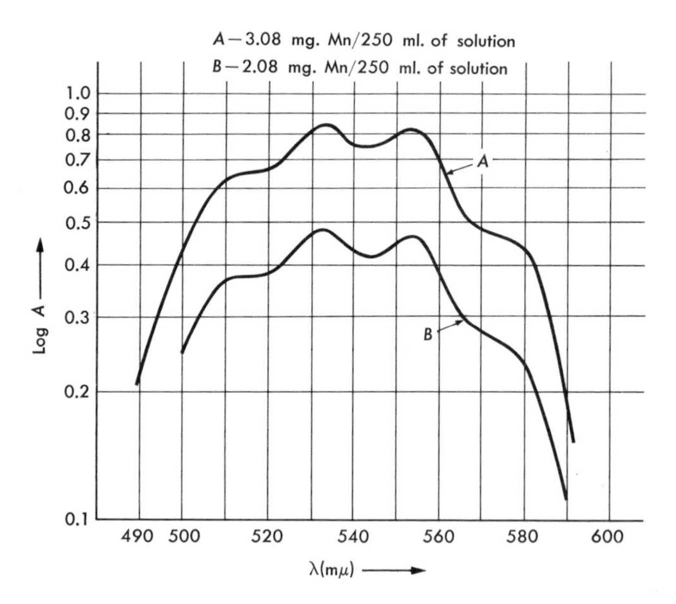

Fig. 15.3. Absorption spectra for aqueous solutions of $KMnO_4$ at two different concentrations. Log A is plotted as a function of wavelength.

Two-Component Analysis

Often it is not necessary to separate a solution formed by two colored constituents into its pure components in order to determine the concentration of each in the mixture.

If there is no overlap of the spectrum of each pure component, then the absorbance of the mixture is measured at the wavelength of maximum absorbance of each pure component. Such a hypothetical case is shown in Figure 15.6. The concentrations of the components I and II of the mixture can be measured at the wavelengths shown as λ_1 and λ_2.

Where there is a single overlap, as shown in Figure 15.7, the absorbance of the mixture can be measured at λ_2 in order to determine the concentration of II. This is possible because component I does not absorb at this wavelength. The absorbance of the mixture measured at λ_1 is composed of the absorbance of I at λ_1 and the absorbance of II at λ_1. The absorbance of II at λ_1 can be calculated knowing its absorptivity, a, at λ_1, which can be obtained with a solution of pure component II of known concentration. The contribution of component I to the total absorbance of the mixture at λ_1 can be obtained by subtracting the absorbance of component II from the absorbance of the mixture.

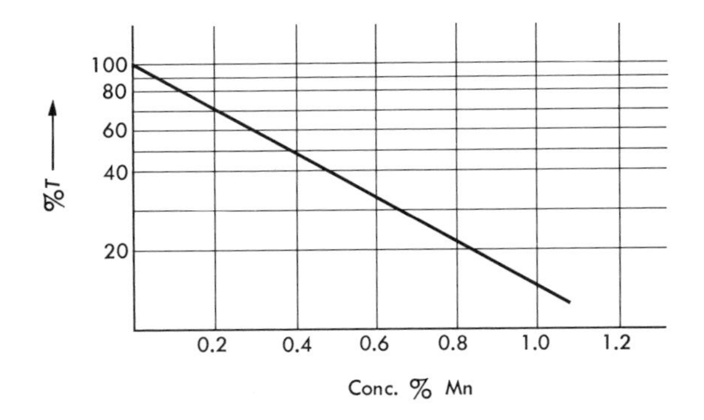

Fig. 15.4. Calibration curve for manganese determination; log $\%T$ *vs.* concentration.

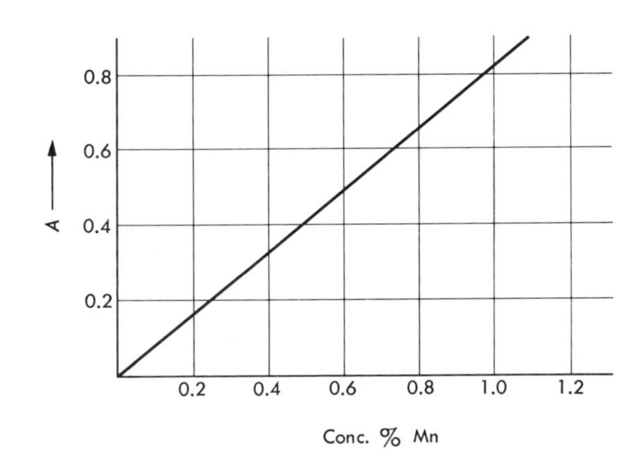

Fig. 15.5. Calibration curve for manganese determination; absorbance *vs.* concentration.

The concentration of component I can then be calculated using the absorptivity of pure component I at wavelength λ_1. This value of the absorptivity can be obtained from the spectrum of pure component I at wavelength λ_1.

When there is a double overlap of the spectra of component I and component II, two wavelengths are chosen. If each substance absorbs strongly at a wavelength where the other absorbs weakly, then it is possible to determine the con-

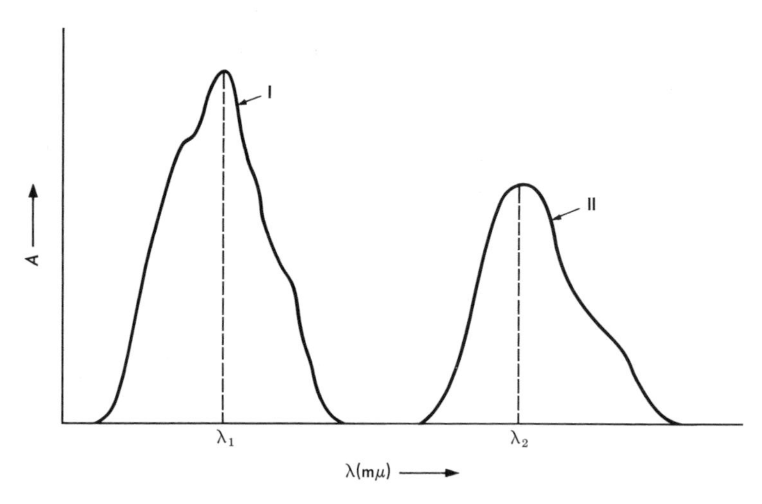

Fig. 15.6. Graph showing no overlap of spectra for pure components I and II of a hypothetical solution.

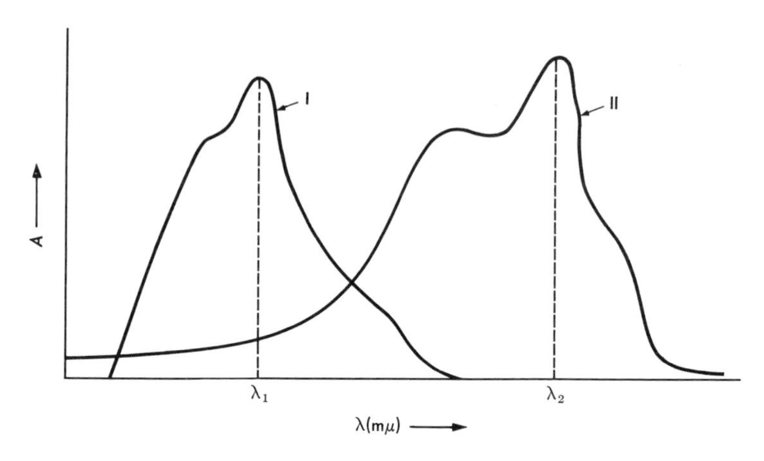

Fig. 15.7. Graph showing overlap of spectra for pure components I and II of a hypothetical solution.

centration of each substance. If the absorbances are additive, then the following is true.

$$a_{1_{\lambda_1}}c_1 + a_{2_{\lambda_1}}c_2 = A_{\lambda_1} \quad \textbf{(15.1)}$$

$$a_{1_{\lambda_2}}c_1 + a_{2_{\lambda_2}}c_2 = A_{\lambda_2} \quad \textbf{(15.2)}$$

where $a_{1_{\lambda_1}}c_1$ = absorbance of component I at wavelength λ_1

$a_{1_{\lambda_2}}c_1$ = absorbance of component I at wavelength λ_2

$a_{2_{\lambda_1}}c_2$ = absorbance of component II at wavelength λ_1

$a_{2_{\lambda_2}}c_2$ = absorbance of component II at wavelength λ_2

The wavelengths λ_1 and λ_2 are chosen in such a manner that at λ_1 one component of the mixture absorbs strongly and the other component shows a weak absorbance. At wavelength λ_2, the reverse must be true. Figure 15.8 gives an illustration of the choice in wavelengths λ_1 and λ_2 in a mixture of potassium permanganate and potassium dichromate.

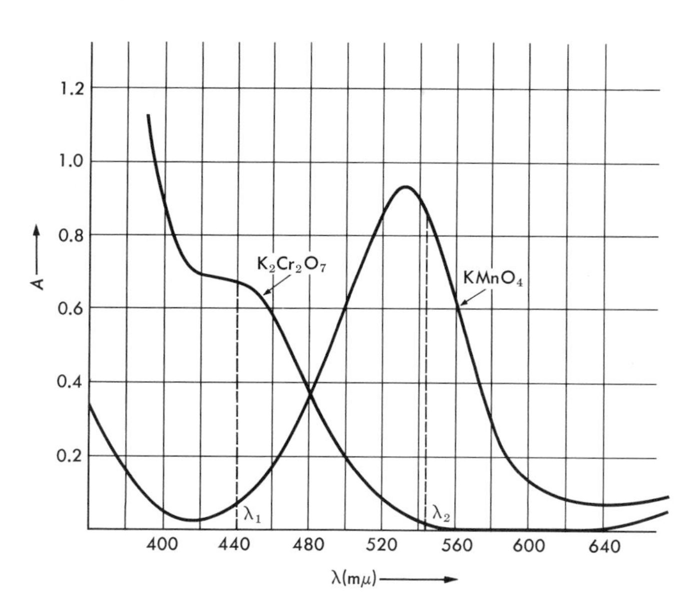

Fig. 15.8. Two-way overlap of spectra of $KMnO_4$ solution (5.78 mg/100 ml.) and $K_2Cr_2O_7$ solution (47.04 mg/100 ml.).

Using equations 15.1 and 15.2, a_1 and a_2 for each wavelength λ_1 and λ_2 can be determined from the spectrum of each pure component at a known concentration. Since a is a constant at a given wavelength, provided the chemical procedure is absolutely duplicated, then the concentration of the pure component in the known solution and the mixture do not have to be identical. Once a_{λ_1} and a_{λ_2} for each component have been determined, then the concentrations of the two components can be determined if the absorbance of the mixture is measured at both wavelengths λ_1 and λ_2. Equations 15.1 and 15.2 can be solved simultaneously for c_1 and c_2. Thus,

$$c_1 = \frac{a_{2_{\lambda_2}} A_{\lambda_1} - a_{2_{\lambda_1}} A_{\lambda_2}}{a_{1_{\lambda_1}} a_{2_{\lambda_2}} - a_{2_{\lambda_1}} a_{2_{\lambda_2}}} \qquad c_2 = \frac{a_{1_{\lambda_1}} A_{\lambda_2} - a_{1_{\lambda_2}} A_{\lambda_1}}{a_{1_{\lambda_1}} a_{2_{\lambda_2}} - a_{2_{\lambda_1}} a_{1_{\lambda_2}}} \qquad \textbf{(15.3)}$$

Solutions containing more than two components can be analyzed using this same method. For multi-component mixtures, equations whose solutions will give the concentration of each absorbing substance in the mixture can be developed.

In the case where the absorbances are not additive, the absorptivity is a function of concentration. The absorptivity, a, is plotted versus concentration, c. The concentration that corresponds to the absorptivity can be determined by reference to the curve. A more detailed discussion of this can be found in the monograph by Mellon listed as reference 2 in the bibliography at the end of the chapter.

Development of an Absorptiometric Method

When a new absorptiometric method is being developed, there are many factors that must be taken into consideration. The effect of each of these factors on the final method must be given careful study.

The most important factor in the development of an analytical method is the selection of the wavelength or filter to be used in the determination. To accomplish this it is necessary to obtain an absorption spectrum of the pure material in the region of the spectrum within which the analyst is working. A spectrum of a blank solution containing all the reagents used except the substance being determined is also necessary. If the system is an aqueous one, distilled water can be used to set the zero absorbance reading. However, if the solvent is an organic one, then it should be used to make the zero absorbance setting. From these spectra, the analyst can select a wavelength or a filter at which the absorbance of the sample is a maximum. A standard calibration curve can then be prepared at this wavelength.

On occasion, a reagent may present an unavoidable interference. The extent of the interference is determined at the desired wavelength and a correction curve can be calculated. The correction can be determined as previously described in multicomponent analyses (see page 262).

Interferences can be classed as either chemical or optical. Chemical interferences are those resulting from a reaction with the desired constituent. These interferences can be eliminated by one of the common separation methods such as precipitation, complex formation, extraction, electrolysis, or volatilization.

Optical interferences are those in which the interfering substance absorbs at the same wavelength as the desired constituent. These may be taken care of by separation methods, complexing methods, or by optical methods. It has been shown earlier (see page 264) that it is possible to determine two substances simultaneously. This method may be applied to determine a substituent in the presence of an interfering substance.

When considering an absorptiometric method, it is necessary to determine the linearity of the absorbance-concentration curve. It is not necessary that the curve be linear for all concentrations, since the concentration can be adjusted so that it will fall within the range where the curve is linear. A system may show a linear plot when data obtained from a spectrophotometer are used, but show a departure from linearity with data obtained from a filter photometer. This happens because the band pass of the filter photometer is much broader than the band pass of the spectrophotometer.

Another of the factors that needs to be considered is the effect of *p*H on the system. In colorimetric methods which use indicators as a means of generating color, this effect is very critical. The control of *p*H is a useful means of eliminating interferences. In many methods used with inorganic materials, the effect of *p*H on extraction procedures is very important. When new methods are being evaluated, absorption measurements should be made in acid, neutral, and basic media. If there is a *p*H effect, it will be observed and means to control this effect can be devised.

There are several other factors that should be listed for consideration. What will be the effect of time of standing on colorimetric measurements? Will changes in procedural steps affect the measurement? What is the range of concentration of this method? What are the accuracy and precision of the method? Each of these questions must be answered before the method is completely acceptable.

Along with a description of the method, specific information as to the type of instrument and attachments and/or modifications employed is necessary to allow this method to be reproduced by another analyst.

Applications

The applications of absorption spectroscopy have increased at an amazing rate. The emphasis in the past has been on absorptiometric determination of colored inorganic ions, the colorimetric determination of *p*H, analyses of metals, and analyses depending on the addition to a clear solution of a color-forming reagent.

Organic reagents that will react with inorganic ions to develop colors are continually being discovered. These reagents have, in many cases, the advantage of being relatively specific in their reactions. Many times, the complex formed between the inorganic ion and the organic reagent can be extracted into an organic solvent from the aqueous solution before measurement. This method is, in effect, a means of separating the desired constituent from its interferences. The determination of heavy metals using dithizone is an example of this procedure. At a given value of *p*H, a selected heavy metal can be extracted as the metal dithizonate into the organic phase, thus separating the metal from the remainder of the interfering substances.

Methods involving absorption measurements have been used to determine trace elements in high purity metals, to test the purity of chemical reagents, and in the determination of reaction rates. The sensitivity of these methods is very high, enabling a few parts per million of many substances to be determined in this manner. The sensitivity varies from one determination to another. The main difficulty in the accuracy of consecutive determinations is not of an instrumental nature but is the result of variations in chemical conditions from one determination to another. Variations in temperature, pH, and in ionic strength are examples of the factors that can cause errors in photometric determinations.

Absorptiometric methods may be employed to determine the equivalence point of titrations. The volume of titrant is plotted against the absorbance, and the equivalence point is indicated by a break in the curve. Titrations of this type are called photometric titrations. Since the equivalence point is determined by the extrapolation of lines determined by points far away on either side of the equivalence point, little or no significance is placed on points in the region of the equivalence point. Therefore, any side reactions that occur in this region are not important in the determination of the exact equivalence point. Many applications of this type of titration are found in the literature. Some examples are: chelometric titrations using ethylenediaminetetraacetic acid; titrations with iodine, permanganate, and dichromate; neutralization reactions; and turbidimetric and nephelometric titrations. Important also is the use of photometric titrations to study equilibria of complex ions and the determination of equilibrium constants.

The application of absorption methods to organic compounds has been centered in the ultraviolet and infrared regions of the spectrum. The increased availability of instrumentation has caused a much greater development of analytical methods in these regions than in the visible region. The development of colored organometallic complexes, however, is causing an increase in the use of the visible region for the determination of many organic compounds.

References

1. Ewing, *Instrumental Methods of Chemical Analysis*, 2nd ed., McGraw-Hill Book Company, Inc., New York, 1960.

2. *Analytical Absorption Spectroscopy*, edited by Mellon, John Wiley and Sons, Inc., New York, 1950.

3. Reilley and Sawyer, *Experiments for Instrumental Methods*, McGraw-Hill Book Company, Inc., New York, 1961.

Laboratory Experiment 27

Principles of Absorption Spectroscopy

Discussion

The Bausch and Lomb Spectronic 20 spectrophotometer can be used as an example for discussing the operation of a spectrophotometer using a diffraction grating monochromator. A schematic diagram of the Spectronic 20 is shown in Figure 15.9, page 271.

The source, a tungsten lamp, radiates white light (light containing all visible wavelengths). This light passes through an entrance slit and falls on the diffraction grating where it is dispersed. A narrow band of the dispersed beam containing light of similar wavelengths passes through an exit slit and through the solution in the sample holder. The light that passes through the solution is directed onto the light sensitive cathode of the phototube. The intensity of the light transmitted by the solution is measured electrically.

The diffraction grating in this instrument is a flat sheet of glass coated with plastic ruled with 600 grooves to the millimeter. The grooves are parallel and accurately spaced. To make it reflect, the surface is aluminized. When white light falls upon the grating, it is dispersed into a spectrum of beams with the short wavelengths (ultraviolet and violet) at one end and the longer wavelengths (red and infrared) at the other.

This spectrum of light is directed on the dark screen containing the exit slit. The portion that illuminates the slit goes through into the sample. By turning the grating, any portion of the spectrum of wavelengths can be directed at the slit. The **wavelength control knob** situated on the top of the instrument is used to turn the grating. Attached to this knob is a wavelength scale that indicates the central wavelength of the band being directed at the slit. This dial may be set at any wavelength between 340 mμ and 900 mμ at intervals of 5 mμ. The band pass of the slit is 20 mμ. Since the dispersion of the diffraction grating is linear, the 20 mμ band width is constant over the entire wavelength region.

Since the tungsten lamp source does not emit light of all wavelengths with equal intensity and the phototube does not respond to light of all wavelengths equally, a means of regulating the amount of light passing through the exit slit is necessary. In addition, the **blank** solution itself may absorb light of certain wavelengths. Thus, to measure the absorbance due only to a particular species in solution, all other factors that affect the percentage transmittance must be taken care of in the original adjustment. To make this adjustment, the **light control knob** (the right hand knob on the front of the instrument) regulates the amount of light passing through the exit slit. The light control is attained by using a wedge shaped exit slit in the light path connected to the light control knob.

The **amplifier control knob** (the left hand knob on the front of the instrument) is used to adjust the percent transmittance to read zero. This adjustment is made after the instrument has had 15 minutes to warm up and when it has no cuvette in the sample holder. A light occluder is always in the light path if there is no cuvette in the sample holder. The meter should read zero at all times when there is no cuvette in the sample holder.

A cuvette containing the solvent used to dissolve the sample (blank solution) is placed in the sample holder, and the occluder is removed from the light path. The light control knob is rotated until the percent reads 100 on the dial. Any absorption due to the blank solution has now been compensated for.

A cuvette containing the sample solution is placed in the sample holder and allowed to come into the path of the light. Any change in the percent transmission reading will be due to the particular species in the sample that is light absorbing. The percent transmittance can be used as a measure of the quantity of the light absorbing species present.

Each time a change in wavelength is made, the zero point and the 100% transmittance must be reset. This is necessary since changes in wavelength, however small, require changes in the amount of compensation needed.

The phototube in the Spectronic 20 is a cesiumantimony surface type photoemissive cell, type S-4. The relative response of this type of phototube to a beam of monochromatic light whose intensity is constant is as follows:

Wavelength (λ) mμ	Relative Response
355	92
380	99
400	100
430	97
455	88
480	78
505	65
510	62
520	56
540	44
570	25
605	9
610	8
620	6

The phototube is much more sensitive to light having a wavelength of 400 mμ than to light having a wavelength of 620 mμ. This indicates that the phototube will require greater intensity of light having a wavelength of 620 mμ than of light having a wavelength of 400 mμ to obtain the same percent transmittance reading on the spectrophotometer meter. Thus the need for the light control is apparent.

USE OF CUVETTES

Since the cuvette determines the length of the light path through the sample, it is necessary that if more than one is used, they must be matched. Any

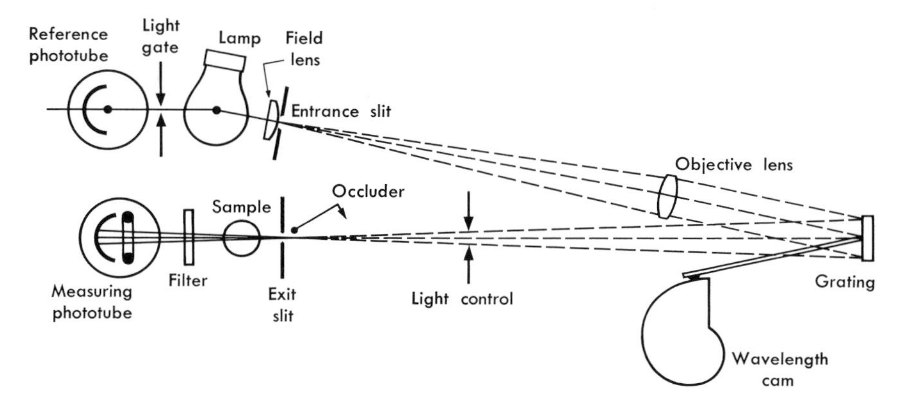

Fig. 15.9. Schematic diagram of optical path of Spectronic 20 spectrophotometer. *Courtesy Bausch and Lomb Incorporated*

variation in the cuvettes, such as strains, smudges, change in cuvette width or curvature of the glass or film of liquid on the outside will cause varying results. Therefore, the handling and care of the cuvettes are extremely important. To minimize such errors, cuvettes should be handled in the following manner:

(1) Hold the cuvette by the top so that the lower part through which the light beam passes will not be covered with finger smudges.

(2) Rinse the cuvette with portions of the sample solution before performing a measurement.

(3) Wipe the lower part of the cuvette with lens tissue to remove any liquid drops or smudges on the outside of the cuvette before making the measurement.

(4) Insert the cuvette in the sample holder in such a manner as to avoid scratches on the portion of the cuvette in the light path.

(5) When using two cuvettes, always use the same one for the blank solution and the other for the various samples being measured. It is not good technique to interchange cuvettes in the middle of a series of measurements.

If the above suggestions are followed carefully, errors due to mishandling of sample cuvettes will be held to a minimum. Most cuvettes are expensive; therefore they should be handled with care.

Apparatus

Bausch and Lomb Spectronic 20 spectrophotometer

Cuvettes (3) two matched and one containing a piece of chalk cut in such a manner as to reflect the color of the light passing through the exit slit.

Reagent

Potassium permanganate standard solution

containing 15 ml. of standard manganese solution prepared for the colorimetric determination of manganese in steel (see page 274).

Procedure

A. CHARACTERISTICS OF SPECTRONIC 20

(1) Place the instrument in operation according to directions given by the instructor. Place approximately 5 ml. of distilled water into a clean cuvette that has been previously rinsed with distilled water, and wipe the outside dry with the lens tissue that is provided. Turn the **light control knob counter-clockwise** as far as it will go to reduce the amount of light falling on the phototube. Place the cuvette containing the distilled water into the sample holder. Align the index line on the cuvette with the line on the sample holder exactly. Close the top of the sample holder.

Rotate the **wave length control knob** to 510 mμ. Turn the **light control knob** clockwise until the meter needle reads about 90% on the transmittance scale. Rotate the wavelength knob, scanning from 400 mμ to 700 mμ (the visible spectrum) and record the manner in which the needle responds as the wavelength is varied. Indicate the wavelength at which the instrument is most responsive. Record this wavelength and set the wavelength scale at this value. Adjust the light control until the meter reads 100% T. Without readjusting the spectrophotometer by moving either the light control or amplifier control, record the percent transmittance (%T) at the following wavelengths: 355, 380, 400, 430, 455, 505, 510, 520, 540, 570, 605, 610, and 620 mμ.

(2) Insert the cuvette containing a piece of chalk into the sample holder. This will allow observation of the color of the light leaving the exit slit. Beginning at 700 mμ, record the color of the light falling on the chalk surface every 50 mμ until a value of 350 mμ has been reached. During this observation it may be necessary to increase or decrease the intensity of the light by rotating the light control knob. At no time should the meter read above 95% transmittance.

(3) Place about 5 ml. of the standard permanganate solution into one of the two matched cuvettes that has been previously rinsed with this permanganate solution. In the other place about 5 ml. of distilled water, after first rinsing it with distilled water. Set the wavelength scale at 380 mμ. With no cuvette in the sample holder and the sample holder lid closed, adjust the instrument so that the meter reads 0% T, using the **amplifier control knob.**

Insert the cuvette with the distilled water into the sample holder, making sure the index lines are exactly lined up, close the lid and by rotating the

light control knob adjust the meter to read 100% T. Remove the cuvette holding the distilled water and insert the cuvette holding the permanganate solution, making certain that the index lines are exactly aligned. Record the percent transmittance as indicated by the position of the meter needle.

Before changing to another wavelength, it is best to rotate the **light control knob** counter-clockwise a few turns to protect the meter from burnout.

Using the procedure of first adjusting the zero reading with no cuvette in the sample holder, and then adjusting for 100% T at each wavelength while the cuvette containing distilled water is in the sample holder, take a reading of the %T of the sample as follows:

every 10 mμ from 380 mμ up to and including 510 mμ;
every 5 mμ from 510 mμ to 550 mμ;
every 10 mμ from 550 mμ to 700 mμ.

B. TREATMENT OF DATA

(1) Plot on a piece of linear graph paper (10 or 20 lines to the inch) the *relative overall response* of the spectrophotometer *vs.* wavelength (λ) using the data obtained in part A-1. Plot the wavelength (λ) along the horizontal axis.

(2) On the same piece of graph paper used in B-1, plot the relative response of the phototube *vs.* wavelength, using the values supplied in the discussion on page 270.

(3) Indicate on this same graph the colors observed at the various wavelengths used in part A-2.

(4) Calculate the relative intensity of the spectrophotometer lamp source over the visible range of the spectrum using the following relationship at each wavelength listed in section A-1.

$$\text{Relative lamp intensity} = \frac{\text{Relative overall response}}{\text{Relative phototube response}} \times \frac{100}{K}$$

The term K is the whole number which is nearest to the maximum value reached by the first factor on the right hand side of the relationship. Multiplying the first factor by $100/K$ will convert all values to a maximum of approximately 100. Usually the value of K is 3–5.

(5) Plot on the same graph as B-1, the **relative lamp intensity** *vs.* wavelength, λ.

(6) On a second sheet of linear graph paper, plot the value of the percent transmittance, %T, of the $KMnO_4$ solution obtained in part A-3 *vs.* wavelength, λ.

(7) Using the relationship $A = 2 - \log \%T$, convert the %T values to absorbance, A, readings. Plot, on a third sheet of linear graph paper, absorbance, A, *vs.* wavelength, λ.

Laboratory Experiment 28

Colorimetric Determination of Manganese in Steel

Apparatus

Available spectrophotometer
Available filter photometer
Available color comparator

Reagents

Acid mix
: prepared by mixing equal parts of HNO_3, H_3PO_4, and H_2O.

KIO_4
: potassium periodate, analytical reagent grade.

0.2 mg./ml. standard manganese solution
: prepared by dissolving 0.6153 gram $MnSO_4 \cdot H_2O$ in a small amount of distilled water in a one liter volumetric flask and then making up to the line with distilled water.

Procedure

A. PREPARATION OF THE STANDARD MANGANESE SOLUTIONS

Weigh to the nearest tenth of a milligram a 0.5000 gram sample of National Bureau of Standards ingot iron containing 0.03% manganese, into each of four Pyrex 250 ml. volumetric flasks. Add 50 ml. of acid mix to each flask and boil on a hot plate to expel the oxides of nitrogen. To three of the flasks add, respectively, from pipets or from a buret, 5, 15, and 25 ml. of the standard manganese solution. Leave one flask for a blank. Dilute the solution in each flask to about 100 ml. with distilled water, cautiously add about 0.2500 gram of KIO_4, and boil for three minutes to oxidize the manganese(II) ion to the permanganate ion. (Three minutes are required to insure complete oxidation; longer boiling, within reason, does no harm.) Cool the solution to room temperature, dilute to the mark with distilled water, and thoroughly mix the solution by inverting the stoppered flasks several times.

B. PREPARATION OF THE UNKNOWN SAMPLES

Into each of three Pyrex 250 ml. volumetric flasks weigh to the nearest tenth of a milligram a sample of 0.200–0.3000 gram of steel. Add 50 ml. of the acid mix to each flask and boil on a hot plate to expel the oxides of nitrogen. Dilute the solution in each flask to about 100 ml. with distilled water, cautiously add about 0.2500 gram of KIO_4 and boil three minutes to oxidize the manganese(II) ion to the permanganate ion. Cool the solution to room temperature, dilute to the mark with distilled water, and mix thoroughly by inverting each of the stoppered flasks several times.

C. ABSORPTION MEASUREMENTS

(1) Using in turn each of the spectrophotometers provided, measure the percent transmittance of two standard solutions and one unknown sample from 400 mμ to 650 mμ, taking readings every 10 mμ. The intervals between readings should be decreased at points of minimum and maximum transmission. Plot the %T *vs.* λ (mμ) for the three samples on the same sheet of rectangular coordinate paper.

(2) Using each spectrophotometer provided, measure each standard sample solution and each unknown sample solution at 440, 480, 500, and 530 mμ. Record the %T of each solution at each wavelength. On the same sheet of semi-log graph paper, plot the %T *vs.* concentration of manganese (mg. per 250 ml.) for each of the standards at each wavelength measured. Draw the best straight line through the four values of %T observed at each wavelength used.

(3) For each filter photometer, place the instrument in operation according to the directions given by the manufacturer. Each of the four standard solutions and the three unknown solutions is measured and the %T values are recorded. Using separate sheets of semi-log graph paper, plot %T *vs.* concentration of manganese (mg. per 250 ml.) for the standard solutions measured on each filter photometer. On each graph, draw the best straight line through the four values of %T obtained.

(4) Select a standard solution whose intensity most nearly matches the three unknown solutions. Using a color comparator (*e.g.*, Duboscq Color Comparator), place a sample of the standard solution in one sample cup and in the other place a sample of an unknown solution. Measure the unknown solution according to the directions provided by the instructor. Each of the two remaining unknown solutions is measured in the same manner.

D. TREATMENT OF DATA

(1) From the standard calibration curve for each instrument and the %T values of the unknown sample solutions measured on each instrument, determine the concentration of manganese in mg. per 250 ml. for each of the unknown samples. Calculate the percentage of manganese in the sample of steel.

(2) Calculate the concentration of manganese of each unknown sample solution from the color comparator readings using the relationship:

$$c_1 b_1 = c_2 b_2$$

where c_1 is the concentration of the standard solution, b_1 is the reading of the standard solution, c_2 is the concentration of the unknown solution and b_2 is the reading of the unknown solution.

(3) Using the results obtained with each instrument, report in tabular form the percentages of manganese found.

ANALYSIS OF A TWO COMPONENT MIXTURE

A mixture of potassium dichromate and potassium permanganate solutions can be used to illustrate the analysis of a two component mixture having a two way overlap of absorption spectra. As can be seen from Figure 15.8, page 265, both potassium dichromate and potassium permanganate absorb strongly in the visible portion of the spectrum. Each spectrum overlaps the other so that the presence of one interferes with the analysis of the other. Nevertheless using the technique described on page 262, a mixture of these two substances can be analyzed.

From solutions of known concentrations the absorptivity, a, can be calculated at a given wavelength. Using this calculated value of the absorptivity and the absorbance of the solution measured at the specified wavelength, the concentration of the desired component can be determined.

Laboratory Experiment 29

Analysis of Potassium Dichromate–Potassium Permanganate Mixture Spectrophotometrically

Apparatus

An available spectrophotometer such as the Bausch and Lomb Spectronic 20; 5 cuvettes

Reagents

0.004 M $K_2Cr_2O_7$

prepared by weighing 0.2942 gram of analytical reagent grade potassium dichromate into a 250 ml. volumetric flask, dissolving in a small amount of distilled water and diluting to the line with distilled water.

0.004 M $KMnO_4$

prepared by weighing 0.1580 gram of analytical reagent grade potassium permanganate into a 250 ml. volumetric flask, dissolving in a small amount of distilled water and diluting to the line with distilled water.

0.5 N H_2SO_4

prepared by adding 14 ml. of concentrated sulfuric acid to 986 ml. of distilled water. Store in a glass stoppered pyrex bottle.

Procedure

Turn on the spectrophotometer to allow for the specified warm up time. In the case of the Spectronic 20 the time is 15 minutes.

A. ABSORPTION SPECTRUM OF POTASSIUM DICHROMATE

Into a 50 ml. volumetric flask pipet 5 ml. of 0.004 *M* $K_2Cr_2O_7$. Dilute to the mark with 0.5 *N* H_2SO_4. Mix thoroughly by inverting the stoppered flask several times. Place about 5 ml. of this solution in a cuvette. This sample will be used to obtain the spectrum of $K_2Cr_2O_7$.

Measure the percent transmittance, $\%T$, of this solution from 355–660 mμ at 5 mμ intervals. Calculate the absorbance, A, at each wavelength using the relationship $A = 2 - \log \%T$. Plot A *vs.* λ (mμ) using rectangular coordinate paper.

B. ABSORPTION SPECTRUM OF POTASSIUM PERMANGANATE

Into a 50 ml. volumetric flask, pipet 5 ml. of 0.004 *M* $KMnO_4$. Dilute to the mark with 0.5 *N* H_2SO_4. Mix thoroughly by inverting the stoppered flask several times. Place about 5 ml. of this solution in a cuvette. This sample will be used to obtain the spectrum of $KMnO_4$.

Measure the percent transmittance, $\%T$, of this solution from 355–660 mμ at 5 mμ intervals. Calculate the absorbance, A, at each wavelength in the same manner as in B-1. Plot A *vs.* λ (mμ) on the same piece of graph paper used in plotting A in B-1.

C. ABSORPTION AT SELECTED WAVELENGTHS BY POTASSIUM DICHROMATE AND POTASSIUM PERMANGANATE

(1) From the spectra plotted in Part B, select two wavelengths for the analysis of the mixture. At each wavelength selected one solution should show a strong absorption and the other should show a weak absorption.

(2) Into each of three 50 ml. volumetric flasks pipet 1, 2, and 4 ml. respectively of 0.004 *M* $K_2Cr_2O_7$. Dilute each solution to the mark with 0.5 *N* H_2SO_4. Mix thoroughly by inverting the stoppered flask several times. Place 5 ml. of each solution into a clean cuvette and measure the percent transmittance, $\%T$, at each of the wavelengths selected in C-1. Calculate the absorbance, A, at each wavelength in the same manner as in B-1. Record these values.

(3) Into each of three 50 ml. volumetric flasks pipet 1, 2, and 4 ml. respectively of 0.004 *M* $KMnO_4$ solution. Dilute each solution to the mark with 0.5 *N* H_2SO_4. Mix thoroughly by inverting the stoppered flask several times. Place 5 ml. of each solution into a clean cuvette and measure the percent transmittance, $\%T$, at each of the wavelengths selected in C-1. Calculate the absorbance, A, at each wavelength in the same manner as in B-1. Record these values.

D. ANALYSIS OF THE UNKNOWN MIXTURE OF POTASSIUM DICHROMATE AND POTASSIUM PERMANGANATE

Obtain in a 50 ml. volumetric flask an unknown aqueous solution of potassium dichromate and potassium permanganate. Dilute the solution to the mark with 0.5 N H_2SO_4. Mix thoroughly by inverting the stoppered flask several times. Place 5 ml. of each solution into a clean cuvette and measure the percent transmittance, $\%T$, at each of the wavelengths selected in C-1. Calculate the absorbance, A, at each wavelength in the same manner as in B-1.

From the values of the absorbance obtained calculate the concentration of $K_2Cr_2O_7$ and the $KMnO_4$ in the unknown solution. Report the number of milligrams of $K_2Cr_2O_7$ and $KMnO_4$ in the sample as received.

CHAPTER 16

Electrogravimetric Analysis

Electrogravimetric analysis, more commonly termed electrolysis, is based on the deposition of the element itself or a well defined compound of the element being determined on an electrode in a weighable form. This method does not require an exact measurement of a quantity of electricity to calculate the amount of the substance being determined. The electrolysis generally employs a constant current with a controlled potential at the working electrode. Being able to control the potential increases the selectivity and the possibility of isolation of the desired electrode reaction. This rather well demonstrated method has come into increased use in the last decade because of the increased development of automatic instrumentation.

PRINCIPLE OF ELECTROLYSIS

In a previous chapter it has been shown that the selection of a proper pair of half-reactions can produce a current as a result of the chemical reactions that take place at the electrodes. These reactions are reversible; thus chemical reactions can be produced by supplying a current at a suitable potential to the electrodes of the cell. The process of decomposition of a solution by the passage of an electric current is termed electrolysis. The cell in which the electrolytic process occurs is called an electrolytic cell. An electrolytic cell is composed of a solution of an electrolyte in which are placed two electrodes. These electrodes are connected externally to a source of direct current. An example of this type of an electrolytic cell is shown schematically in Figure 16.1. In this example, an aqueous solution of copper(II) sulfate is the electrolyte, the electrodes which are inserted in the solution are made of platinum, and the direct current source is a six volt battery. The negative ions in the solution that are attracted to the anode are called **anions.** In the illustration of the copper(II) sulfate solution, the $SO_4^{=}$ ions from the $CuSO_4$ solution and the small number of OH^- ions from the ionization of water are the anions. Those positive ions in the solution that are attracted to the cathode are called **cations.** The Cu^{++} ions from the copper(II) sulfate solution and the H^+ ions from the ionization of water are termed cations.

During the process of electrolysis, the Cu^{++} ion is reduced at the cathode and the water (or OH^- ions from it) is oxidized at the anode according to the following reactions:

$$Cu^{++} + 2e \rightarrow Cu \text{ (cathode reaction)}$$
$$H_2O \rightarrow \tfrac{1}{2}O_2 + 2H^+ + 2e \text{ (anode reaction)}$$

The $SO_4^=$ ions are not discharged at the anode because the OH^- ion is more easily oxidized at the anode. Hydrogen does not appear at the cathode because

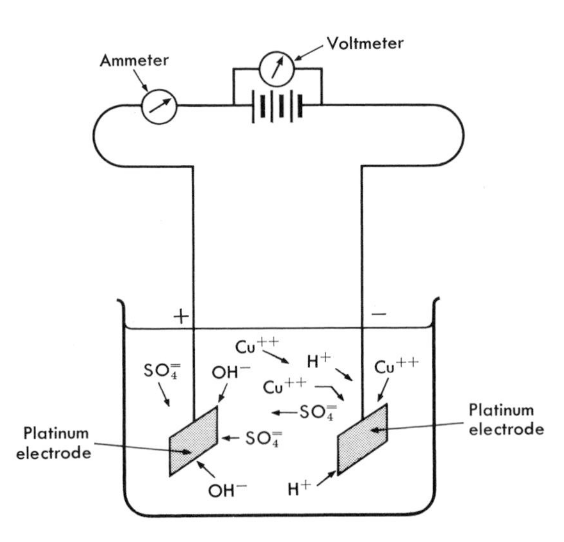

Fig. 16.1. Schematic diagram of an electrolytic cell containing an aqueous solution of copper(II) sulfate.

the Cu^{++} ion is easier to reduce than is the H^+ ion. The reactions that take place at an electrode depend on the ions present in solution and the nature of the electrode. Changes may occur at electrodes without the liberation of an elementary substance. An element may be oxidized to a higher oxidation state at the anode and the oxidized form may be reduced at the cathode. The following reactions of iron(III) and iron(II) can be used as an example.

$$Fe^{++} \rightarrow Fe^{+++} + e \qquad \text{(anode reaction)}$$
$$Fe^{+++} + e \rightarrow Fe^{++} \qquad \text{(cathode reaction)}$$

Electrolytic processes can be used as a means of purification of impure metals. For example, if an impure copper anode is placed in a solution of copper(II) sulfate and a pure copper cathode is used, upon the application of a direct current the Cu^{++} ion will plate out on the cathode as pure copper,

$$Cu^{++} + 2e \rightarrow Cu$$

while at the anode the reverse will happen. The copper will go into solution according to the reaction

$$Cu \rightarrow Cu^{++} + 2e$$

Some metals, under proper conditions, can be separated at the anode. One of the most common examples is that of lead(II) ions which are separated as lead(IV) in the form of PbO_2.

$$Pb^{++} + 2H_2O \rightarrow PbO_2 + 4H^+ + 2e$$

Manganese, uranium, and molybdenum react in a similar manner, being separated at the anode.

Decomposition Potential

If a current is passed through a solution, there is a minimum voltage below which no appreciable decomposition will occur. The lowest externally applied voltage that must be applied to cause steady electrolysis to occur is called the **decomposition potential** of the electrolyte. The decomposition potential can be obtained experimentally by plotting the current versus the externally applied voltage. Until the decomposition potential is reached, practically no current is detected and then with a further increase in potential, the current increases rapidly (see Figure 16.2).

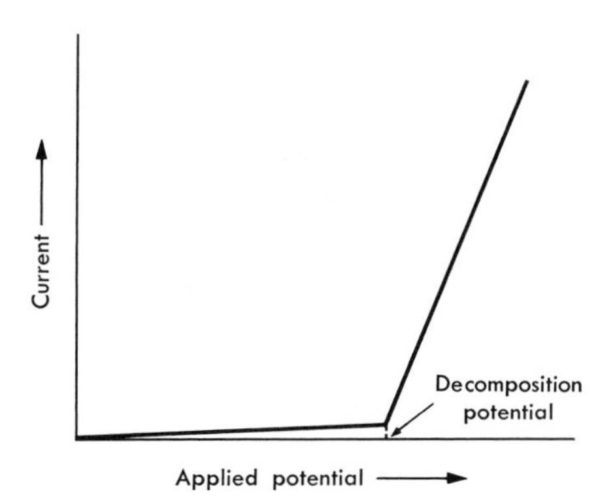

Fig. 16.2. Current-voltage graph illustrating the determination of the decomposition potential.

The decomposition potential can be expressed as

$$E_d = IR + E_{rev} + o.v.$$

where E_d is the decomposition potential, IR is the voltage drop through the entire circuit, E_{rev} is the "back *emf*" that arises from the cell operating as a voltaic cell and *o.v.* is the overvoltage. The IR drop of the circuit can be calculated using Ohm's Law. The "back *emf*" can be determined from the application of the Nernst equation to the voltaic cell produced. For example, in the electrolysis of copper(II) sulfate solution, the voltaic cell set up is

$$\mathrm{Pt} \mid \tfrac{1}{2}\mathrm{O_2}, 2\mathrm{H^+} \parallel \mathrm{Cu^{++}} \mid \mathrm{Cu}$$

the potential of which can be calculated as follows:

$$\begin{aligned} E &= E_1 - E_2 \\ &= \left[E^0_{\mathrm{H_2O}} - \frac{0.0591}{2} \log\,[\mathrm{H^+}]^2[p_{\mathrm{O_2}}]^{1/2}\right] \\ &\quad - \left[E^0_{\mathrm{Cu}} - \frac{0.0591}{2} \log\,[\mathrm{Cu^{++}}]\right] \end{aligned}$$

For the electrolysis to proceed, the voltage that is applied must be larger than this "back *emf*". If the values of the ohmic resistance of the solution and the "back *emf*" are added together and this voltage applied to the electrodes inserted in the solution, continuous deposition of the copper would not occur. It would be necessary to add a small voltage to cause the copper to plate out continuously. This small additional voltage is the overvoltage (see the following section).

As a result of the "back *emf*" factor, the decomposition potential is concentration dependent and, therefore, it will change continuously during the electrolysis.

Overvoltage

The difference between the potential of an electrode when the continuous plating of the substance was observed and the theoretical reversible value for the same solution is called the **overvoltage.** The importance of the overvoltage is greatest at the electrodes where a gas is liberated. For all practical purposes, the overvoltage in the separation of metals can be neglected since, as a general rule, it is very small. The overvoltage may occur at the anode as well as the cathode.

The overvoltage depends on several factors.

(1) The current density employed. The overvoltage usually increases with current density. Current density is the amount of current per unit area of the electrode, usually expressed in amperes per square centimeter of electrode surface (normal density). The increase in overvoltage with current density is greatest at low current densities in any given case. As the normal density (N.D.) increases above N.D. = 0.10 there is comparatively little further effect.

(2) The nature of the electrode. The effect is especially great when a gas is liberated at the electrode. Table 16.1 shows the variation in the overvoltage of hydrogen on a variety of electrodes.

(3) The temperature of the solution. The overvoltage usually decreases as the temperature increases. An exception to this is the hydrogen overvoltage on platinized platinum, which appears to be independent of the temperature.

(4) The concentration gradient in the vicinity of the electrodes. As this increases, the overvoltage also increases.

(5) The nature of the surface of the electrode. The overvoltage on bright metallic electrodes is higher than on those electrodes that have roughened surfaces.

TABLE 16.1
Overvoltage of Hydrogen for Different Electrodes in Acid Solution

TYPE OF ELECTRODE	OVERVOLTAGE	
	C.D. = 0.01	C.D. = 0.1
Pt, smooth	0.07	0.29
Pt, platinized	0.03	0.04
Au	0.39	0.59
Hg	1.04	1.07
Cu	0.58	0.85
Fe	0.56	0.82

C.D. = Current density, amp./$cm.^2$

The analytical chemist can take advantage of the differences of overvoltage arising from the above factors in electrolytic separations. The most important overvoltages are those of hydrogen and oxygen, especially hydrogen. In most electrolyses there is some evolution of hydrogen at the cathode due to the local depletion of the metal ions in the vicinity of the electrode. The deposition of hydrogen would predominate if it were not for the hydrogen overvoltage. The complete removal of many metals from solution would then become difficult. The high overvoltage of hydrogen on mercury can be used to accomplish depositions that could not be made otherwise. The use of a mercury cathode to remove iron and zinc from aluminum is an example of the use of this technique.

Electroanalytical Separations

If there is enough difference between the decomposition potentials of two substances, it is possible to separate these substances using electrogravimetric methods. The separations that can be accomplished by electrolysis can be predicted from the redox potentials of the metal-metal ion half-reactions (activity series). If the half-cell potentials are of different signs, this has a special advantage if the deposition is to be made from acid solution. In the analysis of brass, the copper may be separated from zinc electrolytically because zinc is above hydrogen and the copper is below hydrogen in the activity series.

The discharge of hydrogen at the cathode effectively prevents the deposition of the more active metal. In general, the potential of the working electrode needs to be no more than 0.2 volts greater than the decomposition potential to obtain rapid electrolysis. For irreversible reactions this difference usually is adequate for complete electrolysis. The decomposition potential of a component being deposited from solution may be changed by chemical means. Complexing agents or a change of *p*H can cause the decomposition potential of the component to be changed and thus allow a separation to be made that could not have been accomplished under the original conditions. Polarography takes advantage of electroanalytical separations resulting from differences in the decomposition potentials of substances at a dropping mercury electrode.

Factors Affecting the Nature of the Deposit

There are many factors that affect the nature of the deposit that is formed on the electrode. The most desirable condition is a fine-grained adherent plate. The important factors that affect the physical form of the deposit are:

(1) Concentration of metal ions. The deposit will be fine-grained if the concentration of the metal ion being deposited is kept low. This can be accomplished many times by use of a complex ion, as in the case of plating silver from a cyanide bath. The concentration of free silver ion is kept at a very low value as a result of the following equilibrium:

$$Ag^{+} + 2CN^{-} \rightleftarrows Ag(CN)_2^{-}$$

(2) Nature of the substance being plated. The properties of metals greatly affect the nature of the plate that is obtained. Copper can be plated from an acid solution as a fine-grained adherent deposit; yet, under the same conditions, lead will be plated out on the anode as a spongy nonadherent deposit.

(3) Current density. High current density will cause excessive gassing. Rapid agitation of the solution allows the use of high current densities because fresh solution is constantly being brought into contact with the surface of the electrode.

(4) Evolution of hydrogen. A brittle deposit will result from the excessive evolution of gas. All the conditions that reduce the amount of gas evolution help obtain a better plate. Agitation, low current density, decrease in acidity of the solution, and high temperature are the important factors in the reduction of the evolution of gas. Chemical depolarizers may be used to reduce gas evolution. In the electrolytic deposition of copper, nitric acid is added because it oxidizes the hydrogen atoms at the cathode according to the reaction

$$NO_3^{-} + 2H^{+} + 8H \rightarrow NH_4^{+} + 3H_2O$$

In other electrolyses, such as nickel deposition, nitrates are harmful, and the electrolytic solution must be nitrate ion free.

To obtain a fine-grained adherent plate, the component should be plated from a dilute, well agitated solution, using a low current density.

METHODS OF SEPARATION

The two most common methods that are used for electrodeposition are constant potential analysis and controlled potential analysis.

Constant Potential Analysis

The applied potential is set at a particular value and left there during the entire electrolysis in the constant potential analytical method. Using this method, no separation can be made between two elements whose redox potentials are close together. As the substance is deposited the potential of the cathode will increase greatly, but it must be assumed that the potential of the cathode will not be great enough to exceed the decomposition potential of an unwanted component and cause it to be deposited. In water solution, the evolution of hydrogen at the cathode serves as a means of preventing the cathode potential from increasing to too great a value.

The constant potential analysis is the most common method of electrogravimetric analysis. The electrolytic separation and subsequent determination of copper in brass and bronze alloys is an example of the application of this method.

Controlled Potential Analysis

A separation of two substances whose electrode potentials are very similar can be accomplished by controlling the cathode potential during the entire electrolytic process at a value that is greater than the decomposition potential of one substance and less than that of the other. This process requires a means of measuring the potential of the cathode with respect to the solution near it. One way that this can be done is to place a calomel reference electrode close to the cathode and connect these electrodes to a potentiometer. Figure 16.3 shows a schematic diagram of one type of apparatus that can be used to accomplish this measurement. During the electrolysis the potential is kept from increasing by controlling the external resistance in the circuit. If the control is a manual one, the method requires the constant attention of the analyst. Automatic control of the potential is possible through the use of present day electronic circuitry. This eliminates the necessity of constant attention and makes the method more attractive. One deterring factor in many cases is that the equipment is rather expensive.

Successful separations using the controlled potential method have been made in the cases of copper from antimony, lead, and tin; silver from copper; nickel from aluminum, iron, and zinc; and tin from nickel.

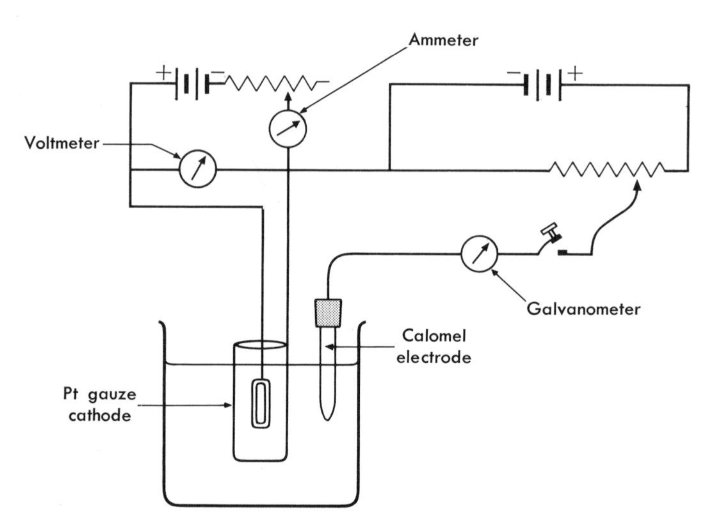

Fig. 16.3. Schematic diagram of apparatus for controlled cathode potential separations.

QUANTITATIVE ELECTROGRAVIMETRY

The quantitative relationship between the amount of material deposited on an electrode and the quantity of electricity is based on Faraday's Laws. These laws can be expressed as follows:

(1) The mass of any component deposited at an electrode is proportional to the quantity of electricity which passes through the solution.
(2) The passage of the same quantity of electricity through different solutions will cause the deposition of substances in amounts proportional to the equivalent weights of the substances.

Application of the two laws of Faraday to the stoichiometric relationships of electrolytic separations results in the following statement:

> One gram-equivalent weight of a substance can be deposited at an electrode by the passage of one faraday of electricity (96,500 coulombs).

If the current efficiency is 100%, then it becomes possible to measure the quantity of electricity that passes through the solution by determining the amount of chemical change produced at the electrode.

It is found by experiment that at 100% current efficiency 96,500 coulombs of electricity will deposit at the cathode:

$$\frac{Ag}{1} = 107.88 \text{ grams of silver from a solution of silver salt}$$

$$\frac{Cu}{2} = 31.77 \text{ grams of copper from a solution of copper(II) salt}$$

$$\frac{Co}{3} = 19.65 \text{ grams of cobalt from a solution of cobalt(III) salt}$$

To illustrate the stoichiometric relationships pertaining to Faraday's Laws and numerical concentration relationships, the following examples are given.

EXAMPLE I. What weight of metal is deposited at the cathode if a $AgNO_3$ solution is electrolyzed for 140 minutes at 0.18 ampere?

Solution:

Number of coulombs $= 140 \times 60 \times 0.18 = 1512$

Number of faradays $= \dfrac{1512}{96,500}$

One faraday will liberate $\dfrac{Ag}{1} = 107.88$ grams of silver at the cathode from the silver nitrate solution.

$$\frac{1512}{96,500} \times 107.88 = 1.68 \text{ g. Ag, } \textit{Ans.}$$

In the solution of the above example it is assumed that the current efficiency is 100%. In most analyses this is not generally the case.

EXAMPLE II. A solution containing 0.250 gram of copper, in solution as Cu^{++}, requires 20 minutes for complete deposition of the copper at 1.250 amperes. What is the current efficiency?

Solution:

At 100% current efficiency the weight of copper deposited is

$$\frac{20 \times 60 \times 1.25 \times Cu}{96,500 \times 2} = 0.493 \text{ g. Cu}$$

Actual deposition of copper is 0.250 gram copper

$$\frac{0.250}{0.493} \times 100 = 50.6\% \text{ current efficiency, } \textit{Ans.}$$

It is a common procedure in the analysis of a brass alloy to deposit the copper on the cathode and the lead on the anode from an acid solution. The composition of the solution at this point in the analysis is generally copper(II) ion, lead(II) ion, zinc ion, hydrogen ion, and the anions of the acid used in the solution of the sample. The following example is used to illustrate the type of calculations that can be made from this procedure.

EXAMPLE III. An acid solution containing 0.635 gram of copper(II) ion, 0.414 gram of lead(II) ion, and 0.326 gram of zinc ion is also 1.00 *N* in acid. It is electrolyzed with an average current of 2 amperes, and the volume of the solution is kept at 100 ml. Assuming 100% current efficiency and assuming that all the lead deposits as PbO_2 at the anode during the copper deposition at the cathode, what is the acid normality of the solution when all the lead is just out? What is the acid normality of the solution when all the copper is just out? What is the total volume of gas that has been liberated at this point? What is the acid normality of the solution after the current is continued for 10 minutes longer? What is the total volume of gas that has been liberated during the entire analysis?

Solution:

To solve this problem it is best to break the electrolytic process into three steps.

Step I. At the beginning of the electrolysis, copper is deposited at the cathode and lead dioxide at the anode.

Step II. The copper that remains in solution is deposited at the cathode and oxygen from the water is deposited at the anode.

Step III. During the time the current passes through the solution after all of the copper has been deposited, hydrogen is evolved at the cathode and oxygen at the anode.

Under the conditions of the problem, zinc cannot deposit at the cathode since the solution remains constantly acid. If the acid solution contains nitrate ion and the electrolytic process is continued for a long time, complete neutralization may result and then zinc could begin to deposit. The reactions listed at the cathode and anode during each step are given below.

	Anode reaction	Cathode reaction
Step I	$Pb^{++} + 2H_2O \rightarrow PbO_2 + 4H^+ + 2e$	$Cu^{++} + 2e \rightarrow Cu$
Step II	$H_2O \rightarrow \frac{1}{2}O_2 + 2H^+ + 2e$	$Cu^{++} + 2e \rightarrow Cu$
Step III	$H_2O \rightarrow \frac{1}{2}O_2 + 2H^+ + 2e$	$2H^+ + 2e \rightarrow H_2$

It can be seen that there is an increase in acidity in Steps I and II. Gas is evolved in Steps II and III.

$$\frac{635.0}{63.5} = 10 \text{ mmoles Cu} \qquad \frac{414}{207} = 2 \text{ mmoles Pb}$$

Gain in acidity in *Step I.*

The passage of 2 faradays of electricity (100% current efficiency) results in the deposition of 1 mole of PbO_2 at the anode; 1 mole of copper at the cathode; increase in acidity of 4 moles of H^+ and no gas evolution.

$$2 \text{ mmoles } Pb^{++} \times 4 = 8 \text{ mmoles } H^+/100 \text{ ml.} = 0.08 \text{ mmole } H^+/\text{ml.}$$
$$= 0.08 \text{ meq. } H^+/\text{ml.}$$

Acid normality $1.00 + 0.08 = 1.08$ *N*, *Ans.* Millimoles of copper deposited during PbO_2 deposition = 2. Millimoles of copper remaining in solution = 8.

Gain in acidity in *Step II.*

The passage of 2 faradays of electricity (100% current efficiency) results in the deposition of 1 mole of copper at the cathode, the evolution of one-half mole of oxygen at the anode, and an increase in acidity of 2 moles of H^+ ions.

$$8 \text{ mmoles } Cu^{++} \times 2 = 16 \text{ mmoles } H^+/100 \text{ ml.} = 0.16 \text{ mmole } H^+/\text{ml.}$$
$$= 0.16 \text{ meq. } H^+/\text{ml.}$$

Acid normality $1.08 + 0.16 = 1.24\ N$, *Ans.*

Gas Evolution in *Step II.*

The passage of 2 faradays of electricity (100% current efficiency) results in the evolution of one half mole of oxygen at the anode and one mole of copper at the cathode.

$$8 \times \tfrac{1}{2} = 4 \text{ mmoles } O_2$$
$$4 \text{ mmoles} \times 22.4 \text{ ml./mmole} = 89.6 \text{ ml. gas evolved,} \quad \textit{Ans.}$$

Gas Evolution in *Step III.*

For each faraday of current flowing through the solution after the deposition of copper is complete, one fourth mole of oxygen is evolved at the anode and one half mole of hydrogen at the cathode. This makes a total of three fourths mole of gas evolved per faraday of current passing through the solution.

$$\frac{10 \times 60 \times 2 \times 3}{96{,}500 \times 4} = 0.00933 \text{ mole gas} = 9.33 \text{ mmoles}$$
$$9.33 \text{ mmoles} \times 22.4 \text{ ml./mmole} = 209 \text{ ml. gas evolved}$$

The total volume of gas liberated during the entire electrolysis is

$$209 + 89.6 = 298.6 \text{ ml.,} \quad \textit{Ans.}$$

References

1. Delahay, *Instrumental Analysis,* The Macmillan Company, New York, 1957.

2. Glasstone, *Introduction to Electrochemistry,* D. Van Nostrand Company, Inc., Princeton, N.J., 1942.

3. Lingane, *Electroanalytical Chemistry,* 2nd ed., Interscience Publishers, Inc., New York, 1958.

4. Willard, Merritt, and Dean, *Instrumental Methods of Analysis,* 3rd ed., D. Van Nostrand Company, Inc., Princeton, N.J., 1958.

Problems

1. How many minutes will it take for a current of 0.700 ampere to cause the deposition of 500.0 mg. of copper from acid solution on the basis of (a) 100% and (b) 70% current efficiency? *Ans. (a) 36.2 min.; (b) 51.7 min.*

2. How many coulombs of electricity are required to deposit 0.100 gram of silver from a nitric acid solution? How many amperes of current would be required to deposit that amount in 17 minutes 35 seconds? *Ans. 89.5 coulombs; 0.085 amp.*

3. With a current of 1.00 ampere, what volume of gas (under standard conditions) will be evolved in 30 seconds in a water coulometer? *Ans. 5.2 ml.*

4. If a current of 0.500 ampere is passed through a copper sulfate solution, what weight of copper would be deposited in 60 minutes? What is the gain in acidity in terms of millimoles of sulfuric acid during the 60 minute period? *Ans. 0.590 gram; 9.3 mmoles* H_2SO_4

5. If 6.5 amperes of current will deposit 0.532 gram of cobalt from a solution of cobalt(II) solution in 10 minutes, what is the current efficiency? *Ans. 44.7%*

6. Assuming 100% current efficiency, what would be the gain in weight of an anode placed in an acid solution containing 0.25 millimole of lead that is electrolyzed until deposition is complete, using a current of 0.900 ampere? How many minutes would be required to complete the deposition of the lead? *Ans. 59.8 mg.; 0.89 min.*

7. What would be the net gain or loss in gram equivalents of hydrogen ion per faraday in the electrolysis of HNO_3 in which 75% of the current goes to the simple decomposition of water and 25% goes to the reduction of nitrate to free nitrogen at the cathode and the liberation of oxygen at the anode? *Ans. 0.05*

8. An alloy consists of 18.62% lead and 77.55% zinc. A one gram sample is dissolved in acid and the solution diluted to one liter. A 500.0 ml. sample of the solution is electrolyzed at 1.5 amperes for exactly 10 minutes (assuming 100% current efficiency) with the deposition of lead as PbO_2. A 50 ml. pipetful of the remaining original sample solution is titrated with 0.050 N NaOH requiring 30.0 ml. to neutralize the acid present.

(a) How many milliliters of gas (under standard conditions) are evolved during this time? *Ans. 146.4 ml.*

(b) After the electrolysis, the volume is brought to 500 ml. What would be the acid normality of the solution? *Ans. 0.034 N*

9. An acid solution of an alloy containing 0.450 gram of copper, 0.350 gram zinc, and 0.1035 gram lead is electrolyzed with an average current of 0.750 ampere. Assuming 100% current efficiency, calculate the total gain in acidity in terms of millimoles of hydrogen ion (a) at the end of the copper deposition at the cathode, and (b) after the current was continued for 10 minutes beyond completion of the copper deposition. What volume of gas (under standard conditions) has been evolved during the entire time of electrolysis? *Ans. (a) 15.2 mmoles; (b) 15.2 mmoles; (c) 152 ml.*

10. A sample of brass weighing 0.750 gram is dissolved, the tin is removed, and the resulting solution is electrolyzed using a current of 1.00 ampere. The cathode gains 0.6950 gram and the anode gains 0.0295 gram. Assuming 100% current efficiency and that the electrolysis is stopped as soon as the copper is completely deposited, calculate (a) the percentage of copper and lead in the sample, (b) the gain in acidity in terms of moles of sulfuric acid, and (c) the volume of gas evolved (under standard conditions). *Ans.* *(a) Cu, 92.7%, Pb, 3.4%; (b) 0.010 mole* H_2SO_4*; (c) 121 ml.*

CHAPTER **17**

Electrometric Methods of Analysis

Methods that depend on the exact measurement of one or more electrical quantities, the magnitude of which can be used as a measure of the amount of a substance being determined, are classed as electrometric methods. These methods are associated with the reactions at metallic electrodes in contact with electrolytic solutions and with the transport of ions through electrolytic solutions.

There are several distinct classifications of electrometric methods. These include potentiometric, conductometric, coulometric, and polarographic methods.

POTENTIOMETRIC METHODS

In earlier discussions of acid-base, oxidation-reduction, and precipitation reactions, it has been shown how the measurement of a potential (*emf*) of a galvanic cell, or of the manner in which the potential changes during a titration, can be used as a means of determining the amount of substance in a solution.

CONDUCTOMETRIC METHODS

Techniques based on a single measurement of resistance of a solution or on measurement of changes in resistance during a titration involving ion-combination reactions are classed as conductometric methods.

Since the conductivity of a solution is dependent continually upon all ions present in solution, any change in the conductivity of the ion species in the solution will cause a change in the overall conductivity of the solution. The analytical chemist is able to use conductance measurements to detect changes in the make-up of the solution, as well as to determine the composition of binary mixtures. Conductance measurements can be used in the determination of ionization constants and in the calculation of the solubilities of slightly soluble salts in pure solvents. These solubilities can be used to evaluate the solubility product. The conductivity of a solution can be used to detect the equivalence point of a titration. Conductometric measurements are limited in their use because of their nonspecific nature.

Conductometric Titration

The conductance of a solution is dependent on the number, size, and charge of the ion species in solution. Ions of different species vary in their contribution to the total conductance. Therefore, if an ion of one species is replaced by one of another, the conductivity of the solution will show a measurable difference. For example, the reaction of neutralization of a strong acid and a strong base

$$H^+ + Cl^- + Na^+ + OH^- \rightarrow Na^+ + Cl^- + H_2O$$

can be used to illustrate the conductometric titration.

The conductance of the original solution—the hydrochloric acid—is the sum of the mobilities of the H^+ and the Cl^- ions. As the strong base, NaOH, is added to the solution, mobile H^+ ions react with the OH^- ions to form essentially undissociated molecules. The net result of the addition is that the Na^+ ion replaces the H^+ ion. From Table 17.1, listing the relative mobilities of ions (ionic conductance at infinite dilution at 25°C), it can be seen that the mobility of the H^+ ion is about seven times that of the Na^+ ion. The conductance of the solution will steadily decrease upon the addition of NaOH until all of the highly mobile H^+ ions have reacted with OH^- ions. Beyond this point—the equivalence point—the addition of excess NaOH places mobile OH^- ions in solution and causes the conductance to increase. The equivalence point is the intersection of the two straight arms of the curve (see Figure 17.1a).

The titration curve can assume various shapes, depending on the substance being titrated. The shape of the curve can be explained by considering the ion mobilities involved, the ionization constants of the reactants, and the hydrolysis of the salt formed during the titration. Examples of the various shapes of representative curves are given in Figure 17.1.

TABLE 17.1
Relative Mobilities of Ions
(Ion Conductances at Infinite Dilution at 25°C)

Cation	Conductance	Anion	Conductance
H^+	349.8	OH^-	198.
K^+	73.5	Br^-	78.4
NH_4^+	73.4	Cl^-	76.3
Ag^+	61.9	NO_3^-	71.4
Na^+	50.1	HCO_3^-	44.5
Li^+	38.6	$C_2H_3O_2^-$	40.9

The reactions that are illustrated by the various curve types are: displacement reactions, such as the titration of sodium acetate by hydrochloric acid; precipitation reactions, shown by the precipitation of chloride ion using silver

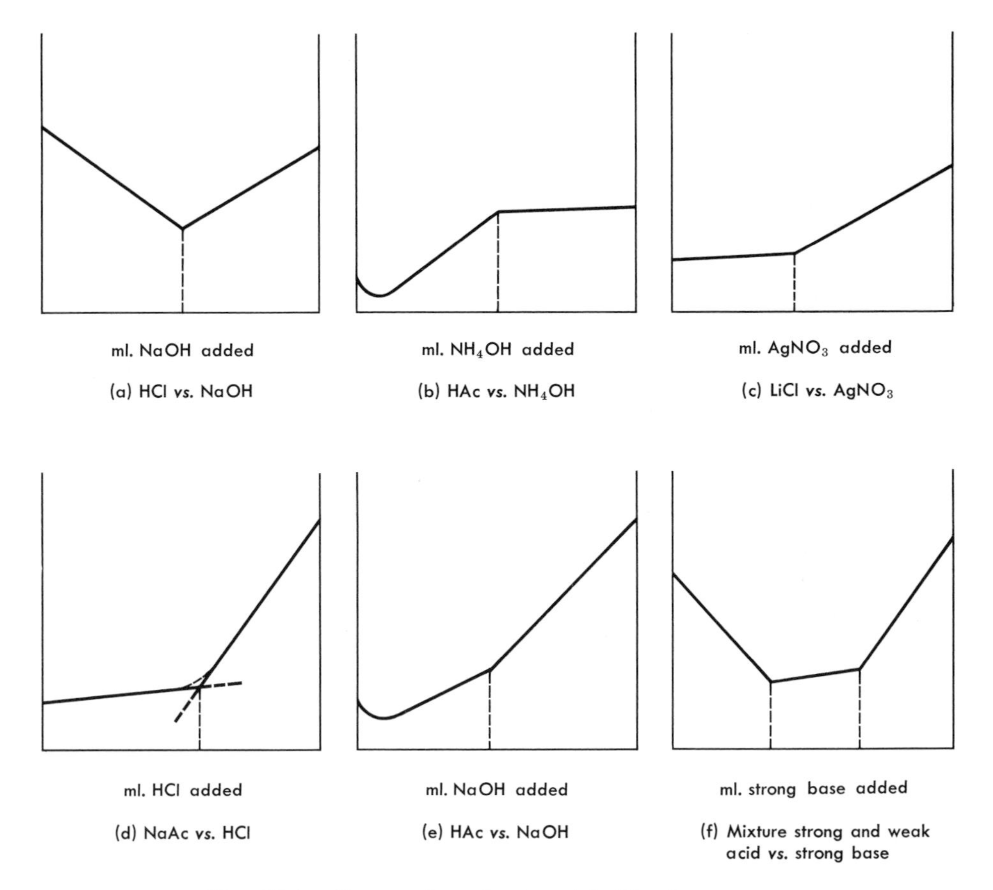

Fig. 17.1. Forms of conductometric titration curves.

ion; and the determination of a binary mixture, exemplified by the titration of a mineral acid in vinegar using sodium hydroxide.

One of the main advantages of conductometric titrations is the fact that such titrations can be performed rapidly on samples of unknown composition without fear of missing the equivalence point. Generally these titrations are selected in place of potentiometric titrations in cases where considerable hydrolysis, solubility, or dissociation of reaction products occurs. Points taken near the equivalence point are not as important as those taken well before and well after this point. The titration curves frequently show curvature in the vicinity of the endpoint due to hydrolysis or solubility of the precipitate.

Conductometric titrations are restricted to applications where foreign electrolytes are known to be either absent or present in very low concentrations. High concentration of foreign electrolytes gives a flattened curve, thus making the endpoint difficult or impossible to distinguish accurately.

Conductance Measurement Apparatus

The apparatus used to make a conductance measurement is of a Wheatstone bridge type. An example is illustrated in Figure 17.2. The variable resistance

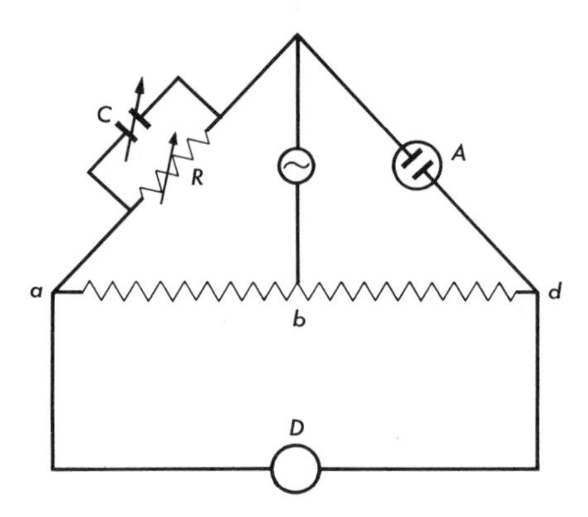

Fig. 17.2. Diagram of a Wheatstone bridge type conductometric apparatus. *Redrawn with permission of Harley and Wiberley,* Instrumental Analysis, *John Wiley and Son, Inc., N.Y., 1954.*

R and the two arms ab and bd of the bridge are adjusted until no current can be detected at D. The resistances are related by the simple proportion

$$\frac{A}{R} = \frac{bd}{ab}$$

Since the resistance R is known and the ratio of ab to bd can be measured, the resistance of the cell A can be calculated. In practice, the resistance of R should be such that the bridge is balanced at the midpoint of the slide wire ad. The error in the setting of R will cause the least error in the final result under these conditions. The current detector (D) can be earphones, an a-c galvanometer, or an oscilloscope. These are commonly used to detect the point of balance of the Wheatstone bridge.

Conductometric Cells

Conductivity cells are made in various forms. The outer shape of the cell is designed to fit the conditions of the experiment. All cells contain two electrodes of given surface area made of platinum coated with platinum black. The platinum electrodes can be platinized by electrolyzing them in a solution of 3% chloroplatinic acid containing a trace of lead acetate. The direction of the direct current is reversed every thirty seconds. After the electrodes are platinized they should be stored in distilled water. Several of the common types of conductivity cells are shown in Figure 17.3.

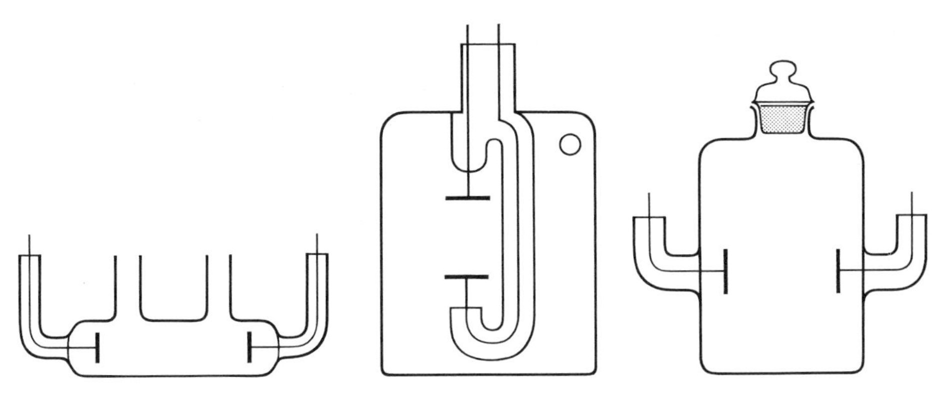

Fig. 17.3. Three types of conductivity cells.

COULOMETRIC METHODS OF ANALYSIS

Although Faraday's Law has been known for more than a hundred years, it is only recently that the relationship between the quantity of electricity and the quantity of the electrode reaction has been used for the purpose of chemical analysis. Coulometric methods are based on the measurement of the quantity of electricity required during the complete reaction of the substance being determined. When the substance being determined reacts directly at one of the electrodes, it is called **primary** coulometric analysis. If it reacts in solution with another reagent generated by an electrode reaction, then it is termed **secondary** coulometric analysis.

Requirements for Coulometric Analysis

The prime requisites for coulometric analysis are that the electrode reaction must proceed with 100% current efficiency and that only one reaction must take place. The reagent must react stoichiometrically and rapidly with the substance being determined. Two different techniques have been developed; one is coulometric titration with a constant current, and the other is coulometric analysis with controlled potential of the working electrode. Both depend on the fact that whenever one faraday of electricity (96,500 coulombs) passes through an electrolyte, it causes one gram-equivalent of chemical change of reactant in the solution. Therefore, if the quantity of electricity, expressed as coulombs, is known, the number of equivalents of the substance transformed can be calculated. The number of coulombs of electricity is equal to the current in amperes multiplied by the time in seconds that it takes for the completion of the reaction. Using a constant value of the current, it is only necessary to measure the time of the electrolysis. Most of the methods used to detect endpoints in ordinary analysis can be used to indicate the completion of the reaction in a coulometric titration.

Coulometric Titrations

The largest number of applications of the coulometric method are found in coulometric titrations. In a coulometric titration the titrant is prepared as a result of an electrode reaction, rather than being introduced by means of a buret as in volumetric titrations. Often the titrant is generated in the electrolysis cell. This preparation illustrates one of the advantages of this type of titration. Many substances that are difficult to employ as standard solutions, such as bromine or iodine, can be generated as needed in the electrolysis cell. The amount of the reagent generated is measured electrically in coulometric titrations. Thus, the standard reagent is the electron.

Advantages of Coulometric Titrations

There are several advantages of coulometric titrations. The common ones are as follows:

(1) Electrical measurements can be made with a high degree of accuracy. Therefore, the method is capable of producing results with a high degree of accuracy.

(2) The need for standard solutions is eliminated. A constant current supply can be used to generate a variety of titrants in virtually any strength required. The primary standard becomes the coulomb instead of some chemical standard.

(3) The titrant can be generated on demand. There is no need of standardizing and storing large volumes of solutions, many of which are unstable.

(4) The method is ideal for automation because of the electrical means of generation of the reagents. It is easy to devise remote operational methods for use in areas where dangerous materials are handled.

(5) Since the electrical switch takes the place of the buret stopcock, the control of the amount of the titrant that enters the reaction is very simple and accurate. The current can be set accurately and controlled at almost any value so that the overall quantity of electricity used during the reaction can be produced precisely for subsequent titrations of the same ion.

Limitations of the Method

For the determination of moderate amounts of material the precision is determined by the precision of the electrical and time measurements in the generating system. The coulometric titration of very small amounts is dependent on the precision with which the endpoint of the reaction is detected.

The major limitations to coulometric titrations when extended to the submicrogram range appear to result from slow electrode processes, adsorption phenomena, and kinetic factors at extreme dilutions.

Applications of Coulometric Titrations

The applications of coulometric titrations are varied. Substances such as arsenic, antimony, thallium, and uranium can be titrated with bromine, which can be generated with 100% current efficiency by the oxidation of bromide ion at a platinum electrode. Slow bromination reactions such as the bromination of aniline can be done coulometrically. In the same manner as bromine, iodine can be generated at a platinum anode from the oxidation of iodide ion and can be used to determine the amount of substances present such as arsenic, antimony, selenium, thiosulfate ion, and sulfide ion. Many other reagents that can be generated electrically can be used in coulometric titrations. For a complete discussion of the applications of coulometric titrations, reference 4 at the end of the chapter should be consulted.

POLAROGRAPHIC METHODS OF ANALYSIS

In 1922, Heyrovsky initiated a new method of analysis depending on the fact that the measurement of the current flow can be a specific property. In polarography, the current due to ion diffusion and subsequent electrolysis is measured. The polarographic method can be used as both a quantitative and qualitative method of analysis.

Polarography, a portion of the general field known as voltammetry, deals with the characteristics of current-voltage curves obtained by the use of a dropping mercury electrode.

Dropping Mercury Electrode

The dropping mercury electrode (DME) consists of a length of capillary tubing that has a very fine bore. The capillary is connected to a mercury reservoir by Tygon tubing. As the mercury flows through the capillary, a very small drop forms on the capillary tip. The drop grows until it reaches a certain perfectly definite size and then falls off. As one drop falls off, another begins to grow, reaching the same size and then dropping off. This process can go on indefinitely. Each drop has a spherical surface, free from scratches or any irregularities. As a result, the calculation of the electrode area is a rather simple one. Since the surface of the electrode is renewed every four or five seconds due to the drop falling from the tip, materials that are deposited or adsorbed are not able to accumulate on the surface. The dropping mercury electrode is much less sensitive to shock than solid electrodes. One drop may be shaken off the tip due to shock with little effect on the next drop.

An additional important advantage of the dropping mercury electrode is that the hydrogen overvoltage on mercury is very large. This extends the cathodic range over which current-voltage curves are obtainable for substances that are difficult to reduce, without interference from the hydrogen ion. Aluminum ion and manganous ion are examples of substances whose polarograms can be obtained with dropping mercury electrodes, but cannot be obtained using a noble metal microelectrode.

There are disadvantages associated with a dropping mercury electrode. Metallic mercury is easily oxidized. This oxidation begins at a potential near +0.4 volt *vs.* a standard calomel electrode, according to the equation

$$Hg \rightarrow Hg^{+} + 1e$$

For this reason, the use of the dropping mercury electrode for analysis of substances whose oxidation potential is near to or greater than this value is definitely limited.

Apparatus for Polarographic Measurements

The apparatus necessary to obtain a current-voltage curve (polarogram) is basically simple. The instrument is called a **polarograph.** It is constructed so that the current flow can be measured as the voltage to the electrodes is gradually increased. The potentials required are not usually larger than two volts. The current flowing is quite small, usually a few microamperes. A variable, direct current voltage source, a sensitive galvanometer to measure the current, and a measuring device for the voltage are needed. These, along with a cell and a pair of electrodes make up the instrument. A schematic diagram of a basic instrument is shown in Figure 17.4.

General Principles

Current-voltage curves, called **polarograms,** that arise at a microelectrode when diffusion is the rate determining step in the discharge of ions, form the basis for the polarographic method. A typical polarogram, one of the cathodic type, that of lead, is illustrated in Figure 17.5. A small residual current is observed as the applied potential is increased. As the decomposition potential of the Pb^{++} ion is reached, the current will increase, gradually at first, then very sharply and finally slowly until the current reaches the limiting value controlled by the diffusion process. Referring to Figure 17.5, the portion of the curve from A to B is composed of the residual current and the migration current. From B to C is the part of the curve resulting from the electrolysis current as the applied voltage is increased.

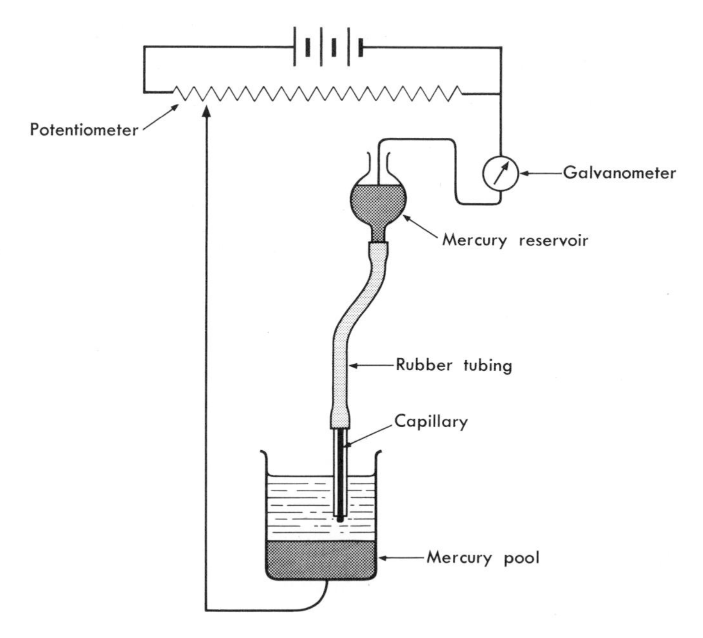

Fig. 17.4. Schematic diagram of a simple polarograph. The mercury reservoir can be raised or lowered to regulate the time of the mercury drop.

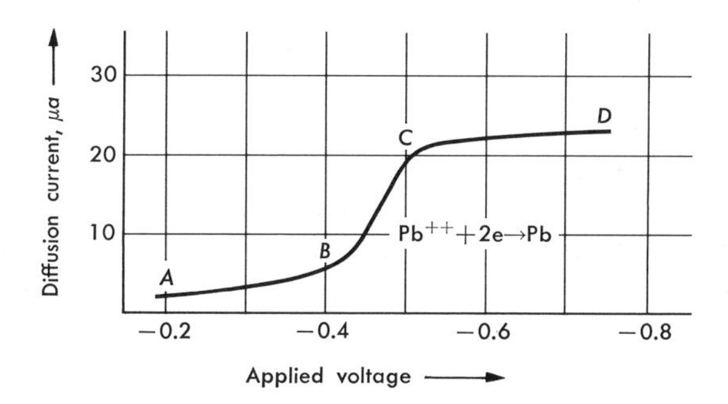

Fig. 17.5. Polarogram of a solution containing lead ions.

When more than one cation is in solution, a polarogram as shown in Figure 17.6 will be obtained. The curve resulting from the decomposition of lead at the cathode is the same as in Figure 17.5. After *D* the applied voltage exceeds the decomposition potential of the Zn^{++} ions and the current again increases, developing the zinc curve (wave). The rise at the end of the zinc is the reduction of the cations in the supporting electrolyte.

Migration Current

The current resulting from the migration of a metal ion under the influence of an electric potential difference between the mercury surface and the solution

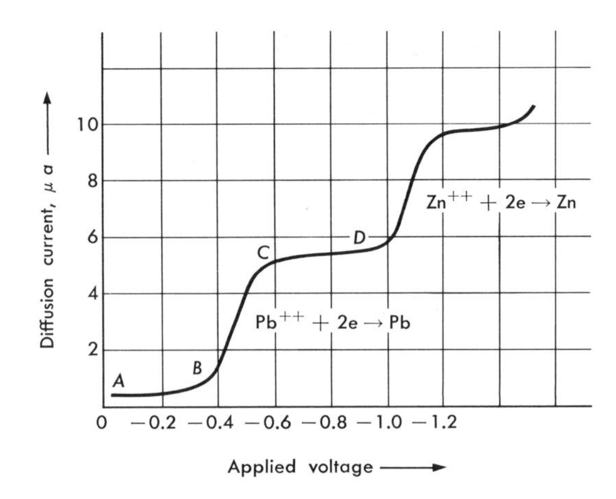

Fig. 17.6. Polarogram of a solution containing lead and zinc ions.

is called the **migration current.** The addition of a large excess of an inert electrolyte, the **supporting electrolyte,** which is not oxidized or reduced in the potential region under consideration, causes the migration current to be carried almost entirely by the inert electrolyte. An example of such a supporting electrolyte is potassium chloride. The result of this addition is that the limiting current corresponding to the plateau of the wave will be solely the diffusion current of the ions being reduced at the dropping mercury electrode.

Diffusion Current

The basis of the diffusion current is a concentration gradient. When the ionic species in the bulk of the solution has a greater concentration than at the electrode surface, the ions tend to diffuse across the interface at a rate proportional to the concentration difference. The current will rise gradually, then very sharply as the applied voltage is increased. As the voltage across the electrode is increased, there will be a point where the concentration gradient at the interface is zero and the diffusion rate becomes constant. No further increase in voltage will change the diffusion rate. The current value levels off since the number of ions plating into the drop equals the maximum number of ions furnished by diffusion from the body of the solution.

The first theoretical equation for the diffusion current obtained with the dropping mercury electrode (DME) was derived by Ilkovic. From the laws governing the diffusion conditions at a DME and the periodic growth and fall of the mercury drop, Ilkovic derived the following equation:

$$i_d = 607nD^{1/2}m^{2/3}t^{1/6}c$$

where i_d = average current during the life of the drop in microamperes
n = number of faradays of electricity per mole of electrode reaction

D = diffusion coefficient of reducible or oxidizable substance in sq. cm. per sec.
m = rate of flow of mercury from DME in mg/sec.
t = time for each drop of mercury to form, in sec.
c = concentration of electroactive substance in mmoles/liter.

In the usual polarographic analytical method the equation can be reduced to

$$i_d = kc$$

where k is a constant and c is the concentration of the electroactive substance in millimoles per liter. This can be accomplished by using the same capillary, same drop time, and a series of standards prepared and measured in the same manner as the unknown solutions.

The Ilkovic equation can be broken down into two parts to show that this relationship will hold under the conditions stated.

(a) $m^{2/3}t^{1/6}$—dependent on the characteristics of the capillary
(b) $nD^{1/2}c$—dependent on the properties of the solution

By using the same capillary and the same drop time, term (a) will become constant. This term can be evaluated by measuring the mass of mercury flowing through the capillary per second and the drop time in the diffusion current region. Diffusion currents obtained with different capillaries can be compared at similar potentials if the value of term (a) is known.

The second term, (b), is a function of the ion in solution. By using standards of the ion in question, prepared and measured in the same manner as the solution of the ion to be determined, n and D become constant. The remaining term, c, is the concentration of the ion in question.

It can be seen that the diffusion current, i_d, is directly proportional to the concentration of the ion in the solution which results in the relationship.

$$i_d = kc$$

Maxima

Frequently the current-voltage curves obtained with the DME contain maxima. These vary from sharp peaks to rounded humps. The current rises sharply, but instead of following a normal increase it increases abnormally until a maximum value is reached. When this point is reached, the current decreases rapidly until the value corresponding to the limiting plateau of the ion in question is reached. This is illustrated in Figure 17.7. It is necessary to eliminate the maxima formed. This can be accomplished in most cases by adding maxima suppressors. These suppressors are surface active agents such as dyes or gelatin. The amount of gelatin added is controlled carefully between 0.01 and 0.2%. Examples of dyes that are added are methyl red, bromthymol blue, and acidic and basic fuchsin. Usually a maxima suppressor is added to every polarographic solution as a precautionary measure.

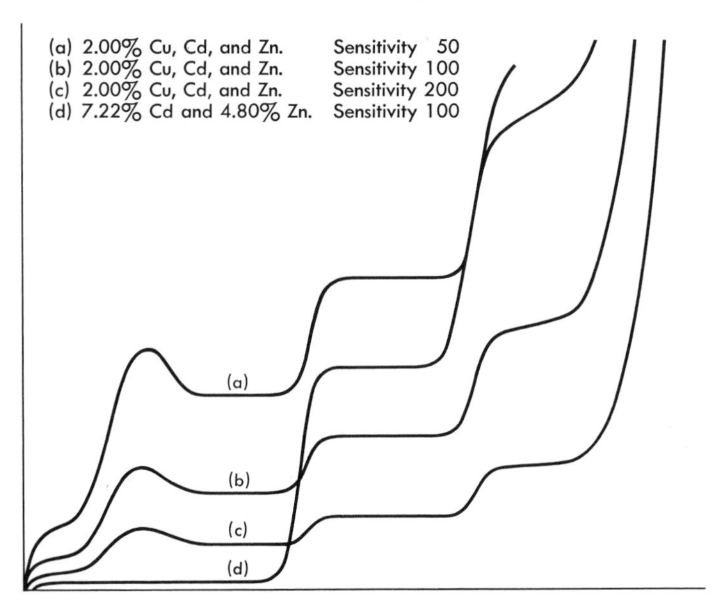

Fig. 17.7. Polarograms taken at different sensitivities of a copper, zinc and cadmium solution on a Sargent-Heyrovsky Recording Polarograph to illustrate the appearance of a polarographic maxima.

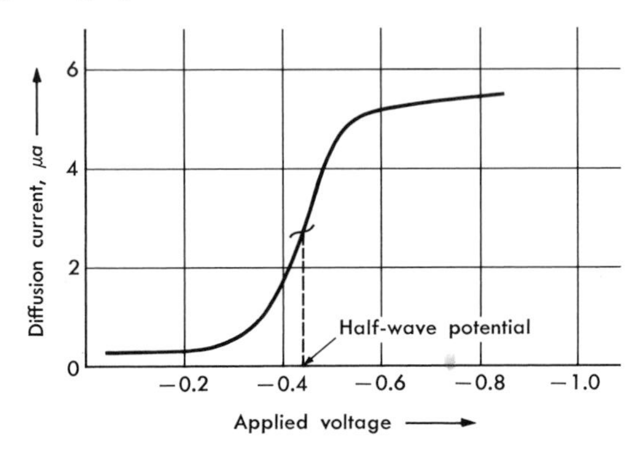

Fig. 17.8. Polarogram showing half-wave potential.

The magnitudes of the maxima appear to depend on the drop time. As the drop time becomes slower, the maxima will be smaller.

Half-Wave Potential

The potential at which the current in a polarographic cell is one half the diffusion current (see Figure 17.8)

$$i = \tfrac{1}{2}i_d$$

is called the **half-wave potential.** Because half-wave potentials are concentration independent and have significance thermodynamically, they are used for qualitative determinations, rather than decomposition potentials, because the latter are concentration dependent. The half-wave potentials are reported with reference to a standard electrode such as a saturated calomel electrode.

Since half-wave potentials are characteristic of the molecular form of the reducible or oxidizable material, they can be shifted by the addition of complexing agents or by varying the *p*H of the solution. This is advantageous when it is necessary to determine two substances simultaneously whose half-wave potentials overlap.

One indication that an electrode reaction is not proceeding reversibly is a serious deviation among the half-wave potentials of a series of solutions differing only in concentration of the ion species.

Kinds of Applications

Polarography can be used both as a quantitative and as a qualitative method. The half-wave potential can be used for the qualitative determination of the ions present in the solution. Since the half-wave potentials of many of the common ions are very near the same value, polarography as a qualitative tool is a special application rather than a general application. Small quantities of substances can be determined quantitatively by polarographic methods. Methods have been devised so that both organic and inorganic substances can be determined quantitatively.

Anodic waves can be used to determine the amount of a substance that forms in soluble salts or a stable complex with the mercurous or mercuric ion. Bromide, iodide, hydroxide, sulfide, and cyanide ion are examples of such substances.

In addition to the analytical applications of these methods, polarography can be used to evaluate the formal potentials of redox couples under varying conditions. Much fundamental physico-chemical information can be obtained from polarographic data. The polarograph is therefore seen to be a very useful tool in modern instrumental methods of analysis.

Amperometric Titration

This is the term used for techniques whereby the diffusion current is plotted versus the volume of titrant added. The endpoint in the titration can be determined from the curve.

The potential is kept at a constant value on the plateau of the wave for the ion to be followed, the titrant is added, and the diffusion current is measured after each addition. At the value of the applied potential selected for the titration, the titrant yields no diffusion current. Therefore, as the titrant is added, the diffusion current will decrease; after the endpoint the current remains essentially at zero. The endpoint is determined graphically, thus it is not necessary to take data around the endpoint. As in conductometric titrations, a few points taken before and a few points taken after the endpoint are sufficient to construct the titration curve.

The amperometric titration of a nonreducible ion by a reagent capable of electrolytic reduction will give a satisfactory titration curve. The diffusion current increases steadily after the endpoint as excess titrant is added, whereas

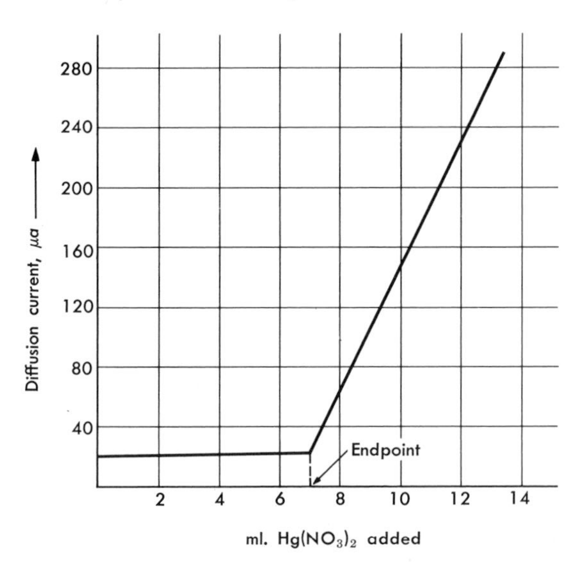

Fig. 17.9. Amperometric titration curve for NaCl solution titrated with mercury(II) nitrate.

prior to the endpoint the current remains essentially constant. Figure 17.9 illustrates a titration curve of this type obtained by titrating sodium chloride solution with mercury(II) nitrate solution.

The application of amperometric titrations is most common in volumetric precipitation reactions, especially those involving small amounts of organometallic precipitates.

References

1. Glasstone, *Introduction to Electrochemistry*, D. Van Nostrand Company, Inc., Princeton, N.J., 1942.

2. Harley and Wiberley, *Instrumental Analysis*, John Wiley and Sons, Inc., New York, 1954.

3. Kolthoff and Lingano, *Polarography*, 2nd ed., Interscience Publishers, Inc., New York, 1952.

4. Lingane, *Electroanalytical Chemistry*, 2nd ed., Interscience Publishers, Inc., New York, 1958.

5. Meites and Thomas, *Advanced Analytical Chemistry*, McGraw-Hill Book Company, Inc., New York, 1958.

6. Willard, Merritt, and Dean, *Instrumental Methods of Analysis*, 3rd ed., D. Van Nostrand Company, Inc., Princeton, N.J., 1958.

Laboratory Experiment 30

Polarographic Titration

Apparatus

Fisher Elecdropode or a similar polarograph

Reagents

0.01 *M* $PbCl_2$
: prepared by weighing 0.6955 gram of $PbCl_2$ into a 250 ml. volumetric flask, adding a small amount of distilled water to dissolve the salt, and diluting to the mark with distilled water.

0.01 *M* $CdCl_2$
: prepared by weighing 0.5710 gram of $CdCl_2 \cdot 2\frac{1}{2}H_2O$ into a 250 ml. volumetric flask, adding a small amount of distilled water to dissolve the salt, and diluting to the mark with distilled water.

0.01 *M* CuCl
: prepared by weighing 0.2475 gram CuCl into a 250 ml. volumetric flask, adding 20 ml. of 1 : 1 HCl solution to dissolve the salt, and diluting to the mark with distilled water.

0.2% gelatin
: prepared by dissolving 0.2 gram gelatin powder in 100 ml. of hot water.

2 *M* KCl
: prepared by dissolving 149.12 grams of reagent grade KCl in a small amount of water in a one liter volumetric flask, and diluting to the mark with distilled water.

Procedure

(1) Place the instrument in operation according to the directions with the instrument.

(2) Into a 100 ml. volumetric flask pipet 10 ml. of the $PbCl_2$ stock solution, 5 ml. of 2 *M* KCl solution, and 2.5 ml. of the 0.2% gelatin solution, and make up to the mark with distilled water.

(3) Run a polarogram of this solution from 0 volts to 1.2 volts negative (with respect to the pool), using 0.025 volt increments of applied voltage. Record the reading on the galvanometer (current, i) after each increment. Record the sensitivity.

(4) Into a 100 ml. volumetric flask, pipet 10 ml. of $CdCl_2$ stock solution, 5 ml. of 2 *M* KCl solution, and 2.5 ml. of 0.2% gelatin solution, and make up to the line with distilled water.

(5) Run a polarogram of this solution from 0 volts to 1.2 volts negative (with respect to the pool), using 0.025 volt increments. Record the reading on the galvanometer (current, i) after each increment. Record the sensitivity.

(6) Into a 100 ml. volumetric flask, pipet 10 ml. of CuCl stock solution, 5 ml. of 2 *M* KCl solution, and 2.5 ml. of 0.2% gelatin solution, and make up to the line with distilled water.

(7) Run a polarogram of this solution from 0 volts to 1.2 volts negative (with respect to the pool), using 0.025 volt increments. Record the reading on the galvanometer (current, i,) after each increment. Record the sensitivity.

(8) A 100 ml. volumetric flask containing an unknown solution is obtained from the instructor. To this solution add 5 ml. 2 *M* KCl solution and 2.5 ml. of 0.2% gelatin solution, and make up to the mark with distilled water.

(9) Run a polarogram of this solution from 0 volts to 1.2 volts negative (with respect to the pool), using 0.025 volt increments of applied voltage. Record the reading on the galvanometer (current, i,) after each increment. Record the sensitivity.

Calculations

(1) On the same piece of linear graph paper, plot a curve of applied voltage versus the current, i, using the horizontal axis for the applied voltage and the vertical axis for the current. Do this for the lead, cadmium, and copper solutions.

(2) Using the same scale as in (1) and a new sheet of graph paper, plot the data obtained from the unknown solution.

(3) From the half-wave potentials obtained from the graph plotted in (1) and the half-wave potentials obtained from the unknown solution plotted in (2), identify the components in the unknown mixture.

(4) From the heights of the waves in (1) and the concentration of the solution used to obtain these heights and the height of the wave of the same substance in the unknown solution, calculate the weight of each component in the unknown solution.

Laboratory Experiment 31

Coulometric Titration

Discussion

Iodine can be generated with 100% current efficiency according to the following reaction at a platinum anode:

$$2I^- \rightarrow I_2 + 2e$$

The iodine formed at the electrode can be used as a titrant in a volumetric titration. The acidity of the supporting electrolyte can range from strongly acid to a *p*H of about 8.5.

The iodine generated by the electrode system can be used to determine arsenic. If an unknown quantity of arsenic is present as $AsO_3^{\equiv}$ in the solution in which the iodine is being generated, then the $AsO_3^{\equiv}$ will be oxidized by the iodine to $AsO_4^{\equiv}$ according to the net equation

$$H_2O + AsO_3^{\equiv} + I_2 \rightarrow 2I^- + AsO_4^{\equiv} + 2H^+$$

When all of the $AsO_3^{\equiv}$ has reacted with I_2, the color of the solution will turn blue-black if starch is present during the titration, due to formation of the starch-iodo complex from the slight excess of iodine generated.

The amount of iodine generated can be calculated from Faraday's Law if the number of coulombs is known. The number of coulombs can be calculated from the number of seconds required for the appearance of the blue-black color and the current in amperes passing through the solution. Once the number of coulombs has been calculated, the number of faradays, and hence the number of equivalents of iodine, can be determined. Since the equivalents of iodine and the equivalents of arsenic are equal, the amount of arsenic can be determined. This relationship can be expressed mathematically,

$$W = \frac{QM}{96{,}500n}$$

where W is the weight of the substance with a formula weight M being titrated, Q is the number of coulombs required to reach the endpoint, 96,500 is the number of coulombs per faraday, and n is the number of faradays corresponding to one formula weight of the substance being titrated.

Apparatus

Constant current coulometric power supply and timer
Platinum electrodes

Reagents

0.16 N As_2O_3

prepared by weighing 7.9100 grams As_2O_3 into a one liter flask, adding enough dilute NaOH to dissolve the salt, making slightly acid with dilute HCl, and diluting to the mark with distilled water.

3% Starch

prepared by dissolving 3 grams starch in 100 ml. boiling water.

Composite KI and $NaHCO_3$ buffer

prepared by dissolving 60 grams KI, 10.25 grams $NaHCO_3$, and 0.25 ml. arsenite solution in a small amount of distilled water, and diluting to one liter in a volumetric flask.

Procedure

A. STANDARD SOLUTION

(1) Into a 100 ml. volumetric flask pipet 25 ml. of 0.16 N As_2O_3 solution, and dilute to the mark with distilled water.

(2) Into a 250 ml. beaker place 75 ml. of the KI-$NaHCO_3$ buffer solution. Pipet 2 ml. of the diluted stock solution prepared in (1) into the beaker and add 4–8 drops of the 3% starch solution. Place the stirring magnet in the beaker and set the beaker on the magnetic stirrer. Start the stirrer and cautiously raise the stirrer until the electrodes are immersed in the beaker to a depth such that the stirring magnet does not come in contact with the electrodes.

(3) Set the milliampere control to 20. Turn the switch to *OA* standby position. Reset the timer to zero.

(4) Turn the switch to titrate. Allow the titration to continue with rapid stirring until a blue-black or light purple color develops. It may be desirable to stop the titration near the endpoint and allow the iodine formed to react. Since the control switch can be compared to a buret stopcock, it is possible to stop the addition of iodine. Also the titrant, iodine, can be added in very small amounts. The iodine will appear as blue streaks streaming from the platinum generating electrode. By observing the time necessary for these blue streaks to disappear, it is possible to judge whether or not the endpoint is being approached. Thus, small additions of iodine can be made by turning the control switch on and off. As soon as a permanent blue-black color develops, stop the titration.

(5) Record the time in seconds from the timer. Record the exact value of the current shown in milliamperes on the ammeter.

(6) Pipet 2 ml. of the diluted stock solution into the beaker and repeat steps (3) through (5).

(7) Repeat the procedure, using 2 ml. aliquots, until the times agree within one second.

B. UNKNOWN SOLUTION

(1) From the instructor obtain an unknown solution in a 100 ml. volumetric flask. Dilute the solution to the mark with distilled water and shake well.

(2) Into a beaker containing 75 ml. of the KI-$NaHCO_3$ buffer solution and 4–8 drops of 3% starch solution, pipet 2 ml. of the unknown solution. Place the

beaker on the stirrer and insert the stirring magnet. Immerse the electrodes such that the stirring bar will not come in contact with the electrodes. Start the stirrer.

(3) Titrate the unknown solution according to steps A(3) through A(5) in the standardization procedure.

(4) Repeat the procedure, using 2 ml. aliquots, until the times agree within one second.

C. CALCULATIONS

(1) From the amperage and time, calculate the original normality of the stock solution prior to the dilution. Compare this with the normality calculated from the weight of the stock solution.

(2) Calculate the weight of As_2O_3 in milligrams in the unknown solution prepared by the instructor.

Laboratory Experiment 32

Conductometric Titration

Discussion

With the apparatus ready as it is set up, the square wave generator is turned on and the output set at 1000 cycles per second. The oscilloscope is turned on and allowed to warm up for 15 minutes. The conductometric cell is placed in the solution and the wave pattern is observed on the face of the oscilloscope. By adjusting the resistance of the decade resistance box, the wave pattern on the face of the oscilloscope is brought as nearly as possible to a horizontal line. The resistance value is recorded. An increment of titrant is added and the bridge is brought into balance again by adjusting the resistance until a horizontal line is obtained on the face of the oscilloscope. This procedure is repeated for each increment added.

Upon the completion of the experiment, the conductivity cell should be rinsed thoroughly and left immersed in distilled water. The oscillator and oscilloscope are turned off and the plugs disconnected from their sockets.

Apparatus

Standard Wheatstone bridge
Electronic oscillator square wave generator
Cathode ray oscilloscope
Conductometric cell (dipping type)

Reagents

0.100 N

hydrochloric acid prepared by diluting 8.5 ml. concentrated hydrochloric acid to one liter with distilled water.

0.100 N

sodium hydroxide prepared by dissolving 4.0 grams reagent grade sodium hydroxide in distilled water and diluting to one liter with distilled water.

$KHC_8H_4O_4$

potassium acid phthalate analytical reagent grade.

Procedure

(1) Accurately weigh a sample of previously dried potassium acid phthalate of about 0.200 gram. Dissolve the sample in about 500 ml. of distilled water in an 800 ml. beaker. Titrate the sample with 0.100 N sodium hydroxide. Measure the conductance at 2 ml. increments to 20 ml.

(2) Pipet 10 ml. of 0.100 N hydrochloric acid into an 800 ml. beaker and dilute to about 500 ml. with distilled water. Titrate the acid solution using 0.100 N sodium hydroxide. Measure the conductance at 2 ml. increments to 20 ml.

(3) Pipet a 50 ml. sample of vanilla extract into an 800 ml. beaker and dilute to 500 ml. with distilled water. Titrate with 0.100 N sodium hydroxide. Measure the conductance, using 1 ml. increments from 0–10 ml. of sodium hydroxide added and 2 ml. increments from 10–20 ml. of sodium hydroxide added.

(4) Pipet a 50 ml. sample of vinegar into an 800 ml. beaker and dilute to 500 ml. with distilled water. Titrate the solution using 0.100 N sodium hydroxide. Measure the conductance at 1 ml. increments until 25 ml. of sodium hydroxide is added and then at 2 ml. increments until 50 ml. of sodium hydroxide is added.

Calculations

(1) Plot $1/R$ *vs.* milliliters of sodium hydroxide added for each of the four solutions titrated.

(2) Determine the endpoint in each titration graphically.

(3) From the data obtained in Procedure (1), calculate the normality of the sodium hydroxide.

(4) Using the normality of the sodium hydroxide and the data obtained from Procedure (2), calculate the normality of the hydrochloric acid.

(5) Calculate the grams of vanillin per liter of vanilla extract from the data obtained in Procedure (3).

(6) Calculate the weight of hydrochloric acid in grams per liter, using the data obtained in Procedure (4). Calculate the weight of acetic acid in grams per liter in the vinegar sample.

Laboratory Experiment 33

Amperometric Titration

Apparatus

Fisher Elecdropode or similar manual Polarograph

Reagents

0.025 *N* $HgNO_3$

prepared by dissolving 3.5078 grams of analytical reagent grade $HgNO_3 \cdot H_2O$ in distilled water and diluting to approximately one liter in a pyrex bottle.

0.002 *N* NaCl in 0.1 *N* KNO_3

prepared by dissolving 0.1169 gram of reagent grade sodium chloride in 0.1 *N* KNO_3 in a one liter volumetric flask and diluting to the line with 0.1 *N* KNO_3.

0.1 *N* HNO_3

prepared by adding 6.6 ml. of concentrated nitric acid to a one liter volumetric flask and diluting to the mark with distilled water.

Procedure

A. STANDARDIZATION OF $HgNO_3$

Pipet a 100 ml. aliquot of 0.002 *N* NaCl into a titration beaker. Pour a layer of mercury on to the bottom of the beaker and put the beaker in place on the apparatus. Bubble nitrogen through the solution for five minutes. Adjust the applied voltage to 0.06 volt and read the galvanometer scale. Record the reading. Add 2 ml. of 0.025 *N* $HgNO_3$ and bubble nitrogen through the solution for one minute. Record the reading on the galvanometer after the gas is shut off. Repeat this procedure for each 2 ml. increment added until 14 ml. have been added.

B. TITRATION OF SOLUBLE CHLORIDE SAMPLE

Into a 500 ml. volumetric flask weigh to the nearest tenth of a milligram about 0.100 gram of the sample of the soluble chloride previously dried at 100–105°C. Add 50 ml. of distilled water, 5 drops of bromthymol blue indicator solution and neutralize with 0.1 *N* HNO_3. Dilute the solution to the mark with 0.1 *N* KNO_3. Mix the solution thoroughly by inverting the stoppered volumetric flask several times.

Pipet a 100 ml. aliquot into the titrating beaker. Pour a layer of mercury on to the bottom of the beaker and put the beaker in place on the apparatus. Bubble nitrogen through the solution for five minutes. Adjust the applied voltage to 0.06 volt and read the galvanometer scale. Record the reading. Add 2 ml. of the standard 0.025 *N* $HgNO_3$ and bubble nitrogen through the solution for one minute. Record the reading on the galvanometer after the gas is shut off. This procedure is followed using 2 ml. increments until 20 ml. of 0.025 *N* $HgNO_3$ have been added.

C. CALCULATIONS

(1) From the data obtained in the standardization of $HgNO_3$, plot the galvanometer reading *vs.* ml. of $HgNO_3$ added. Use a scale such that the endpoint can be determined to 0.01 ml. From the volume obtained at the endpoint and the normality of the sodium chloride solution calculate the normality of the $HgNO_3$.

(2) From the data obtained in the titration of the soluble chloride sample, plot the galvanometer reading *vs.* ml. of $HgNO_3$ added. Use a scale such that the endpoint can be determined to 0.01 ml. From the volume obtained at the endpoint, calculate the percentage of NaCl in the sample.

PART V

APPENDICES

APPENDIX I

Treatment of Analytical Measurements

In analytical chemistry, as in other related fields of science, any measurements that are made are subject to error. Determinations on the same sample, obtained independently and reported by different analysts using the same methods of analysis will not be in complete agreement with each other. Thus one of the main objectives of a beginning quantitative analysis course is to help the student analyst understand the limits of accuracy that can be expected from a given chemical method and appreciate the significance of the measurements involved. Measurements depend on the instruments involved in the measurement and the type of observation made by the individual analyst. For instance, if it is necessary to titrate a solution to the nearest 0.01 ml., a 50 ml. buret graduated in 0.1 ml. would not be satisfactory, since the design of the buret is such that it will not deliver measurable amounts less than 0.05 ml. with any degree of reproducibility. Therefore, in this measurement as in all others, there is an amount of doubt as to the final measurement being exact. Since the measurements made usually have an error that is built into them, it would be well to try to classify these errors into general types.

TYPES OF ERRORS

Errors are generally classified into two main types: **determinate** and **indeterminate.**

Determinate Errors

Determinate errors are those that are tangible and can be determined. They can either be avoided or corrections can be applied to compensate for the error. Some of the common sources of errors that are usually classified under this type are

(1) *Errors due to impurities in reagents.* These impurities may be in the form of an interference to a desired analysis, may cause secondary reactions, or may prevent the desired reaction.

(2) *Errors due to equipment.* The equipment may be faulty; for example, volumetric equipment not calibrated correctly, analytical balance not in cor-

rect operating order due to faulty construction, and reagents contaminated as a result of chemical attack of the containers used.

(3) *Errors due to method.* These errors are most common and many times the most troublesome. They result from coprecipitation of impurities, side reactions, and/or the slight solubility of insoluble precipitates. Many times the choice of method contributes to the errors involved since it is not the best method or most applicable method for the determination of the desired constituent.

(4) *Personal errors.* These can arise from the tendency to under titrate or over titrate consistently due to the lack of ability to discriminate between shades of color. Often color blindness is a serious source of error in analytical measurements. Many times when titrating identical aliquots, the analyst will make the value of the titrant added agree with the others done before, even though there is a slight uncertainty, because he knows that the values should be identical. Perfect agreement of values resulting from a conscious attempt on the part of the analyst is inexcusable. There is a fine line between prejudice and dishonesty in this area and many times it is difficult to decide where the line should be drawn. Slight variation in measurement is a desirable characteristic; on the other hand wide variation in values is not desirable.

Indeterminate Errors

Those errors that are more or less intangible and can not be predicted or estimated are called **indeterminate errors.** Because of their unpredictability, these errors follow the laws of chance and are often referred to as random errors. As a result it is possible to apply the mathematical laws of probability to measurements having inherent in them errors of an indeterminate nature. In order to apply these rules a number of measurements are required. If the measurements are to be subject to statistical evaluation, the laws of probability, namely, that large errors occur very seldom, that the frequency of small errors is high, and that positive and negative errors appear equally, must hold.

The numerical relationship between the frequency of the occurrence of the indeterminate error and its magnitude can be represented graphically, as in Figure A–1, by a curve known as the normal distribution curve, normal frequency curve, or the Gaussian distribution curve. The arithmetic mean of the results is shown by point M. The arithmetic mean is the average of all the measured values. In relation to the mean, positive and negative differences are equally likely to occur, and the occurrence of values with large error is less likely than of those with small discrepancies. The result of a series of measurements made with equal care and under conditions that are essentially the same can best be expressed as the arithmetic mean.

There are other common statistical means of expressing the relationship between the frequency and magnitude of indeterminate errors.

Deviation (d) is the difference between an observation and the arithmetical mean.

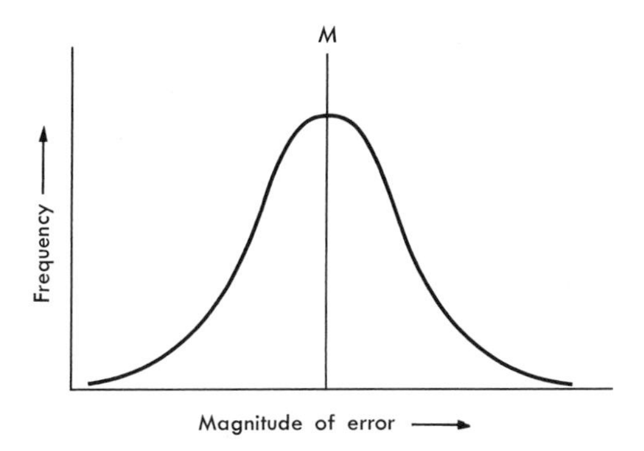

Fig. A–1. Normal distribution curve.

Average deviation ($a.d.$) of a single measurement is the average of the deviation of the individual measurements from the mean, without regard to sign. It is the amount by which an average single measurement deviates from the mean value.

Standard deviation of a single measurement ($s.d.$ or σ) is the square root of the quotient obtained by dividing the sum of the squares of the deviations (d) of a series of values by the number of measurements made.

$$s.d.(\sigma) = \sqrt{\frac{\Sigma(d)^2}{N}}$$

If the number of measurements is small, then $(N - 1)$, where N is the number of measurements, is used instead of N.

The following can be used to illustrate the use of the above ways of expressing values of analytical measurements. The values for the analysis of a soluble sulfate expressed as percent SO_3 are as follows:

	$\%SO_3$	d	d^2
(a)	15.63	0.02	0.0004
(b)	15.71	0.06	0.0036
(c)	15.58	0.07	0.0049
(d)	15.68	0.03	0.0009
	4|62.60	4|0.18	0.0098
	15.65 Mean	0.04 $a.d.$	$\sqrt{\frac{.0098}{4-1}} = .06\ s.d.(\sigma)$

The average deviation of the mean value ($A.D.$) is found by

$$A.D. = \frac{a.d.}{\sqrt{N}}$$

where $a.d.$ is the average deviation of a single determination. In the case above,

$$A.D. = \frac{.04}{\sqrt{4}} = .02$$

and the mean value for the analysis could be expressed as 15.65% ± 0.02%.

Accuracy versus Precision

Precision is defined as the degree of agreement between replicate measurements of the same quantity. A precise measurement does not assure the analyst that the measurement is accurate. There is a familiar cliché among analytical chemists that states, "You can be very precise in your error." What this does is to emphasize the difference between precision and accuracy.

Accuracy is the degree of agreement between the measured value and the true value. Since absolute true values are seldom known except in counting discrete objects, accuracy then is the difference between the measured value and the accepted true value.

One of the best ways to explain the difference is to look at the problems involved in firing in a rifle match. The object is to place as many shots in the bull's eye as possible. To cluster them in the center is an example of being both precise and accurate. To place the shots just inside the perimeter of the bull's eye but not clustered illustrates accuracy but poor precision. For the shooter that forgets to allow for windage, the shots may be clustered but outside the bull's eye area, illustrating good precision but poor accuracy. The latter also shows that the shooter was very precise in his error. This same thing can happen to the analytical chemist if he carries a constant error in his analysis. The agreement among his values is good but his accuracy is very poor.

Methods of Expressing Precision

Each value that is reported for an analysis should be accompanied by an indication of the precision of the value. This can be expressed as an absolute value of the difference or a relative difference. The absolute difference is the actual difference between the values. The relative difference is the difference between the measured values, divided by the average value. If the true value is known, the relative difference may be expressed as the actual difference between the measured value and the true value, divided by the true value. It is often expressed in parts per thousand.

If the values of duplicate analyses of manganese dioxide in a pyrolusite ore are found to be 36.05% and 36.22% and the true percentage of the manganese dioxide in the ore is 36.04%, the analyst would report the arithmetic mean of the two values as 36.13%, which would differ from the true value by 0.09%. This is the absolute error in the analysis. If this error is expressed in parts per thousand, the relative error would be

$$\frac{0.09}{36.04} \times 1000 = 2.5 \text{ parts per thousand}$$

The two experimentally obtained values differ by 0.17% or, if expressed in parts per thousand,

$$\frac{0.17}{36.13} \times 1000 = 4.7 \text{ parts per thousand}$$

If the true value is not known, as is the case in the majority of student analyses, the precision of the determination is generally expressed as the relative agreement of the replicate values that are obtained.

Rejection of Measurements

There are many times when making measurements that one value is considerably different from the others and the analyst must decide whether to reject this value or not. There are several arbitrary rules that have been proposed to aid in the rejection process. Tables have been prepared setting up factors for calculating confidence limits. Quality control charts are maintained in many routine analytical procedures, which give the average value and the range of results plotted versus time. In this manner values of analyses obtained can be compared and those values that are outside the range can be rejected.

One rule that can be used to aid in the rejection of a value is, if the suspected value has a deviation from the mean established without the inclusion of the suspected value that is four times the average deviation of the individual values from the mean, then the value can be rejected.

There is no simple easy answer to the rejection problem. Whether to reject extreme results and run the risk of being misled by retaining only the results of high precision, or to proceed with additional analyses, is a decision which is usually governed by the relative costs which may be incurred. Much has been written concerning the application of statistics in chemical analysis. Three reviews of this literature can be found in references 1, 2, and 3.

Significant Figures

Significant figures are the digits necessary to express the results to the precision with which the measurements are made. Each digit denotes the actual quantity which it specifies. For instance, the number *1654* indicates that there is 1 thousand, 6 hundreds, 5 tens, and 4 units. It is then apparent that the digit *0* can be used in two ways. It can be used as a significant figure or used to locate the decimal. For example in the number 30403, both zeros are significant, while in 0.0005 the zeros are not significant since all they do in this case is to locate the decimal. In order to save confusion when the zeros are not significant in a value such as 635,000, where the measurement is accurate to three figures only, the value should be expressed as 6.35×10^5.

The number of significant figures that are retained in a result, and in data in general, is such that there will only be one uncertain figure. When adding and subtracting numbers, only the number of significant figures that appear in the individual value having the greatest uncertainty should be retained in the sum or the difference. For example, adding

$$\begin{array}{r} 10.2635 \\ 1.25 \\ \hline 11.51 \end{array}$$

The answer is expressed with two figures to the right of the decimal point rather than four.

In multiplication and division, the product or the quotient may be expressed with the number of significant figures to indicate a certainty comparable to the least certain of the factors. If the following multiplication is performed,

$$7.2586 \times 0.25 = 1.8$$

it is not justifiable to express this result as 1.8144, because of the relative uncertainty of the value 0.25.

Applying these rules to analytical operations, it is advisable to measure quantities to about the same absolute uncertainty when adding or subtracting, and to the same relative uncertainty where other arithmetical operations are involved. It is very apparent that it is not worthwhile to spend the time to weigh a sample to the nearest tenth of a milligram and then use the value obtained in a calculation where the reading of a volume was made to the nearest tenth of a milliliter. In the first case, there are four significant figures on a sample less than one gram and for volumes greater than 10 ml. there are three significant figures. Carrying more significant figures than are necessary through a calculation is a waste of time and effort on the part of the analyst.

In rounding numbers to the proper number of significant figures, increase by 1 the last figure retained if the rejected figure is 5 or over. If less than 5, retain the last figure as it is written.

LOGARITHMS AND THEIR USE

The common logarithm is the logarithm of a number to the base 10. Each number can be expressed as a power of 10. Since $10^1 = 10$, and $10^2 = 100$, the logarithm of 10 is 1 and the logarithm of 100 is 2. The logarithm (log) of a number that is not an exact power of 10 cannot be expressed exactly but can be expressed only in an approximate manner. The logarithm between 10 and 100 is 1 plus a continuing decimal term. Thus $10^{1.6232} = 42$; therefore the log of 42 is 1.6232.

The logarithm is made up of two parts: the **characteristic** is the series of numbers to the left of the decimal point and the **mantissa** is the series of numbers to the right of the decimal point. For example, the log of 42 is 1.6232; the characteristic is 1 and the mantissa is .6232. The characteristic may be either a positive or a negative integer. The mantissa is **always** positive. The characteristic establishes the decimal point and the mantissa gives the digits that make up the number. The mantissa of the logarithm is given in a table of logarithms. Tables of logarithms of numbers give mantissas of a variety of significant figures. The table used in this text will have four significant figures.

To determine the characteristic of the logarithm, the following rules are followed:

(1) The characteristic of a logarithm of a number that is larger than 1 is one less than the number of digits to the left of the decimal point. The following examples can be used to illustrate this rule.

Number	*Characteristic*	*Logarithm*
10.26	1.	1.0111
6.73	0.	0.8280
37658.0	4.	4.5758

(2) The characteristic of a logarithm of a number less than 1 and greater than zero has a negative value of one more than the number of zeros between the decimal point and the first significant figure to the right of the decimal point. These examples illustrate negative characteristics.

Number	*Characteristic*	*Log*	*Log*
0.923	$\bar{1}$.	$\bar{1}.9652$	9.9652–10
0.00923	$\bar{3}$.	$\bar{3}.9652$	7.9652–10
0.0923	$\bar{2}$.	$\bar{2}.9652$	8.9652–10

The logarithm can be expressed in either form but in each case the mantissa is a positive number. From the examples above, it can be seen that the mantissas of the numbers having the same sequence of digits are identical. It is only the characteristic that is different.

To find the logarithm of a number using the tables on pages 339–345, the following procedure is used.

Locate the first two digits in the first column; then proceed to the right until the column is reached that is headed by the third digit. To the number thus found, add the number that is listed opposite the fourth significant figure in the appropriate column of proportional parts. The mantissa of 305.8 is .4843 plus .0011 = .4854. The log of the number is 2.4854.

To determine the number whose logarithm is known, it is necessary to reverse the procedure of finding the logarithm. The antilogarithm of 1.2653 is the number that has 1.2653 for a logarithm. The antilogarithm of 1.2653 is 18.42.

To find the antilogarithm of a number, the following steps are taken. First the mantissa of the logarithm is located in the table, or at least the nearest value to the mantissa of the logarithm desired. Then after the mantissa has been located, the significant figures are obtained by taking the interpolated figure obtained using the proportional parts as the fourth significant figure, the figure at the top of the column is the third significant figure and then to the left for the first two significant figures which are obtained from the first column of the table.

The logarithm of a product is equal to the sum of the logarithms of its factors. The logarithm of a quotient is equal to the difference of the logarithms of its factors. To illustrate the use of logarithms in the solution of multiplication and division operations the following example is given.

$$\frac{21.35 \times 0.0821 \times 100}{625.4} = Y$$

$$\begin{aligned}
\log 21.35 &= 1.3294 \\
\log 0.0821 &= 8.9143 - 10 \\
\log 100 &= \underline{2.0000} \\
& 12.2437 - 10 \\
-\log 625.4 &= \underline{-2.7961} \\
\log Y &= 9.4476 - 10 \\
Y &= 0.2803
\end{aligned}$$

The logarithm of a power of a quantity is equal to the logarithm of the quantity multiplied by the exponent. For example, the log of $(62.1)^3 = 3 \times \log 62.1 = 3(1.7931) = 5.3793$.

To take the root of a quantity, the logarithm of the quantity is divided by the index of the root. The log of $\sqrt[3]{16.76}$ is $1/3 \log 16.76 = (1/3)(1.2243) = 0.4081$.

Many analytical terms as defined require for their use facility in handling negative logarithms. For example, what is the hydrogen ion concentration of a solution whose pH = 3.2?

$$pH = -\log [H^+]$$
$$3.2 = -\log [H^+]$$
$$\log [H^+] = -3.2 = (-4 + 0.8)$$

The number -3.2 is a negative number and the decimal part as such can not be treated as a mantissa and located in the log table. By making the number -3.2 become two numbers, one with a negative sign and the other with a positive sign as shown above $(-4 + 0.8)$, then the number having the negative sign can be the characteristic and the number having the positive sign can be the mantissa. The antilog of -4 is 10^{-4} and the antilog of 0.8 is 6.3, thus.

$$[H^+] = 6.3 \times 10^{-4}$$

References

(1) Hader and Youden, *Analytical Chemistry* **24,** 120 (1952).
(2) Mandel and Linnig, *Analytical Chemistry* **28,** 770 (1956). **30,** 739 (1958).
(3) Wernmint, *Analytical Chemistry* **21,** 115 (1949).

APPENDIX II

Ionization Constants of Some Acids, Bases, and Complex Ions, 25°C

ACIDS

Acetic Acid	$HC_2H_3O_2$	1.86×10^{-5}		
Arsenic Acid	H_3AsO_4	5×10^{-3}	4×10^{-5}	6×10^{-10}
Benzoic Acid	$HC_7H_5O_2$	6.6×10^{-5}		
Boric Acid	H_3BO_3	5.5×10^{-10}		
Carbonic Acid	H_2CO_3	3.3×10^{-7}	5×10^{-11}	
Formic Acid	$HCHO_2$	2.1×10^{-4}		
Hydrogen Sulfide	H_2S	9.1×10^{-8}	1.2×10^{-15}	
Oxalic Acid	$H_2C_2O_4$	3.8×10^{-2}	4.9×10^{-5}	
Phosphoric Acid	H_3PO_4	1.1×10^{-2}	2×10^{-7}	4×10^{-13}
Tartaric Acid	$H_2C_4H_4O_6$	1.1×10^{-3}	6.9×10^{-5}	

BASES

Acetamide	CH_3CONH_2	3.1×10^{-15}
Ammonium Hydroxide	NH_4OH	1.75×10^{-5}
Aniline	$C_6H_5NH_2$	4×10^{-10}
Ethyl Amine	$C_2H_5NH_2$	5.6×10^{-4}
Pyridine	C_5H_5N	2.3×10^{-9}
Urea	$CO(NH_2)_2$	1.5×10^{-14}

COMPLEX IONS

$Ag(NH_3)_2^+$	6.8×10^{-8}
$Co(NH_3)_6^{+++}$	2×10^{-34}
$Cu(NH_3)_4^{++}$	4.6×10^{-14}
$Ag(CN)_2^-$	1.0×10^{-21}
$Hg(CN)_4^=$	4.0×10^{-42}
$Ni(CN)_4^=$	1.0×10^{-22}
$CaY^=$	2.5×10^{-11}
$MgY^=$	2.0×10^{-9}
$ZnY^=$	3.2×10^{-17}

($Y^{\equiv}$ is ethylenediaminetetraacetate ion. See page 158.)

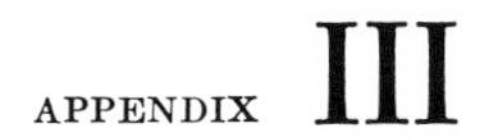

APPENDIX III

Solubility Product Constants of Some Common Compounds

COMPOUND	FORMULA	K_{sp}
Aluminum		
Hydroxide	$Al(OH)_3$	5.0×10^{-33}
Barium		
Carbonate	$BaCO_3$	8.1×10^{-9}
Chromate	$BaCrO_4$	3.0×10^{-10}
Fluoride	BaF_2	1.7×10^{-6}
Iodate	$Ba(IO_3)_2$	6.0×10^{-10}
Oxalate	BaC_2O_4	1.7×10^{-7}
Sulfate	$BaSO_4$	1.1×10^{-10}
Cadmium		
Sulfide	CdS	3.6×10^{-29}
Calcium		
Carbonate	$CaCO_3$	1.6×10^{-8}
Chromate	$CaCrO_4$	2.3×10^{-2}
Fluoride	CaF_2	3.2×10^{-11}
Iodate	$Ca(IO_3)_2$	6.4×10^{-9}
Oxalate	CaC_2O_4	2.6×10^{-9}
Sulfate	$CaSO_4$	6.4×10^{-5}
Copper(II)		
Sulfide	CuS	8.0×10^{-45}
Copper(I)		
Chloride	$CuCl$	1.0×10^{-6}
Bromide	$CuBr$	4.1×10^{-8}
Iodide	CuI	5.0×10^{-12}
Sulfide	Cu_2S	1.0×10^{-45}
Thiocyanate	$CuCNS$	1.6×10^{-11}

Iron(III)		
Hydroxide	$Fe(OH)_3$	1.1×10^{-36}
Iron(II)		
Hydroxide	$Fe(OH)_2$	1.6×10^{-14}
Sulfide	FeS	1.5×10^{-19}
Lead		
Carbonate	$PbCO_3$	5.6×10^{-14}
Chloride	$PbCl_2$	2.4×10^{-4}
Chromate	$PbCrO_4$	1.8×10^{-14}
Fluoride	PbF_2	3.7×10^{-8}
Iodate	$Pb(IO_3)_2$	9.8×10^{-14}
Oxalate	PbC_2O_4	3.3×10^{-11}
Sulfate	$PbSO_4$	1.1×10^{-8}
Sulfide	PbS	4.2×10^{-28}
Magnesium		
Ammonium Phosphate	$MgNH_4PO_4$	3.0×10^{-13}
Carbonate	$MgCO_3$	2.6×10^{-5}
Fluoride	MgF_2	6.4×10^{-9}
Hydroxide	$Mg(OH)_2$	3.4×10^{-11}
Oxalate	MgC_2O_4	8.6×10^{-5}
Manganese		
Hydroxide	$Mn(OH)_2$	4.0×10^{-14}
Sulfide	MnS	1.4×10^{-15}
Mercury(I)		
Chloride	Hg_2Cl_2	1.1×10^{-18}
Bromide	Hg_2Br_2	1.4×10^{-21}
Iodide	Hg_2I_2	1.2×10^{-28}
Nickel		
Sulfide	NiS	1.4×10^{-24}
Silver		
Bromate	$AgBrO_3$	5.0×10^{-5}
Bromide	$AgBr$	5.0×10^{-13}
Carbonate	Ag_2CO_3	6.2×10^{-12}
Chloride	$AgCl$	1.0×10^{-10}
Chromate	Ag_2CrO_4	9.0×10^{-12}
Cyanide	$Ag_2(CN)_2$	1.2×10^{-12}
Hydroxide	$AgOH$	1.5×10^{-8}
Iodide	AgI	1.0×10^{-16}

Silver (*cont.*)		
Oxalate	$Ag_2C_2O_4$	1.3×10^{-11}
Phosphate	Ag_3PO_4	1.8×10^{-18}
Sulfate	Ag_2SO_4	7.0×10^{-5}
Sulfide	Ag_2S	1.6×10^{-49}
Thiocyanate	$AgCNS$	1.0×10^{-12}
Strontium		
Carbonate	$SrCO_3$	1.6×10^{-9}
Chromate	$SrCrO_4$	3.0×10^{-5}
Fluoride	SrF_2	2.8×10^{-9}
Oxalate	SrC_2O_4	5.6×10^{-8}
Sulfate	$SrSO_4$	2.8×10^{-7}
Zinc		
Carbonate	$ZnCO_3$	3.0×10^{-6}
Hydroxide	$Zn(OH)_2$	1.8×10^{-14}
Sulfide	ZnS	1.2×10^{-23}

APPENDIX IV

Standard Reduction Potentials

IONIC HALF-REACTION	$E°$
$F_2 + 2e = 2F^-$	2.65
$S_2O_8^= + 2e = 2SO_4^=$	2.01
$H_2O_2 + 2H^+ + 2e = 2H_2O$	1.77
$MnO_4^- + 4H^+ + 3e = MnO_2 + 2H_2O$	1.69
$Ce^{++++} + 1e = Ce^{+++}$	1.61
$MnO_4^- + 8H^+ + 5e = Mn^{++} + 4H_2O$	1.51
$PbO_2 + 4H^+ + 2e = Pb^{++} + 2H_2O$	1.455
$BrO_3^- + 6H^+ + 6e = Br^- + 3H_2O$	1.45
$Cl_2 + 2e = 2Cl^-$	1.359
$Cr_2O_7^= + 14H^+ + 6e = 2Cr^{+++} + 7H_2O$	1.33
$MnO_2 + 4H^+ + 2e = Mn^{++} + 2H_2O$	1.23
$O_2 + 4H^+ + 4e = 2H_2O$	1.23
$IO_3^- + 6H^+ + 6e = I^- + 3H_2O$	1.087
$Br_2(l) + 2e = 2Br^-$	1.065
$NO_3^- + 4H^+ + 3e = NO + 2H_2O$	0.96
$NO_3^- + 3H^+ + 2e = HNO_2 + H_2O$	0.93
$2Hg^{++} + 2e = Hg_2^{++}$	0.92
$Hg^{++} + 2e = Hg$	0.85
$Ag^+ + 1e = Ag$	0.799
$Hg_2^{++} + 2e = 2Hg$	0.789
$Fe^{+++} + 1e = Fe^{++}$	0.77
$C_6H_4O_2 + 2H^+ + 2e = C_6H_4(OH)_2$	0.70
$O_2 + 2H^+ + 2e = H_2O_2$	0.68
$HAsO_4^= + 2H^+ + 2e = HAsO_3^= + H_2O$	0.559
$I_2 + 2e = 2I^-$	0.536
$Cu^+ + 1e = Cu$	0.52
$Fe(CN)_6^{\equiv} + 1e = Fe(CN)_6^{\equiv}$	0.36
$Cu^{++} + 2e = Cu$	0.337
0.1 *N* Calomel Cell	0.338
1.0 *N* Calomel Cell	0.280
Saturated Calomel Cell	0.246

IONIC HALF-REACTION	$E°$
$AgCl + 1e = Ag + Cl^-$	0.22
$SO_4^{=} + 4H^+ + 2e = H_2SO_3 + H_2O$	0.17
$Cu^{++} + 1e = Cu^+$	0.15
$Sn^{++++} + 2e = Sn^{++}$	0.15
$S + 2H^+ + 2e = H_2S$	0.14
$AgBr + 1e = Ag + Br^-$	0.095
$UO_2^{++} + 1e = UO_2^+$	0.05
$2H^+ + 2e = H_2$	0.00
$Pb^{++} + 2e = Pb$	−0.13
$Sn^{++} + 2e = Sn$	−0.136
$AgI + 1e = Ag + I^-$	−0.15
$CuI + 1e = Cu + I^-$	−0.185
$Ni^{++} + 2e = Ni$	−0.25
$Cd^{++} + 2e = Cd$	−0.40
$Fe^{++} + 2e = Fe$	−0.44
$2CO_2 + 2H^+ + 2e = H_2C_2O_4$	−0.49
$Cr^{+++} + 3e = Cr$	−0.74
$Zn^{++} + 2e = Zn$	−0.763
$SiO_2 + 4H^+ + 4e = Si + 2H_2O$	−0.86
$Mn^{++} + 2e = Mn$	−1.18
$Mg^{++} + 2e = Mg$	−2.37
$Na^+ + 1e = Na$	−2.71
$Ca^{++} + 2e = Ca$	−2.87
$Ba^{++} + 2e = Ba$	−2.90
$K^+ + 1e = K$	−2.925
$Li^+ + 1e = Li$	−3.045

APPENDIX **V**

Formula Weights

Formula	Weight	Formula	Weight
AgBr	187.80	CaF_2	78.08
AgCl	143.34	$Ca(NO_3)_2$	164.10
$Ag_2Cr_2O_7$	331.77	CaO	56.08
AgI	234.80	$Ca(OH)_2$	74.10
$AgNO_3$	169.89	$Ca_3(PO_4)_2$	310.19
Ag_3PO_4	418.62	$CaSO_4$	136.15
Ag_2SO_4	311.83	CaS	95.61
$AlBr_3$	266.73	$Ce(SO_4)_2 \cdot 2(NH_4)_2SO_4 \cdot 2H_2O$	632.59
$AlCl_3$	133.35		
Al_2O_3	101.96	CO_2	44.01
$Al(OH)_3$	78.00	$CO(NH_2)_2$	60.06
$Al_2(SO_4)_3$	342.16		
		$CrCl_3$	158.38
As_2O_3	187.82	Cr_2O_3	152.02
As_2O_5	229.82	$Cr_2(SO_4)_3$	392.22
As_2S_3	246.02		
		CuO	79.54
$BaBr_2$	297.19	CuS	95.61
$BaCl_2$	208.27	Cu_2S	159.20
$BaCl_2 \cdot 2H_2O$	244.31	$CuSO_4 \cdot 5H_2O$	249.69
$BaCO_3$	197.37		
$BaCrO_4$	237.37	$FeCl_3$	162.22
BaF_2	175.36	$FeCl_3 \cdot 6H_2O$	270.34
BaI_2	391.18	$FeCO_3$	115.86
BaO	153.36	FeO	71.85
$Ba(OH)_2$	171.38	Fe_2O_3	159.70
$BaSO_4$	233.43	Fe_3O_4	231.55
		$Fe(OH)_3$	106.87
BeO	25.01	FeS_2	119.97
		Fe_2Si	139.79
$CaCl_2$	110.99	$FeSO_4 \cdot 7H_2O$	278.03
$CaCO_3$	100.09	$FeSO_4(NH_4)_2SO_4 \cdot 6H_2O$	392.16

Formula	Weight
HBr	80.92
$HCHO_2$	46.03
$HC_2H_3O_2$	60.05
$HC_7H_5O_2$	122.12
HCl	36.47
$HClO_4$	100.46
$H_2C_2O_4 \cdot 2H_2O$	126.07
HNO_3	63.02
H_2O	18.02
H_2O_2	34.02
H_3PO_4	98.00
H_2S	34.08
HSO_3NH_2	97.10
H_2SO_4	98.08
Hg_2Cl_2	472.14
HgO	216.61
KBr	119.02
$KBrO_3$	167.01
KCl	74.56
$KClO_3$	122.56
$KClO_4$	138.56
KCN	65.12
$KCNS$	97.19
K_2CrO_4	194.21
$K_2Cr_2O_7$	294.22
$KHC_4H_4O_6$	188.18
$KHC_8H_4O_4$	204.13
$KHC_2O_4 \cdot 1H_2O$	146.14
$KHC_2O_4 \cdot H_2C_2O_4 \cdot 2H_2O$	254.20
$KH(IO_3)_2$	389.93
KI	166.01
$KMnO_4$	158.04
$KNaC_4H_4O_6 \cdot 4H_2O$	282.22
KNO_3	101.11
K_2O	94.20
KOH	56.11
K_2PtCl_6	486.16
$LiCl$	42.40
Li_2CO_3	73.89

Formula	Weight
Li_2O	29.88
$LiOH$	23.95
$MgCl_2$	95.23
$MgCO_3$	84.33
$MgNH_4AsO_4$	181.27
$MgNH_4PO_4$	137.34
MgO	40.32
$Mg(OH)_2$	58.34
$Mg_2P_2O_7$	222.59
$MgSO_4$	120.39
$MgSO_4 \cdot 7H_2O$	246.50
MnO	70.94
MnO_2	86.94
Mn_2O_3	157.88
Mn_3O_4	228.82
$Mn_2P_2O_7$	283.83
NH_3	17.03
NH_4Cl	53.50
$(NH_4)_2C_2O_4 \cdot H_2O$	142.12
$(NH_4)_3PO_4 \cdot 12MoO_3$	187.65
NH_4OH	35.05
NO	30.01
NO_2	46.01
Na_3AsO_3	191.88
Na_3AsO_4	207.88
$NaBr$	102.91
$NaCHO_2$	68.01
$NaC_2H_3O_2$	82.04
$NaCl$	58.45
Na_2CO_3	106.00
$Na_2C_2O_4$	134.00
$NaHCO_3$	84.01
$NaHC_2O_4$	112.02
NaI	149.90
$NaNO_3$	85.00
Na_2O	61.98
Na_2O_2	77.98
$NaOH$	40.00

$Na_2S_2O_3$	158.11	Sb_2S_3	339.72
$Na_2S_2O_3 \cdot 5H_2O$	248.19		
		SiO_2	60.09
$NiC_8H_{14}O_4N_4$	288.86		
		$SnCl_2$	189.61
P_2O_5	141.95	$SnCl_4$	260.53
		SnO_2	150.70
$PbCl_2$	278.12		
PbC_2O_4	295.23	$SrCO_3$	103.63
$PbCrO_4$	323.22		
PbI_2	461.03	TiO_2	79.90
PbO	223.21		
PbO_2	239.21	UO_3	286.07
Pb_3O_4	685.63	U_3O_8	842.21
$PbSO_4$	303.28		
		$ZnNH_4PO_4$	178.40
SO_2	60.09	ZnO	81.38
SO_3	80.07	$Zn_2P_2O_7$	304.71

FOUR-PLACE LOGARITHMS OF NUMBERS

N	0	1	2	3	4	5	6	7	8	9
10	.0000	0043	0086	0128	0170	0212	0253	0294	0334	0374
11	.0414	0453	0492	0531	0569	0607	0645	0682	0719	0755
12	.0792	0828	0864	0899	0934	0969	1004	1038	1072	1106
13	.1139	1173	1206	1239	1271	1303	1335	1367	1399	1430
14	.1461	1492	1523	1553	1584	1614	1644	1673	1703	1732
15	.1761	1790	1818	1847	1875	1903	1931	1959	1987	2014
16	.2041	2068	2095	2122	2148	2175	2201	2227	2253	2279
17	.2304	2330	2355	2380	2405	2430	2455	2480	2504	2529
18	.2553	2577	2601	2625	2648	2672	2695	2718	2742	2765
19	.2788	2810	2833	2856	2878	2900	2923	2945	2967	2989
20	.3010	3032	3054	3075	3096	3118	3139	3160	3181	3201
21	.3222	3243	3263	3284	3304	3324	3345	3365	3385	3404
22	.3424	3444	3464	3483	3502	3522	3541	3560	3579	3598
23	.3617	3636	3655	3674	3692	3711	3729	3747	3766	3784
24	.3802	3820	3838	3856	3874	3892	3909	3927	3945	3962
25	.3979	3997	4014	4031	4048	4065	4082	4099	4116	4133
26	.4150	4166	4183	4200	4216	4232	4249	4265	4281	4298
27	.4314	4330	4346	4362	4378	4393	4409	4425	4440	4456
28	.4472	4487	4502	4518	4533	4548	4564	4579	4594	4609
29	.4624	4639	4654	4669	4683	4698	4713	4728	4742	4757
30	.4771	4786	4800	4814	4829	4843	4857	4871	4886	4900
31	.4914	4928	4942	4955	4969	4983	4997	5011	5024	5038
32	.5051	5065	5079	5092	5105	5119	5132	5145	5159	5172
33	.5185	5198	5211	5224	5237	5250	5263	5276	5289	5302
34	.5315	5328	5340	5353	5366	5378	5391	5403	5416	5428
35	.5441	5453	5465	5478	5490	5502	5514	5527	5539	5551
36	.5563	5575	5587	5599	5611	5623	5635	5647	5658	5670
37	.5682	5694	5705	5717	5729	5740	5752	5763	5775	5786
38	.5798	5809	5821	5832	5843	5855	5866	5877	5888	5899
39	.5911	5922	5933	5944	5955	5966	5977	5988	5999	6010
40	.6021	6031	6042	6053	6064	6075	6085	6096	6107	6117
41	.6128	6138	6149	6160	6170	6180	6191	6201	6212	6222
42	.6232	6243	6253	6263	6274	6284	6294	6304	6314	6325
43	.6335	6345	6355	6365	6375	6385	6395	6405	6415	6425
44	.6435	6444	6454	6464	6474	6484	6493	6503	6513	6522
45	.6532	6542	6551	6561	6571	6580	6590	6599	6609	6618
46	.6628	6637	6646	6656	6665	6675	6684	6693	6702	6712
47	.6721	6730	6739	6749	6758	6767	6776	6785	6794	6803
48	.6812	6821	6830	6839	6848	6857	6866	6875	6884	6893
49	.6902	6911	6920	6928	6937	6946	6955	6964	6972	6981
50	.6990	6998	7007	7016	7024	7033	7042	7050	7059	7067
N	**0**	**1**	**2**	**3**	**4**	**5**	**6**	**7**	**8**	**9**

Prop. Parts

	28	27	26
1	2.8	2.7	2.6
2	5.6	5.4	5.2
3	8.4	8.1	7.8
4	11.2	10.8	10.4
5	14.0	13.5	13.0
6	16.8	16.2	15.6
7	19.6	18.9	18.2
8	22.4	21.6	20.8
9	25.2	24.3	23.4

	22	21	20
1	2.2	2.1	2.0
2	4.4	4.2	4.0
3	6.6	6.3	6.0
4	8.8	8.4	8.0
5	11.0	10.5	10.0
6	13.2	12.6	12.0
7	15.4	14.7	14.0
8	17.6	16.8	16.0
9	19.8	18.9	18.0

	16	15	14
1	1.6	1.5	1.4
2	3.2	3.0	2.8
3	4.8	4.5	4.2
4	6.4	6.0	5.6
5	8.0	7.5	7.0
6	9.6	9.0	8.4
7	11.2	10.5	9.8
8	12.8	12.0	11.2
9	14.4	13.5	12.6

	13	12	11
1	1.3	1.2	1.1
2	2.6	2.4	2.2
3	3.9	3.6	3.3
4	5.2	4.8	4.4
5	6.5	6.0	5.5
6	7.8	7.2	6.6
7	9.1	8.4	7.7
8	10.4	9.6	8.8
9	11.7	10.8	9.9

	43	42	41	40	39		38	37	36	35	34		33	32	31	30	29	
1	4.3	4.2	4.1	4.0	3.9	**1**	3.8	3.7	3.6	3.5	3.4	**1**	3.3	3.2	3.1	3.0	2.9	**1**
2	8.6	8.4	8.2	8.0	7.8	**2**	7.6	7.4	7.2	7.0	6.8	**2**	6.6	6.4	6.2	6.0	5.8	**2**
3	12.9	12.6	12.3	12.0	11.7	**3**	11.4	11.1	10.8	10.5	10.2	**3**	9.9	9.6	9.3	9.0	8.7	**3**
4	17.2	16.8	16.4	16.0	15.6	**4**	15.2	14.8	14.4	14.0	13.6	**4**	13.2	12.8	12.4	12.0	11.6	**4**
5	21.5	21.0	20.5	20.0	19.5	**5**	19.0	18.5	18.0	17.5	17.0	**5**	16.5	16.0	15.5	15.0	14.5	**5**
6	25.8	25.2	24.6	24.0	23.4	**6**	22.8	22.2	21.6	21.0	20.4	**6**	19.8	19.2	18.6	18.0	17.4	**6**
7	30.1	29.4	28.7	28.0	27.3	**7**	26.6	25.9	25.2	24.5	23.8	**7**	23.1	22.4	21.7	21.0	20.3	**7**
8	34.4	33.6	32.8	32.0	31.2	**8**	30.4	29.6	28.8	28.0	27.2	**8**	26.4	25.6	24.8	24.0	23.2	**8**
9	38.7	37.8	36.9	36.0	35.1	**9**	34.2	33.3	32.4	31.5	30.6	**9**	29.7	28.8	27.9	27.0	26.1	**9**

FOUR-PLACE LOGARITHMS OF NUMBERS

N	0	1	2	3	4	5	6	7	8	9
50	.6990	6998	7007	7016	7024	7033	7042	7050	7059	7067
51	.7076	7084	7093	7101	7110	7118	7126	7135	7143	7152
52	.7160	7168	7177	7185	7193	7202	7210	7218	7226	7235
53	.7243	7251	7259	7267	7275	7284	7292	7300	7308	7316
54	.7324	7332	7340	7348	7356	7364	7372	7380	7388	7396
55	.7404	7412	7419	7427	7435	7443	7451	7459	7466	7474
56	.7482	7490	7497	7505	7513	7520	7528	7536	7543	7551
57	.7559	7566	7574	7582	7589	7597	7604	7612	7619	7627
58	.7634	7642	7649	7657	7664	7672	7679	7686	7694	7701
59	.7709	7716	7723	7731	7738	7745	7752	7760	7767	7774
60	.7782	7789	7796	7803	7810	7818	7825	7832	7839	7846
61	.7853	7860	7868	7875	7882	7889	7896	7903	7910	7917
62	.7924	7931	7938	7945	7952	7959	7966	7973	7980	7987
63	.7993	8000	8007	8014	8021	8028	8035	8041	8048	8055
64	.8062	8069	8075	8082	8089	8096	8102	8109	8116	8122
65	.8129	8136	8142	8149	8156	8162	8169	8176	8182	8189
66	.8195	8202	8209	8215	8222	8228	8235	8241	8248	8254
67	.8261	8267	8274	8280	8287	8293	8299	8306	8312	8319
68	.8325	8331	8338	8344	8351	8357	8363	8370	8376	8382
69	.8388	8395	8401	8407	8414	8420	8426	8432	8439	8445
70	.8451	8457	8463	8470	8476	8482	8488	8494	8500	8506
71	.8513	8519	8525	8531	8537	8543	8549	8555	8561	8567
72	.8573	8579	8585	8591	8597	8603	8609	8615	8621	8627
73	.8633	8639	8645	8651	8657	8663	8669	8675	8681	8686
74	.8692	8698	8704	8710	8716	8722	8727	8733	8739	8745
75	.8751	8756	8762	8768	8774	8779	8785	8791	8797	8802
76	.8808	8814	8820	8825	8831	8837	8842	8848	8854	8859
77	.8865	8871	8876	8882	8887	8893	8899	8904	8910	8915
78	.8921	8927	8932	8938	8943	8949	8954	8960	8965	8971
79	.8976	8982	8987	8993	8998	9004	9009	9015	9020	9025
80	.9031	9036	9042	9047	9053	9058	9063	9069	9074	9079
81	.9085	9090	9096	9101	9106	9112	9117	9122	9128	9133
82	.9138	9143	9149	9154	9159	9165	9170	9175	9180	9186
83	.9191	9196	9201	9206	9212	9217	9222	9227	9232	9238
84	.9243	9248	9253	9258	9263	9269	9274	9279	9284	9289
85	.9294	9299	9304	9309	9315	9320	9325	9330	9335	9340
86	.9345	9350	9355	9360	9365	9370	9375	9380	9385	9390
87	.9395	9400	9405	9410	9415	9420	9425	9430	9435	9440
88	.9445	9450	9455	9460	9465	9469	9474	9479	9484	9489
89	.9494	9499	9504	9509	9513	9518	9523	9528	9533	9538
90	.9542	9547	9552	9557	9562	9566	9571	9576	9581	9586
91	.9590	9595	9600	9605	9609	9614	9619	9624	9628	9633
92	.9638	9643	9647	9652	9657	9661	9666	9671	9675	9680
93	.9685	9689	9694	9699	9703	9708	9713	9717	9722	9727
94	.9731	9736	9741	9745	9750	9754	9759	9763	9768	9773
95	.9777	9782	9786	9791	9795	9800	9805	9809	9814	9818
96	.9823	9827	9832	9836	9841	9845	9850	9854	9859	9863
97	.9868	9872	9877	9881	9886	9890	9894	9899	9903	9908
98	.9912	9917	9921	9926	9930	9934	9939	9943	9948	9952
99	.9956	9961	9965	9969	9974	9978	9983	9987	9991	9996
N	**0**	**1**	**2**	**3**	**4**	**5**	**6**	**7**	**8**	**9**

Prop. Parts

	25	**24**	**23**
1	2.5	2.4	2.3
2	5.0	4.8	4.6
3	7.5	7.2	6.9
4	10.0	9.6	9.2
5	12.5	12.0	11.5
6	15.0	14.4	13.8
7	17.5	16.8	16.1
8	20.0	19.2	18.4
9	22.5	21.6	20.7

	19	**18**	**17**
1	1.9	1.8	1.7
2	3.8	3.6	3.4
3	5.7	5.4	5.1
4	7.6	7.2	6.8
5	9.5	9.0	8.5
6	11.4	10.8	10.2
7	13.3	12.6	11.9
8	15.2	14.4	13.6
9	17.1	16.2	15.3

	10	**9**
1	1.0	0.9
2	2.0	1.8
3	3.0	2.7
4	4.0	3.6
5	5.0	4.5
6	6.0	5.4
7	7.0	6.3
8	8.0	7.2
9	9.0	8.1

	8	**7**
1	0.8	0.7
2	1.6	1.4
3	2.4	2.1
4	3.2	2.8
5	4.0	3.5
6	4.8	4.2
7	5.6	4.9
8	6.4	5.6
9	7.2	6.3

	6	**5**	**4**
1	0.6	0.5	0.4
2	1.2	1.0	0.8
3	1.8	1.5	1.2
4	2.4	2.0	1.6
5	3.0	2.5	2.0
6	3.6	3.0	2.4
7	4.2	3.5	2.8
8	4.8	4.0	3.2
9	5.4	4.5	3.6

Index